ENVIRONMENTAL RESEARCH ADVANCES

HEAVY METAL REMEDIATION

TRANSPORT AND ACCUMULATION IN PLANTS

ENVIRONMENTAL RESEARCH ADVANCES

Additional books in this series can be found on Nova's website
under the Series tab.

Additional e-books in this series can be found on Nova's website
under the e-book tab.

ENVIRONMENTAL RESEARCH ADVANCES

HEAVY METAL REMEDIATION

TRANSPORT AND ACCUMULATION IN PLANTS

DHARMENDRA KUMAR GUPTA
AND
SOUMYA CHATTERJEE
EDITORS

nova publishers

New York

NOTICE TO THE READER

The Publisher has taken reasonable care in the preparation of this book, but makes no expressed or implied warranty of any kind and assumes no responsibility for any errors or omissions. No liability is assumed for incidental or consequential damages in connection with or arising out of information contained in this book. The Publisher shall not be liable for any special, consequential, or exemplary damages resulting, in whole or in part, from the readers' use of, or reliance upon, this material. Any parts of this book based on government reports are so indicated and copyright is claimed for those parts to the extent applicable to compilations of such works.

Independent verification should be sought for any data, advice or recommendations contained in this book. In addition, no responsibility is assumed by the publisher for any injury and/or damage to persons or property arising from any methods, products, instructions, ideas or otherwise contained in this publication.

This publication is designed to provide accurate and authoritative information with regard to the subject matter covered herein. It is sold with the clear understanding that the Publisher is not engaged in rendering legal or any other professional services. If legal or any other expert assistance is required, the services of a competent person should be sought. FROM A DECLARATION OF PARTICIPANTS JOINTLY ADOPTED BY A COMMITTEE OF THE AMERICAN BAR ASSOCIATION AND A COMMITTEE OF PUBLISHERS.

Additional color graphics may be available in the e-book version of this book.

Library of Congress Cataloging-in-Publication Data

Heavy metal remediation : transport and accumulation in plants / edited by Dharmendra Kumar Gupta and Soumya Chatterjee (Gottfried Wilhelm Leibniz Universitdt, Hannover Institut f|r Radiovkologie und Strahlenschutz (IRS), Germany).
    pages cm
 Includes bibliographical references and index.
 ISBN: 978-1-63321-568-9 (hardcover)
1. Phytoremediation. 2. Plants--Effect of heavy metals on. 3. Heavy metals--Environmental aspects. I. Gupta, Dharmendra Kumar (Phytoremediation researcher), editor. II. Chatterjee, Soumya, editor.
 TD192.75.H43 2014
 628.4--dc23
                          2014027182

Published by Nova Science Publishers, Inc. † New York

CONTENTS

PREFACE

Heavy metals (HM) are ubiquitous environmental contaminants in rapid technologically advanced societies. HM like Cu, Zn, Mn, Fe, Ni and Co are crucial micronutrients for plant development but when these present in excess become extremely toxic for the plant growth; further, non-essential metals such as Cd, Hg, As and Pb, can be toxic even at low concentrations (Gupta et al. 2013).

In plants, HM accumulation is affected by various factors i.e. plant type, growth phase and elemental characteristics which control uptake, accumulation and translocation of metals from root to shoot. Sometimes, physiological adaptations also control HM accumulations by making complexes of metals at the root level. Complexation with ligands is a process associated to heavy metal pollutants, and it can be an extracellular or an intracellular molecular event. These ligands can be chelators as organic acids or peptides such phytochelatins (PCs), methallothioneins (MTs) or glutathione (GSH). In plants, several multiple transporters are known. For instance in *Arabidopsis thaliana*, has 150 different cation transporters were known (Axelsen and Palmgren 2001). More than 14 transporters are known for sulfate only. Individual transporter proteins have inimitable properties with reverence to transport rate, substrate specificity, substrate affinity (low affinity transporters tend to be more promiscuous) and follow Michaelis-Menton kinetics (Marschner 1995). These properties may be subjected to regulate by metabolic rates or regulatory proteins (e.g. Kinases). Although there is no direct evidence on the role of plasma membrane efflux transporters in heavy metal tolerance in plants, recent research has revealed that plants possess several classes of metal transporters that must be involved in metal uptake and homeostasis in general and, thus, could play a key role in tolerance (Yang et al. 2005a). Several classes of proteins have been implicated in heavy metal transport in plants. These include the heavy metal (or CPx-type) ATPases that are involved in the overall metal-ion homeostasis and tolerance in plants, the natural resistance-associated macrophage protein (Nramp), the cation diffusion facilitator (CDF) family proteins (Williams et al. 2000), and the zinc–iron permease (ZIP) family proteins, etc. (Yang et al. 2005b).

Heavy metal binding to the cell wall is not the only plant mechanism responsible for metal immobilization into roots and subsequent inhibition of ion translocation to the shoot. Major consequences of HM action in the cell is the enhanced generation of reactive oxygen species (ROS) which usually damage the cellular components such as membranes, nucleic acids, chloroplast pigments and alteration in enzymatic and non-enzymatic antioxidants (Gupta et al. 2013).

The success of phytoremediation as an environmental cleaning tool depends on numerous factors including bioavailability of HM in soil/water, selection of plant type and its ability to uptake, growth and biomass production, plant-microbe interactions, translocation and accumulation of metals in shoots and plants' tolerance and detoxification mechanism to counter HM stress. Plants tolerate HM through the development of effective protective mechanisms either effluxing chelated metals from cytoplasm or sequestering in vacuoles, which excludes HM from cellular sites where important metabolic processes such as cell division, respiration take place (Hall 2002).

For the researchers, it is always an endeavor to decontaminate of heavy metals from contaminated environment. The main purpose of this book is to present a holistic view of recent advancement in the field of accumulation and remediation using plants, the green solar powered alternative to ameliorate heavy metal from the polluted environment. The key features of the book are related to metal transporters and metal accumulation mechanisms under heavy metal stress in plants, plant transcriptional regulation and responses under metal contamination, multiple toxic metal contaminations and its phytoremediation approaches etc. Based on the advancement of research in recent years, the information compiled in this book will bring an in-depth knowledge on bioaccumulation of metals, its transportation in natural condition or genetically modified plants and their strategy to cope up with the toxicity to survive in the hostile environment.

Drs. Dharmendra Kumar Gupta and Soumya Chatterjee are personally thankful to the authors for contributing their knowledge, enthusiasm, valuable time and kind cooperation to bring this book into the present form.

Hannover, Germany   **Dr. Dharmendra Kumar Gupta**
Assam, India   **Dr. Soumya Chatterjee**

REFERENCES

Axelsen KB, Palmgren MG (2001) Inventory of the superfamily of P-type ion pumps in *Arabidopsis*. Plant Physiol 126: 696–706.

Gupta DK, Corpas FJ, Palma JM (2013) Heavy Metal Stress in Plants. Springer-Verlag, Germany.

Hall JL (2002) Cellular mechanisms for heavy metal detoxification and tolerance. J ExpBiol 53: 1–11.

Marschner H (1995) Mineral Nutrition of Higher Plants.Academic Press, San Diego pp 889.

Williams LE, Pittman JK, Hall JL (2000) Emerging mechanisms for heavy metal transport in plants.Biochim Biophys Acta 1465:104–126.

Yang X, Feng Y, He Z, Stoffella P (2005a) Molecular mechanisms of heavy metal hyperaccumulation and phytoremediation. J Trace Elem Med Biol 18:339–353.

Yang X, Jin XF, Feng Y, Islam E (2005b) Molecular mechanisms and genetic bases of heavy metal tolerance/hyperaccumulation in plants. J Integr Plant Biol 47:1025–1035.

In: Heavy Metal Remediation   ISBN: 978-1-63321-568-9
Editors: Dharmendra Kumar Gupta and Soumya Chatterjee © 2014 Nova Science Publishers, Inc.

Chapter 1

MECHANISM OF METAL TRANSPORTERS IN PLANTS

*Anindita Mitra[1], Soumya Chatterjee[*2],*
Sibnarayan Datta[2], Sonika Sharma[2], Vijay Veer[2],
Bam H. M. Razafindrabe[3], Clemens Walther[4]
and Dharmendra K. Gupta[4]

[1]Department of Zoology, Bankura Christian College, Bankura, West Bengal, India
[2]Defence Research Laboratory, DRDO, Tezpur, Assam, India
[3]Faculty of Agriculture, University of the Ryukyus, Okinawa, Japan
[4]Gottfried Wilhelm Leibniz Universität Hannover, Institut für Radioökologie und
Strahlenschutz (IRS), Hannover, Germany

ABSTRACT

Plants absorb a range of heavy metals from soil. Some of them such as Cu, Zn, Mn, Fe, Ni and Co are essential micronutrients while some are nonessential (Cd, Hg, and Pb) for plants. The nonessential heavy metal ions as well as essential ones can have toxic effect when present in supra-optimal values. Thus for normal plant growth, mechanisms must exist that satisfy the requirements of cellular metabolism by regulating the uptake and distribution of these metal ions within different cells and organelles, thereby avoiding hazardous effect from the toxic metals. Membrane transport systems are likely to be involved in transition metal transport. These include CDF family, Nramps, ZIP family, ABC transporters, heavy metal ATPases (HMAs) and CAX family antiporters, Cyclic Nucleotide Gated Channels (CNGC) and copper transporter. This review aims to provide an overview of the range of potential transport systems presently thought to be involved in the acquisition, distribution and homeostasis of heavy metals in plants. It will focus on the general properties of different transporter families apart from the detailed molecular structure with an additional note on transport of some essential and nonessential metals in plants.

Keywords: Heavy metals, Metal transporters, Vacuole, ZIP family, ABC transporter

---

* Corresponding Author: Dr. Soumya Chatterjee, Defence Research Laboratory, DRDO, Tezpur 784001, Assam, India, Phone: 0091- 3712 258 836, Fax: 0091- 3712 258 534, E. Mail: drlsoumya@gmail.com

1. INTRODUCTION

Environment plays a crucial role in the development of any organism. Being sessile in nature, plants use to deal with a range of environment with fluctuating climatic conditions like, temperature, precipitation, moisture, soil quality. Along with essential growth materials like water, nutrients, and minerals, plants use to take up a diversity of natural and noxious compounds through their root system from soil and ground water. Among these substances numerous elements including a range of metals from soil are also being absorbed at the root level through different transporters, either through active or passive mechanisms and developing diverse mechanisms for their survival (Chatterjee et al. 2013).

Physical properties like the ability to conduct heat, electricity, ductility, malleability and luster distinguish metals from nonmetals (Housecroft and Sharpe 2005). Interestingly, the temperature dependent conductivity, the most distinctive physical property of metals is usually lost when the metal is chemically converted into a (chemical) compound (Shaw et al. 2004). However, metals at their elemental (zero valence state) forms are not available to plants and other living organisms unless the metal is available in solution and transformed into compounds (as for example, salts) (Appenroth 2010).

Metals with atomic mass over 20 and specific gravity higher than 5 gm/cm^3 are often termed as 'heavy' metals. However, density of a metal cannot be detected by plants and thus there seems to be no correlation between density dependent up-take of metals. Some of the metals like, copper (Cu), iron (Fe), manganese (Mn), nickel (Ni), molybdenum (Mo), cobalt (Co) and zinc (Zn) are referred to as essential micronutrients for plant as they are required in minute quantity but are vital to normal growth, enzyme catalyzed redox reaction, electron transfer, metalloprotein formations etc. (Zenk 1996; Puig and Penarrubia 2009; Rastgoo et al. 2011). As for example, Cu, an important micronutrient, is an integral component of certain proteins involved in redox-reaction in photosynthesis and respiration processes, protein trafficking machinery, lignification and oxidative stress responses (Hirayama et al. 1999; Yruela 2005). Zinc is another essential element which also has structural and/or catalytic roles in many enzymes, auxin production, carbohydrate and protein metabolism, protecting cells against oxidative stress, photosynthesis reaction and maintaining the membrane structure and functions (Brennan and Bolland 2006). Fe is a key component of different haem proteins (cytochrome, catalase and ferredoxin) and a range of other enzymes (Hall and Williams 2003). In contrast, elements like chromium (Cr), cadmium (Cd), lead (Pb), mercury (Hg) and arsenic (As) are considered as toxic and nonessential for plants because no physiological role has been reported for these metals (Michalak 2006). However even micronutrients become toxic for plants when their concentrations rise above supra-optimal values (Peralta-Videa et al. 2009).A study on the growth parameters (multiplication rate, fresh weight, dry weight, chlorophyll a, chlorophyll b and total carotenoid content) on application of ten different heavy metals (eight transition elements and two leadgroup elements) on *Lemna minor* revealed interesting result with a following toxicity series: $Ag^+> Cd^{2+}> Hg^{2+}> Ti^+> Cu^{2+}> Ni^{2+}> Zn^{2+}> Co^{6+}> Cr^{6+}> As^{3+}> As^{5+}$ (Naumann et al. 2007; Appenroth 2010).

The adverse effect of heavy metal toxicity includes alterations of numerous physiological processes at cellular/molecular levels by inactivation of enzyme, blockage of metabolically important molecules, displacement or substitution of essential elements and disruption of membrane integrity (Sergio et al. 2000; Rakhshaee et al. 2009; Douchiche et al. 2010a).The main threat lies in their ability to produce reactive oxygen species (ROS) (Gratao et al. 2005) due to interference with electron transport activities, especially that of chloroplast membranes (Pagliano et al. 2006; Rocca et al.2009). On exposure to ROS, cells experience oxidative stress leading to lipid peroxidation, biological macromolecule deterioration, membrane dismantling, ion leakage, and DNA-strand cleavage (Quartacci et al. 2001; Navari-Izzo et al. 1998, 1999). Unfortunately, the non-essential metals as well as the essential ones can also produce ROS (Rodriguez-Serrano et al. 2009; Martins et al. 2011). However, plants have developed a series of defense mechanisms that regulate uptake, accumulation, and translocation of these toxic elements and detoxify them by excluding the free ionic forms from the cytoplasm. There are some plants that can survive, grow and reproduce on sites contaminated with high concentration of heavy metals. Majority of these plant species that tolerate heavy metal concentrations, which are highly toxic to the other plants, behave as hypertolerant "non-hyperaccumulators". The hypertolerance strategies help these plants in limiting metal entrance by (i) establishment of symbiotic associations with soil microorganisms such as mycorrhiza that confine movement of heavy metal ions and uptake by the plant (Lin et al. 2007; Amir et al. 2008; Arriagada et al. 2009; Iram et al. 2009), (ii) binding to the anionic groups of the cell walls and eventually to root exudates (Douchiche et al. 2010b; Colzi et al. 2011; Lang and Wernitznig 2011), (iii) reduce influx through the plasma membrane (Courbot et al. 2007; Gonzalez-Mendoza and Zapata- Perez 2008; Xiao et al. 2008; Lang and Wernitznig 2011), (iv) action of proteins connected with the stress caused by heavy metals (heat shock proteins) (Neumann et al. 1994; Wollgiehn and Neumann 1999). Most of the heavy metals that do enter the plant are then kept in root cells, where they are detoxified by chelation with various ligands such as phytochelatins and metallothioneins and/or are sequestered into vacuoles (Hall 2002; Hasan et al. 2009). This greatly restricts translocation to the above-ground organs thus protecting the leaf tissues, particularly the metabolically active photosynthetic cells from heavy metal related damage. On the other hand the "hyperaccumulators" exhibit an opposite behavior by active uptake of exceedingly large amounts of one or more heavy metals from the soil. Moreover, the heavy metals are not retained in the roots but are translocated to the shoot and accumulated in aboveground organs, especially leaves, at concentrations 100–1000-fold higher than those found in non-hyperaccumulating species without exhibiting any symptoms of phytotoxicity (Reeves 2006).

This review aims to provide an overview of the range of potential transport systems presently thought to be involved in the acquisition, distribution and homeostasis of heavy metals in plants. It will focus on the general properties of different transporter families with an additional note on transport of some essential and nonessential metals in plants.

2. METAL ION AND THEIR UPTAKE FROM SOIL

In soil, metals exist as a variety of chemical species in a dynamic equilibrium governed by soil physical, chemical, and biological properties (Chaney 1988). But, only a fraction of soil metal is readily available for plant uptake because of the insoluble nature of the compounds, thus unavailable for transport into roots. Metal availability and mobility in the rhizosphere is influenced by root exudates and microorganisms (Wenzel et al. 2003).

In non-accumulator or 'excluder' plants the first line of defense against heavy metals is achieved by secretion of root exudates into the soil matrix. Root exudates prevent the uptake inside the cells by chelating metals (Marschner 1995). For example, Ni-chelating histidine and citrate are present in root exudates and these reduce the uptake of Ni from soil in nonaccumulator *Thalspi* (Salt et al. 2000). The plant cell wall also plays a key role in the immobilization of toxic heavy metal ions by providing hystidyl groups, and extracellular carbohydrates such as callose and mucilage, and thus prevents heavy metals uptake into the cytosol (Manara 2012).

In contrast, root exudates play important role in uptake by increasing bioavailability of heavy metals. For example, Arsenic bioavailability in the rhizosphere of hyperaccumulator *Pteris* is increased by reducing pH via root exudation of large amount of dissolved organic carbon (Gonzaga et al. 2009). Decrease in the pH in fact enhances the accessibility of water soluble As that can be taken up by the roots (Fitz and Wenzel 2002; Gonzaga et al.2009).

2.1. Major Metal Transporters in Plants

Transport of metal ions across root cellular membrane permits the access of metals into plant tissues. Metals are first taken into apoplast, a free intercellular space directed towards the xylem, of the roots. A portion of total amount of metal is transported into the cells, while some are transported further into the apoplast and some are bound to the cell wall substances (Gregor 1999). Root surfaces are characterized by the presence of high affinity chemical receptors (Salt et al. 1995; Salt and Kramer 2000; Dushenkov et al. 1997) mediating the transport of ions into cells. Heavy metals are translocated apoplastically into plant tissue due to continuum of root epidermis and cortex. The metals in root cells have to cross the endodermis and casparian strip to reach the xylem. The cell walls of the endodermis and casparian strip act as a barrier for apoplastic diffusion into the vascular system. For root–shoot translocation of metals, metal transporters carry metal ions from root symplast into xylem apoplast (Marschner 1995) and are probably driven by transpiration pump (Salt et al. 1995). Physiological concentrations of heavy metals in the plant cell are regulated by tonoplast as well as metal transporters on the plasma membrane.

Different classes of membrane proteins are known to involve in uptake of metals in plants, but still, there is a lacuna in understanding the molecular level transport of heavy metals across plant membranes. Therefore, a complete knowledge of transport processes in plants is crucial to create transgenic plants that can accumulate specific metals to improve the process of soil decontamination and remediation.

2.1.1. NRAMP Family

NRAMP (Natural resistance associated macrophage proteins), a highly conserved family of integral membrane proteins act as metal transporters and are known to transport a wide range of metals, such as Mn^{2+}, Zn^{2+}, Cu^{2+}, Fe^{2+}, Cd^{2+}, Ni^{2+}, and Co^{2+} across membranes. Nramp homologous sequences have been identified in a wide range of organism like bacteria, fungi, plants, and animals (Nevo and Nelson 2006). The mammalian Nramp was the first gene to be characterized in this family (Hall and Williams 2003) encoding an integral membrane protein found in the phagosomes of infected macrophages in mouse where it is thought to regulate the propagation of engulfed bacteria by controlling divalent cation such as Fe and Mn concentrations within the endosomal compartment (Govoni and Gros 1998). Nramp 1 mutant mice are susceptible to pathogenic bacterial infection (Supek et al.1997; Nelson 1999). In plants, Nramp genes encode metal transporters expressing in roots and shoots that transport metal ions through the plasma membrane and the tonoplast (Kramer et al. 2007). Nramp family was first identified in *Oryza sativa*, and three Nramps (OsNramp 1-3) were reported (Belouchi et al. 1995, 1997). In a number of higher plants Nramp gene family have also been localized including six Nramps in *Arabidopsis* (Williams et al. 2000; Maser et al. 2001). Like other Nramps, the plant proteins are evolutionary highly conserved sequences containing 12 predicted transmembrane (TM) domains with a characteristic `*consensus transport motif*` between TM-8 and TM-9 (Gunshin et al. 1997; Curie et al. 2000; Williams et al. 2000). In *A. thaliana* the same gene is involved in Fe and Cd transport, with Nramp1 playing a specific role in Fe transport and homeostasis (Thomine et al. 2000). Transgenic *A. thaliana* overexpressing AtNramp1 showed higher resistance to toxic iron concentration (Curie et al. 2000). According to Hall and Williams (2003) some of the Nramp genes among the different members of the Nramp gene family are involved in Fe and Cd uptake and homeostasis along with performing different physiological functions.

2.1.2. CDF Family

CDF (Cation diffusion facilitator) proteins are a family of heavy metal transporters associated in the transport of Zinc, Cobalt and Cadmium found in bacteria and eukaryotes (Paulsen and Saier 1997; Eide 1998; van der Zaal et al. 1999). These proteins are predicted to possess six transmembrane domains, an N-terminal signature sequence and a C-terminal cation binding domain (Paulsen and Saier 1997; Maser et al. 2001). Members of this family exhibit highly variable size, ranging from about 280 to 740 residues (Paulsen and Saier 1997). Among four phylogenetic groups of CDF gene family (Maser et al. 2001) only group I and III in plants are involved in metal tolerance and accumulation (Kramer et al. 2007). CDF transporter gene ZAT was first identified in *Arabidopsis* (van der Zaal et al. 1999) and shows 35-40% identity to the mammalian ZnT (Zinc transporter) gene and plays a role in vesicular/vacuolar sequestration of Zn (van der Zaal et al. 1999). A ZAT gene designated as ZTP1, has been identified in the Zn hyperaccumulator, *Thlaspi caerulescens* (Assuncao et al. 2001) where it is expressed in the leaves and roots. In transgenic plants, grown in high levels of Zn containing soil, overexpression of ZTP1 confers resistance to Zn toxicity and leads to Zn accumulation in the roots (van der Zaal et al. 1999). In another hyperaccumulator, *Thlaspi goesingense*, a CDF transporter, TgMTP1 (*Thlaspi goesingense* metal tolerance protein1) was found to play a role in accumulation of metal ions within the shoot vacuoles (Persans et al. 2001). The study also supports the view that TgMTP1t1 (derived from unspliced TgMTP1 transcript) confers tolerance to Cd, Co and Zn, while TgMTP1t2 (derived from spliced TgMTP1 transcript) confers tolerance to Ni.In the tropical legume *Stylosanthes hamata*, that can grow in acid and high Mn^{2+} contaminated soils, another CDF transporter, ShMTP1, has been identified (Delhaize et al. 2003). In transgenic Yeast and *Arabidopsis* ShMTP1 was found to function as a proton/Mn^{2+} antiporter and sequestered Mn^{2+} into internal organelles, conferring increased tolerance to Mn^{2+} (Delhaize et al. 2003).

2.1.3. ZIP Family

One of the principal metal transporter family involved in metal uptake is the ZIP (ZRT, IRT-like proteins) family, identified in many plant species as well as bacteria, fungi and animals (Maser et al. 2001). ZIP family members are involved in the translocation of divalent cations (Fe, Zn, Mn, and Cd) across membranes differing in their substrate range and specificity (Guerinot 2000; Maser et al. 2001).The ZIP proteins are predicted to have eight transmembrane domains with the amino- and carboxyl- terminal ends situated on the outer surface of the plasma membrane (Guerinot 2000). ZIP proteins range from 309 to 476 amino acids in length; this difference is largely due to the length between TM- 3 and TM-4 domains designated as the `variable region' that contains a potential metal-binding domain rich in histidine residues, and is predicted to be cytoplasmic. The ZIP family includes a set of transport proteins, all sharing an important feature i.e., they all can transport Zn^{2+} and other metal ions from the extracellular or organelle lumen into the cytosol (Saier 1999).

2.1.4. ABC Transporter

The ABC (ATP-binding cassette) transporter superfamily constitutes a diverse family of membrane proteins and are present in organisms ranging from bacteria to humans (Henikoff et al. 1997).In most cases functional ABC transporter act as ATP driven pump with a wide range of substrate specificity including ions, sugars, lipids, peptides, pigments, xenobiotics, antibiotics and heavy metals that are transported into the vacuole (Martinoia et al. 2002; Hall and Williams 2003). All ABC transporters share a common structural feature, a highly hydrophobic membrane spanning domain (MSD), and ATP-binding domain or nucleoside binding domain (NBD) oriented toward cytoplasm (Rea 1999; Theodoulou 2000). Two major sub-classes of ABC ATPase superfamily have been identified in plants, one is multidrug resistance associated proteins (MRPs) particularly active in the sequestration of chelated heavy metals and the other is multidrug resistance proteins (MDRs). A tonoplastic ABC transporter of *Schizosaccharomyces pombe*, HMT1 was the first identified ABC transporter (Ortiz et al. 1992), capable of mobilizing Phytochelatin-Cd complexes into the vacuole in a Mg-ATP-dependent manner (Ortiz et al. 1995). A similar mechanism has also been proposed to operate in oat root, where transport of a phytochelatin-Cd across root tonoplast was found to be energized by Mg-ATP and highly sensitive to orthovanadate (Salt and Rauser 1995). Functional homologs of SpHMT1 have been reported in *Caenorhabditis elegans* and *Drosophila* (Vatamaniuk et al. 2005; Sooksa-Nguan et al. 2009). In *Saccharomyces cerevisiae*, another ABC transporter, YCF1 (Yeast Cadmium Factor1) was found to contribute to heavy metal tolerance (Szczypka et al. 1994; Li et al. 1997). This vacuolar transporter detoxifies bis-glutathione heavy metal/metalloid complexes, such as Glutathione-S-Cd and Glutathione-S-As. Overexpression of ScYCF1 in *Arabidopsis* resulted in plants that were more tolerant to cadmium (Song et al. 2003). Some ABC proteins were suggested to participate in plant iron homeostasis also (Yamaguchi et al. 2002). However, the MRP subclass of ABC transporter is proposed to transport phytochelatin-Cd or Glutathione-S-Cd complexes across the tonoplast (Rea et al. 1998). A possible role for ABC transporters in Mn^{2+} transport has also been suggested in the cyanobacterium *Synechocystis* (Hall and Williams 2003).Subsequent research revealed the possibility of involvement of ABC transporters in Hg(II) tolerance in plants (Park et al. 2012). Another iron-regulated ABC transporter, IDI7, has been identified in barley root tonoplast (Yamaguchi et al. 2002) which is induced by Fe-deficiency, although the nature of the transported substrate is not known (Hall and Williams 2003).

2.1.5. P Type ATPase

P-type ATPases transporting a variety of substrates across the plasma membrane are present in all life forms. Surprisingly, the largest numbers of P-type ATPases occur in higher plants. For example, 45 different ATPases are predicted in the *Arabidopsis* genome (Axelsen and Palmgren 1998), and 43 are found in rice (Baxter et al. 2003). Why do plants possess so many ATPases, with similar functions (Axelsen and Palmgren 1998) is still debatable. One possible explanation may lie in the fact that due to immobile nature of the plants they need to adjust rapidly to the fluctuating environmental conditions such as water, nutrient availability, temperature, and having large number of highly selective transporters may help plants to more finely adapt to their environment. Five major subfamilies of P-type ATPases are classified according to their substrate specificity. For instance, P_{II}-ATPases include the well-characterized sarcoplasmic reticulum Ca^{2+}- ATPase, Na^+/K^+-ATPase, H^+-ATPases and H^+/K^+-ATPase (Palmgren and Axelsen 1998). However, Type I and III ATPases are responsible for transport of heavy metals and divalent cations across the plasma membrane respectively (Axelsen and Palmgren 2001).

2.1.6. P_{IB}-ATPases

P_{1B}-ATPases members of the type I ATPase subfamily also designated as HMA (Heavy Metal ATPase) transporters. Phylogenetic analysis of P_{1B} subfamily suggested the existence of two main groups based on the metals they can transport : divalent cation transporters fall into HMA1-4 (predicted to transport $Zn^{2+}/Cd^{2+}/Co^{2+}/Pb^{2+}$) and monovalent cation transporters fall into HMA5-8 (proposed to be Cu^+/Ag^+ ATPases) (Axelsen and Palmgren 2001; Arnesano etal. 2002; Mills et al. 2003). These HMA ATPases are also referred as CPx-type ATPases since they contain conserved cysteine-proline-cysteine/histidine/serine motif that is thought to be involved in translocation of the metal (Solioz and Vulpe 1996). All P-type ATPases share some common features like formation of a phosphorylated intermediate during their catalytic cycle; all exist at least in two conformations associated with metal translocation; all contain one or two heavy metal binding domains and in all, phosphorylation occurs invariably in the aspartic acid residue present in the cytoplasmic DKTGT consensus sequence (Cobbett et al. 2003; Williams et al. 2005). Another common feature to all the P-type ATPases is the inhibition by vanadate and thus arresting the metal translocation cycle (Lutsenko and Kaplan 1995).

2.1.6.1. Zn/Cd/Co/Pb Subgroup of P_{1B}-Type ATPases

Chloroplast envelope-targeted proteomics approach in *Arabidopsis thaliana* revealed that HMA1 is expressed in the chloroplast envelope (Seigneurin-Berny et al. 2006) therefore, expression is limited to the green tissues. This study also showed that *hma1* knockout mutants in *Arabidopsis* exhibit decreased chloroplast copper content. Yeast cells transformed with AtHMA1have an increased accumulation of copper. This result was explained by the targeting of HMA1 protein to one of the endomembrane compartments in yeast, and the resulting depletion of copper from the cytoplasm triggering elevated Cu influx into the yeast cell (Seigneurin-Berny et al. 2006).

AtHMA2 another member of this P_{1B}-type ATPase subgroup, has been extensively studied. HMA2 transporter functions as a classical ATPase, forming an acid stable phosphorylated intermediate and is inhibited by vanadate (Eren et al. 2004). From the study of Hussain and coworkers (2004), it was shown that HMA2 is mainly expressed in vascular tissues in both roots and shoots, acts as an efflux transporter and it may be involved in xylemand possibly phloem loading. The HMA2 enzyme has high affinity for Zn^{2+} and Cd^{2+}, suggesting it may transport both of these ions (Eren et al. 2004).

AtHMA3 is the most poorly understood transporter and little information is available on the physiological role of HMA3 in the plants. In mutant yeast cells, HMA3 expression rescued the Cd^{2+}/Pb^{2+}-hypersensitivity phenotype. With this observation, a role in intracellular Cd^{2+} sequestration was proposed for HMA3 (Gravot et al. 2004).

2.1.6.2. Cu/Ag Subgroup of P_{1B}-Type ATPases

Copper is an essential micronutrient and integral component of many enzymes. However, it is also very toxic at elevated tissue concentrations. Therefore, plants have evolved transporters and detoxification mechanisms for copper to avoid its phytotoxic effects. The first P_{1B}-type ATPases of plants to be characterized were PAA1 and PAA2, later renamed as HMA6 and HMA8, respectively. Both of these transporters play a crucial role in Cu transport. PAA2 is only expressed in shoots transporting Cu into the thylakoid lumen for incorporation into Cu requiring steps in photosynthetic electron transfer (Tabata et al. 1997; Shikanai et al. 2003; Abdel-Ghany et al. 2005).While PAA1 is expressed in both roots and shoots and transports Cu across the plastid envelope to be incorporated into stromal Zn/Cu superoxide dismutase (Shikanai et al. 2003). The AtHMA7 (also known as RAN1) protein falls into the Cu^+/Ag^+ cluster and is thought to act by delivering Cu^+ across post-Golgi membranes to create functional ethylene receptors (Hirayama et al. 1999; Woeste and Kieber 2000). Apart from PAA1, PAA2 and RAN1 another gene AtHMA5 is expressed mainly in *Arabidopsis* roots and its expression is strongly and exclusively upregulated by copper (Andres-Colas et al. 2006).

2.1.7. CaCA Transporter

The CaCA superfamily of proteins are membrane transporters that regulate cytosolic Ca^{2+}concentration, using a counter electrochemical gradient of other ions, such as H^+, Na^+, or K^+ (Emery et al. 2012) across tonoplast membrane. MHX and CAX are the members of CaCA family that are believed to be involved in metal homeostasis. MHX is a vacuolar Mg^{+2} and Zn^{+2}/H^+ antiporter expressed principally in xylem-associated cells (Shaul et al.1999). The CAX family is Ca^{+2}/H^+ antiporter that also recognize Cd^{+2}, suggesting this as an important route for Cd sequestration in the vacuole (Salt and Wagner 1993). Two genes, CAX1 and CAX2, have been cloned from *Arabidopsis* and are shown to be high and low efficiency Ca^{+2}/H^+ exchangers, respectively (Hirschi et al. 1996). Further study revealed another gene AtCAX4 together with AtCAX2 seem to be involved in the vacuolar accumulation of Cd (Korenkov et al. 2007). According to Shigaki et al. (2003) CAX2 is the low affinity Mn^{+2}transporters capable of vacuolar transport of Mn.

2.1.8. CNGC Transporter

An additional membrane located non-selective channel for the uptake of both monovalentand divalent cations was found in *Arabidopsis* known as cyclic nucleotide gated channels (CNGCs), a large gene family comprises of 20 members (Schuurink et al. 1998; White et al. 2002; Talke et al. 2003). All members of this family shared the common feature of six putative trans-membrane spans and a pore region between transmembrane (TM) domain 5 and 6. A domain in the TM-4 shows similarity to the Shaker type K^+ voltage sensor and a C-terminal domain is believed to bind both cyclic nucleotides and calmodulin (Koehler and Neuhaus 2000). CNGC voltage gated channels are activated by direct binding of cyclic nucleotide cAMP and/or cGMP (Leng et al. 2002; Balague et al. 2003). Like the animal counterpart, their activation by cyclic nucleotides is blocked in the presence of calmodulin (Hua et al. 2003b).Functional analysis in heterologous systems further showed that all CNGCs freely conduct K^+ and apart from CNGC2, Na^+ (Leng et al. 2002; Balague et al. 2003; Hua et al. 2003a). CNGCs are also reported to conduct Ca^{2+} through the plant cell plasma membrane (Ma et al. 2009). Plant CNGCs proteins have been proposed to involve in multiple physiological processes including root growth and gravitropism, pollen tube growth, sodium stress tolerance, leaf senescence, plant disease resistance and innate immunity (Ma et al. 2006; Frietsch et al. 2007; Gobert et al. 2006; Kohler et al. 2001; Ali et al. 2007). Some evidence suggests a role of CNGCs in heavy metal homeostasis in plants. For example, in tobacco, overexpression of NtCBP4 led to improved tolerance to Ni^{2+} hypersensitivity to Pb^{2+} (Arazi et al. 1999). A role of this protein in the Pb^{2+} transport was strengthened from the findings that plants expressing a truncated version of NtCBP4 showed improved tolerance to Pb^{2+} and reduced accumulation of the metal (Sunkar et al. 2000). However, paucity of knowledge about the substrate range of these channels need further study.

2.1.9.Copper Transporter

A putative Cu transporter (CTR) gene has been isolated in *Arabidopsis* (Kampfenkel et al. 1995) that encodes 169 amino acids long highly hydrophobic protein. The CTR protein predicted to have three potential transmembrane domains (Hall and Williams 2003) and a putative metal-binding motif in the extracellular domain (Puig and Thiele 2002). In *A. thaliana*, copper transporter COPT1 has been shown to transport copper, and it also has a role in growth and pollen development (Sancenon et al. 2003). COPT1 transcripts showed highest expression in leaves and were also found in stems and flowers, but were absent from roots (Kampfenkel et al. 1995).

3. Metal Ion Uptake and Transport in Root

3.1. Iron (Fe) Uptake and Transport

Iron, an essential nutrient is not readily available to plants growing in soil. Fe is present as hydroxides and other insoluble complexes in soil and sparing solubility of Fe limits the availability of this nutrient to plants (Marschner 1995). Uptake and storage of iron is therefore, a highly regulated process. Plants are thought to rely on a reductive mechanism to mobilize rhizospheric soil Fe [III] (Guerinot and Yi 1994; Fox and Guerinot 1998). The initial reduction of Fe^{III} to Fe^{II} is carried out by a root plasma membrane-bound ferric chelate reductase, encoded by the FRO2 gene (Robinson et al. 1999). This reduction enhances the Fe solubility because Fe^{II} is more soluble than Fe^{III} and also prepares the Fe for transport across the root epidermal cell membrane by a Fe^{II} specific transporter (Conte and Walker 2011; Eide et al. 1996). Iron regulated transporter protein or IRT1, the first member of the ZIP gene family to be identified, is a Fe^{II} transporter that takes up iron from the soil (Guerinot 2000). IRT1 is the high affinity Fe transporter andis considered as the major transporter (Connolly et al. 2002; Vert et al. 2002) as mutants of IRT1 also showed significant changes in photosynthetic efficiency and developmental defects that were consistent with a deficiency in Fe transport and homeostasis (Henriques et al. 2002; Varotto et al. 2002). Transgenic plants overexpressing *A. thaliana* AtIRT1were shown to accumulate higher concentrations of Cd and Zn than wild types under Fe deficient conditions (Connolly et al. 2002). Similar report was obtained from the study of Palmgren et al. (2008), which stated that, after the treatment of Fe limitation, IRT1 protein levels were found to increase in the root which in turn leads to IRT1 dependent Cd and Zn accumulation in the roots. Another study reported that AtIRT1 gene is induced in response to excess Ni and is involved in Ni^{2+} transport and accumulation (Assuncao et al. 2001; Nishida et al. 2011). In addition, uptake of Cadmium from soil into the root cells and transport of it to the aboveground tissue was shown to be performed by ZIP transpoters in plants (Kramer et al. 2007). Therefore, it can be said that, in plants, the IRT1 gene is transcriptionally responsive to Fe deficiency but once expressed, it may be capable of transporting other divalent metals like Cd, Zn and Ni in addition to Fe.

Another protein IRT2 has been reported in *Arabidopsis,* which, like IRT1, belongs to ZRT/IRT related protein (IP) family of metal transporter. Like IRT1, IRT2 is up-regulated under Fe deficiency but unlike IRT1, IRT2 is localized in the cortical vesicles within root epidermal cells. Also IRT2 cannot complement the growth defect of irt1- 1 mutant (Vert et al. 2009).

3.2. Zinc (Zn) Uptake and Transport

Zinc is an essential component of more than 300 enzymes such as RNA polymerase, alkaline phosphatase, alcohol dehydrogenase, Cu/Zn superoxide dismutase, and carbonic anhydrase and many protein motifs have characteristic of zinc binding structural domains such as the zinger finger domain (Clarke and Berg 1998). Zn is taken up as a divalent cation (Marschner 1995) and within root cells zinc act as divalent cation that has a strong tendency to form tetrahedral complexes without undergoing further oxidation and reduction (Berg and Shi 1996). Besides IRT1, ZRT1 and ZRT2 of yeast, the next two members of the ZIP family are proposed to perform as high affinity and low affinity Zn^{2+} transporters respectively (Zhao and Eide 1996a,b). ZRT1 and ZRT2 are responsible for the absorption of Zn^{2+} across the plasma membrane from outside environment, while ZRT3 in the vacuole membrane is responsible for shipping Zn^{2+} from the vacuole back to the cytoplasm (Macdiarmid et al. 2000).

3.3. Arsenic (As) Uptake and Transport

The As accumulation and resistance varies between plant species due to genetic differences and diversity in detoxification processes (Meharg and Whitaker 2002). Ma et al. (2001) first reported that the Chinese brake fern (*Pteris vittata*) is able to hyperaccumulate more than 1000 mg As kg^{-1} of shoot. Within root cell As^{V} is reduced to As^{III} after uptake, translocated through the xylem with water and minerals as an As^{III} -S compound, and then it isstored as As^{III} in the fronds (Ma et al. 2001). Generally, in plants, As is transported through the phosphate transport channel because of their chemical similarity with phosphate (Tripathi et al. 2007; Gupta et al. 2013a) thereby competing with phosphate for root uptake and interferes with metabolic processes like ATP synthesis and oxidative phosphorylation (Tripathi et al. 2007; Gupta et al. 2013a). Report from Ma et al. (2008) revealed that in the rice cultivars Oochikara, T-65, and Koshihikari, As^{III} is transported in the form of arsenous acid As $(OH)_3$ through silicic acid transporters (Lsi1 and Lsi2). Inside plant tissues, As^{V} is reduced to As^{III} and/or biotransformed by arsenate reductase to less toxic organic compounds such as DMA (dimethylarsinic acid), MMA (monomethylarsonic acid), or as inorganic As^{III} complexed with thiol groups (Pickering et al. 2000; Dhankher et al. 2006). Within plant tissue, solubility of Arsenic increased through chelation with cyclohexylenedinitrotetraacetic acid, nitrilotiacetic acid, or As-sulfur complexes and thus facilitates mobilization. Arsenic translocation to the shoots and vascular tissues in hyperaccumulator plants as predominant arsenite form probably occurs through a different transporter like aquaglyceroporins of the NIP (Nodulin 26- like Intrinsic protein) family members (Ma et al. 2008; Kamiya et al. 2009; Zhao et al. 2009).

3.4. Cadmium (Cd) Uptake and Transport

Earlier transport studies by Salt and Wagner (1993) suggested that a Cd^{2+}/H^{+} antiporter belonging to CAX family of proteins (Hirschi et al. 2000) might be involved in the accumulation of Cd^{2+} into the vacuole. A tonoplast transporter capable of transporting both phytochelatin (PCs) and Cd-PC complexes from the cytoplasm into the vacuole has also been identified in plants (Salt and Rauser 1995). The major driving force of uptake of Cd by root cells is the electrochemical potential gradient of the plasmamembrane in the root cells of plants (Blaylock and Huang 2000; Huang et al. 1992; Wang et al. 1994).Other external factors such as Fe and Mn concentration also can reduce or promote uptake of Cd (Sharma et al. 2004 a,b; Ramos et al. 2002). For example, in *Thlaspi caerulescens*, Fe deficiency upregulates the expression of genes encoding for Fe^{II} uptake, which in turn promotes the uptake of Cd (Lombi et al. 2002). Transport of Cd may partially be shared with Zn and/or Fe transport as reported in *Arabidopsis halleri* (Ueno et al. 2008). Report of Diatloff et al. (2006) suggesting the role of low affinity cation transporter (LCT1) responsible for Ca transport in wheat is also responsible for Cd transport in the yeast *Pichia pastoris*. Therefore, the role of LCT protein in transport of Cd in higher plants can't be denied.

3.5. Chromium (Cr) Uptake and Transport

Although Cr is considered as nonessential for plants, but, low concentrations of Cr (0.05–1mgL^{-1}) was found to promote growth and increase yield in crops (Peralta-Videa et al. 2009). In soil, concentration of Cr greater than 1 mgL^{-1} induces alterations of metabolic processes in plants such as retarding growth, decrease in chlorophyll synthesis, and chlorosis (Dube et al. 2003). Moreover, hexavalent Cr^{VI} damages root membranes because it has a high oxidation power. In addition, Cr^{VI} reduces the uptake of the essential elements like Fe, K, Mg, Mn P, and Ca (Gardea-Torresdey et al. 2005). Differently, crops from the Brassicaceae family (cauliflower, kale, and cabbage) can accumulate more Cr than other plant species without presenting any phytotoxic symptoms (Zayed and Terry 2003). Both Cr^{VI} and Cr^{III} enter into the root cells by the symplast pathway where Cr ^{VI} is reduced and accumulated in the cortex (Shanker et al. 2005). Within root cells Cr forms complex with root exudates, such as organic acids, which increase the solubility and mobility of Cr through the root xylem (Bluskov et al. 2005). Even though Cr is poorly translocated to aerial parts, it is mobilized and accumulated inside tissues depending on its chemical form (James and Barlett 1983). According to the report of Kim et al. (2006) uptake of Cr^{VI} in *Nicotiana tabacum* occurs through sulfate or phosphate transporter or active mechanism and is retained in the vacuoles. Tetrahedral Cr^{VI} compounds at neutral pH are transported across cell membranes through similar tetrahedral ion channels, while octahedral Cr^{III} is transported through diffusion across membranes (Cohen et al. 2006).

3.6. Lead (Pb) Uptake and Transport

The major source of environmental lead is metal smelting (Caussy et al. 2003), but human activities also have a major contribution in Pb pollution (Marchiol et al. 2004). Plants do not have any channels or specific transporter for Pb uptake, as Pb is not an essential element (Peralta-Videa et al. 2009). Like other toxic metals, excess of Pb is known to interfere with different metabolic processes like seed germination, growth and chlorophyll synthesis (Begonia et al. 2004; Gupta et al. 2013b; Xiong 1998). Reports exist about the binding of this metal to carboxylic groups of mucilage uronic acids on root surfaces (Morel et al. 1986; Sharma and Dubey 2005), but the detail method of transport of Pb from soil to root tissue is still not known. Once inside the roots, most of the Pb is bound to ion exchangeable sites in the cell walls and extracellular precipitation as phosphate and carbonate (Blaylock and Huang 2000; Sahi et al. 2002; Sharma and Dubey 2005). Several studies supports the view that in most plants the absorbed Pb remain stored within root tissue and never translocated to the above ground parts (Blaylock and Huang 2000) but presence of Pb in the phloem tissues of few plants suggest the movement of Pb through the xylem to leaves, returning through the phloem to the plant body (Peralta-Videa et al.2009). Studies of Huang and Cunningham, (1996) and Antosiewicz (2005) suggest that the unbound Pb is moved through Ca^{+2} channels accumulating near the endodermis. However, in *Sesbania drummondii* Pb is transported to stems and leaves as Pb-acetate, Pb-nitrate, and Pb sulfide (Sharma et al. 2004a,b). As described by Cobbett (2000), Pb like other toxic elements is complexed by phytochelatins.

4. ROOT TO SHOOT METAL TRANSLOCATION

As discussed in previous sections, non-hyperaccumulators, retain heavy metals in root cells by detoxifying them and/or chelation in the cytoplasm and/or store them into vacuoles (fig. 1). On the other hand, once taken up by the roots of hyperaccumulators, these metal ions are loaded into the xylem and transported to the shoots as complexes with various chelators (fig. 1). According to Leea et al. (1977), organic acids, mainly malate and citrate, are major chelators for Fe and Ni in the xylem. But the role of these organic acids in the root cells is still controversial, due to their low association constants with metals at cytosolic pH values. The complex formation is more stable within the acidic vacuolar environment (Haydon and Cobbet 2007). Free amino acids also seem to play key role in heavy metal hyperaccumulation such as histidine and nicotinamine, which form stable complexes with bivalent cations within the root cells (Callahan et al. 2006). Free histidine (His) is regarded as the most important ligand involved in Ni hyperaccumulation (Callahan et al. 2006). Fast and efficient root-to-shoot translocation of large amounts of heavy metals in hyperaccumulator plants rely on enhanced xylem loading by constitutive overexpression of genes coding for transport systems common to non-hyperaccumulators (Rascio and Navari-Izzo 2011).

The P_{1B} type ATP ases reclassified as HMAs, function not only as efflux pump to remove metal ion from cells, but also as internal transporter to xylem loading of heavy metals. They play a role in metal homeostasis and tolerance (Axelsen and Palmgren 1998). For example, AtHMA4 is a plasma membrane transporter of divalent ions required for Zn homeostasis and Cd detoxification also participates in the cytosolic efflux and in the root-to-shoot translocation of these metals (Mills et al. 2003; Verret et al. 2004). Overexpression of the AtHMA4 protein not only increases Zn and Cd tolerance, but also enhances the root-to-shoot translocation of both metals suggesting an indispensible role in root-to-shoot metal transport (Verret et al. 2004). Interestingly, it has been demonstrated that the HMA4 activity positively affects other candidate genes particularly those implicated in heavy metal uptake such as ZIP family transporter genes. This strongly suggests that the root-to-shoot translocation acts as a driving force for hyperaccumulation, by creating a permanent metal deficiency response in roots (Hanikenne et al. 2008).

The MATE (Multidrug and Toxin Efflux) family proteins are membrane localized efflux proteins actively participate in heavy metal translocation in hyperaccumulating plants. FRD3 (Ferric Reductase Defective 3), a member of MATE family protein localized at root pericycle plasma membrane are known to load Fe and citrate into vascular tissues in the roots (Durrett et al. 2007).

Involvement of YSL (Yellow strip 1 like) family protein in root to shoot translocation has also been suggested, which mediate the loading into and unloading out of xylem of nicotinamine-metal-chelators (Colangelo and Guerinot 2006). Three genes, TcYSL3,TcYSL5 and TcYSL7 are constitutively overexpressed in roots and shoots of *T. caerulescens* participating in vascular loading and translocation ofnicotinamine-metal-complexes (Gendre et al. 2007). The role of YSL transporters and NA (nicotianamine) in metal distribution in plants has recently been reviewed (Curie et al. 2009).

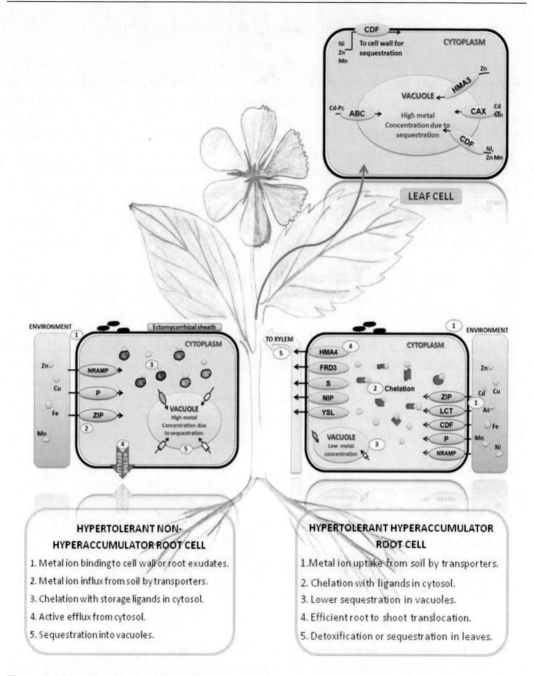

Figure 1. Mechanism involved in metal tolerance and sequestration in plants. (Modified from: Hall 2002; Rascio and Navari-Izzo 2011; Yang and Chu 2011).

5. DETOXIFICATION AND SEQUESTRATION OF TOXIC METALS

On the shoot level, non-hyperaccumulator plants employ metal binding ligands such as metallothioneins, phytochelatins, and organic acids to detoxify heavy metals (Cobbett et al. 2002). Whereas, in hyperaccumulator plants, heavy metals are detoxified by sequestering them into the vacuoles (Kramer et al. 2010) or storing them in specialized epidermal cells (Kupper et al. 2000). Great efficiency in detoxification and sequestration is a key property of hyperaccumulators which allows them to concentrate huge amounts of heavy metals in above-ground organs without suffering any phytotoxic effect. High heavy metal accumulation principally occurs in leaves because the photosynthetic apparatus is the major target for most of these toxic metals. The preferential heavy metal detoxification/sequestration in hyperaccumulators do occur in epidermis (Bidwell et al. 2004; Ma et al. 2005; Asemanehet al. 2006; Freeman et al. 2006), trichomes (Kupper et al. 2000) and even cuticle (Robinson et al. 2003).

The main pathways of heavy metal detoxification/sequestration in hyperaccumulators involve metal complexation with ligands and/or in their removal from metabolically active cytoplasm by moving them into inactive compartments, mainly vacuoles and cell walls in the aerial organs (Rascio and Navari-Izzo 2011). Comparative study of hyperaccumulator and related non-hyperaccumulator species have demonstrated that sequestration trait relies, at least in part, on constitutive overexpression of genes that encode proteins operating in heavy metal transfer across the tonoplast and/or plasma membrane and involved in excluding them from cytoplasm. The CDF (Cation Diffusion Facilitator) family, P_{1B} ATPase, CAX gene encoding members are regarded as important candidates in this detoxification mechanism (Kim et al. 2004; Gustin et al. 2009; Cracium et al. 2006).

CONCLUSION

Anthropogenic activities (e.g. mining and smelting) play a major role in increased metal concentrations in soils rather than their natural sources. Due to their persistent nature, heavy metal contamination is a major problem in the world even though in developed countries the emissions have declined. For example, Cd may accumulate into fields over a time due to its presence as a contaminant in fertilizers (Mortvedt 1996). On the other hand, mineral deficiencies are common worldwide. For example, more than 25% of the world's population is estimated to be at risk of Zn deficiency (Maret and Sandstead 2006) which is, according to WHO, as serious as Fe and vitamin A deficiencies. Both essential micronutrients as well as toxic heavy metals may enter the food chain from the soil via plants. Genetic variations of the plants render them different in tolerant potential of the heavy metals. The extreme examples are the hyperaccumulator plants, which may contain hundred-fold higher metal concentrations in their shoots as compared to other plants. Plant metal tolerance and accumulation are thus very important topics as they influence the content of nutritional or toxic metals in the crops, including food crops. Understanding the mechanisms of heavy metal homeostasis may enable the selective breeding of more tolerant varieties or varieties with increased concentrations of essential minerals or decreased concentrations of heavy metals in the edible parts of the crops. Moreover, such knowledge could be used for developing plants for the purpose of phytoremediation. Enhanced accumulation of heavy metals in the above ground biomass is the ultimate goal in creating plants that can be useful for phytoremediation.

Thus heavy metal transport is a very exciting and developing field in plant biology and we are poised at the discovery of a range of new ion transporters that have undoubtedly changed our concept of metal nutrients acquisition and homeostasis in higher plants. Therefore, a future challenge will be to determine the transfer mechanisms and kinetics, specificity, localization, regulation and especially interaction partners of the transporters in plants.

REFERENCES

Abdel-Ghany SE, Muller-Moule P, Niyogi KK, Pilon M, Shikanai T (2005) Two P-Type ATPases are required for copper delivery in *Arabidopsis thaliana* Chloroplasts. *Plant Cell* 17: 1233–1251.

Ali R, Ma W, Lemtiri-Chlieh F, Tsaltas D, Leng Q, von Bodman S, Berkowitz GA (2007) Death don't have no mercy and neither does calcium: *Arabidopsis* cyclic nucleotide gated channel 2 and innate immunity. *Plant Cell* 19: 1081–1995.

Amir H, Jasper DA, Abbott LK (2008) Tolerance and induction of tolerance to Ni of arbuscularmycorrhizal fungi from New Caledonian ultramafic soils. *Mycorrhiza* 19: 1–6.

Andres-Colas N, Sancenon V, Rodriguez-Navarro S, Mayo S, Thiele DJ, Ecker JR, Puig S, Penarrubia L (2006) The *Arabidopsis* heavy metal P-type ATPase HMA5 interacts with metallochaperones and functions in copper detoxification of roots. *Plant J* 45: 225–236.

Antosiewicz DM (2005) Study of calcium-dependent lead-tolerance on plants differing in their level of Ca-deficiency tolerance. *Environ Pollut* 134: 23–34.

Appenroth KJ (2010) Definition of "Heavy Metals" and their role in biological systems. In: SherametiI, Varma A (eds) *Soil Heavy Metals, Soil Biology*, Vol 19, Springer-Verlag Berlin Heidelberg.

Arazi T, Sunkar R, Kaplan B, Fromm H (1999A) Tobacco plasma membrane calmodulin binding transporter confers Ni^{2+} tolerance and Pb^{2+} hypersensitivity in transgenic plants. *Plant J* 20: 171–182.

Arnesano F, Banci L, Bertini I, Cioffi-Baffoni S, Molteni E, Huffman DL, O'Halloran TV (2002) Metallochaperones and metal-transporting ATPases: A comparative analysis of sequences and structures. *Genome Res* 12: 255–271.

Arriagada C, Aranda E, Sampedro I, Garcia-Romera I, Ocampo JA (2009) Interactions of*Trametes versicolor, Coriolopsis rigida* and the arbuscular mycorrhizal fungus *Glomus deserticola* on the copper tolerance of *Eucalyptus globulus*. *Chemosphere* 77: 273–278.

Asemaneh T, Ghaderian SM, Crawford SA, Marshall AT, Baker AJM (2006) Cellular and subcellular compartmentation of Ni in the Eurasian serpentine plants *Alyssum bracteatum, Alyssum murale* (Brassicaceae) and *Cleome heratensis* (Capparaceae). *Planta* 225: 193–290.

Assuncao AGL, Costa Martins PDA, De Folter S, Vooijs R, Schat H, Aarts MGM (2001) Elevated expression of metal transporter genes in three accessions of the metal hyperaccumulator *Thlaspi caerulescens*. Plant Cell Environ 24: 217–226.

Axelsen KB, Palmgren MG (1998) Evolution of substrate specificities in the P type ATPase superfamily. *J Mol Evol* 46: 84–101.

Axelsen K, Palmgren M (2001) Inventory of the superfamily of P-Type ion pumps in *Arabidopsis*. *Plant Physiol* 126: 696–706.

Balague C, Lin BQ, Alcon C, Flottes G, Malmstrom S, Kohler C, Neuhaus G, Pelletier G, Gaymard F, Roby D (2003) HLM1, an essential signaling component in the hypersensitive response, is a member of the cyclic nucleotide-gated channel ion channel family. *Plant Cell* 15: 365–379.

Baxter I, Tchieu J, Sussman M, Boutry M, Palmgren M, Gribskov M, Harper J, Axelsen B (2003) Genomic comparison of P-Type ATPase ion pumps in *Arabidopsis* and Rice. *Plant Physiol* 132: 618–628.

Begonia MT, Begonia GB, Miller GS, Gilliard D (2004) Effects of chelate application time on the phytoextraction of lead-contaminated soils. *Bull Environ Cont Toxicol* 73: 1033-1040.

Belouchi A, Cellier M, Kwan T, Saini HS, Leroux G, Gros P (1995) The macrophage-specific membrane protein Nramp controlling natural resistance to infections in mice has homologues expressed in the root system of plants. *Plant Mol Biol* 29: 1181–1196.

Belouchi A, Kwan T, Gros P (1997) Cloning and characterization of the OsNramp family from *Oryza sativa*, a new family of membrane proteins possibly implicated in the transport of metal ions. *Plant Mol Biol*33: 1085–1092.

Berg JM, Shi Y (1996) The galvanization of biology: A growing appreciation for the roles of zinc. *Science* 271: 1081–1085.

Bidwell SD, Crawford SA, Woodrow IE, Sommer-Knudsen J, Marshall AT (2004) Sub-cellular localization of Ni in the hyperaccumulator, *Hybanthus floribundus* (Lindley) F. Muell. *Plant Cell Environ* 27: 705–716.

Blaylock MJ, Huang JW (2000) Phytoextraction of metals. In: Raskin I, Ensley BD (eds) *Phytoremediation of toxic metals: Using plants to clean up the environment*. John Wiley, New York pp 53–71.

Bluskov S, Arocena JM, Omotoso OO, Young JP (2005) Uptake, distribution, and speciation of chromium in *Brassica Juncea*. *Int J Phytorem* 7: 153–155.

Brennan RF, Bolland MDA (2006) Zinc sulfate is more effective at producing wheat shoots than zinc oxide in an alkaline soil but both sources are equally effective in an acid soil. *Aust J Exp Agric* 46: 1615–1620.

Callahan DL, Baker AJM, Kolev SD, Wedd AG (2006) Metal ion ligands in hyperaccumulating plants. *J Biol Inorg Chem* 11: 2–12.

Caussy D, Gochfeld M, Gurzau E, Neagu C, Ruedel H (2003) Lessons from case studies of metals: investigation exposure, bioavailability, and risk. *Ecotoxicol Environ Safe* 56:45–51.

Chaney RL (1988) Metal speciation and interactions among elements affect trace element transfer in agricultural and environmental food-chains.In: Kramer JR, Allen HE (eds) *Metal speciation: Theory, analysis and applications*. Lewis Publisher Chelsea MI pp 218–260.

Chatterjee S, Mitra A, Datta S, Veer V (2013) Phytoremediation protocols: An overview. In: Gupta DK (ed) *Plant Based Remediation Processes, Soil Biology*, Vol. 35, Springer-Verlag Berlin Heidelberg.

Clarke ND, Berg JM (1998) Zinc. *Science* 282: 2018–2022.

Cobbett CS (2000) Phytochelatins and their roles in heavy metal detoxification. *Curr Opin Plant Biol* 3: 211–216.

Cobbett CS, Goldsbrough P (2002) Phytochelatins and metallothioneins: Roles in heavy metal detoxification and homeostasis. *Annu Rev Plant Biol* 53: 159–182.

Cobbett CS, Hussain D, Haydon MJ (2003) Structural and functional relationships between type 1B heavy metal-transporting P-type ATPases in *Arabidopsis*. *New Phytol* 159: 315–332.

Cohen MD, Prophete C, Sisco M, Chen L, Zelikoff JT (2006) Pulmonary immunotoxic potentials of metals are governed by select physicochemical properties: Chromium agents. *J Inmunotoxicol* 3: 69–81.

Colangelo EP, Guerinot ML (2006) Put the metal to the petal: Metal uptake and transport throughout plants. *Curr Opin Plant Biol* 9: 322–330.

Colzi I, Doumett S, Del Bubba M, Fornaini J, Arnetoli M, Gabbrielli R, Gonnelli C (2011) On the role of the cell wall in the phenomenon of copper tolerance in *Silene paradoxa* L. *Environ Exp Bot* 72: 77–83.

Connolly EL, Fett JP, Guerinot ML (2002) Expression of the IRT1 metal transporter is controlled by metals at the levels of transcript and protein accumulation. *Plant Cell* 14: 1347–1357.

Conte Sarah S, Walker Elsbeth L (2011) Transporters contributing to iron trafficking in plants. *Mol Plant* 4: 464–476.

Courbot M, Willems G, Motte P, Arvidsson S, Roosens N, Saumitou-Laprade P, Verbruggen N (2007) A major quantitative trait locus for cadmium tolerance in *Arabidopsis halleri* colocalizes with HMA4, a gene encoding a heavy metal ATPase. *Plant Physiol* 144: 1052–1065.

Craciun AR, Courbot M, Bourgis F, Salis P, Saumitou-Laprade P, Verbruggen N(2006) Comparative cDNA-AFLP analysis of Cd-tolerant and - sensitive genotypes derived from crosses between the Cd hyperaccumulator *Arabidopsis halleri* and *Arabidopsis lyrata* spp. petraea. *J Exp Bot* 57: 2967–2983.

Curie C, Alonso JM, Le Jean M, Ecker JR, Briat JF (2000) Involvement of NRAMP1 from *Arabidopsis thaliana* in iron transport. Biochem J 347: 749–755.

Curie C, Cassin G, Couch D, Divol F, Higuchi K, Le Jean M, Mission J, Schikora A, Czernic P, Mari S (2009) Metal movement within the plant: Contribution of nicotianamine and yellow stripe 1-like transporters. *Ann Bot* 103: 1–11.

Delhaize E, Kataoka T, Hebb DM, White RG, Ryan RR (2003)Genes encoding proteins of the cation diffusion facilitator family that confer manganese tolerance. *Plant Cell* 15: 1131–1142.

Dhankher OP, Rosen BP, McKinney EC, Meagher RB (2006) Hyperaccumulation of arsenic inthe shoots of *Arabidopsis* silenced for arsenate reductase (ACR2). *PNAS USA* 103: 5413–5418.

Diatloff E, Forde BG, Roberts SK (2006) Expression and transport characterisation of the wheat low-affinity cation transporter (LCT1) in the methylotrophic yeast *Pichia pastoris*. *Bichem Biophys Res Comm* 344: 807–813.

Douchiche O, Driouich A, Morvan C (2010a) Spatial regulation of cell-wall structure in response to heavy metal stress: Cadmium-induced alteration of the methyl-esterification pattern of homogalacturonans. *Ann Bot* 105: 481–491.

Douchiche O, Soret-Morvan O, Chaibi W, Morvan C, Paynel F (2010b) Characteristics of cadmium tolerance in 'Hermes' flax seedlings: Contribution of cell walls. *Chemosphere* 81: 1430–1436.

Dube BK, Tewari KK, Chatterjee J, Chatterjee C (2003) Excess chromium alters uptake and translocation of certain nutrients in citrullus. *Chemosphere* 53: 1147–1153.

Durrett TP, Gassmann W, Rogers EE (2007) The FRD3-mediated efflux of citrate into the root vasculature is necessary for efficient iron translocation. *Plant Physiol* 144: 197– 205.

Dushenkov S, Vasudev D, Gleba D, Fleisher D, Ting KC, Ensley B (1997) Removal ofuranium from water using terrestrial plants. *Environ Sci Technol* 31: 3468–3474.

Eide D, Broderius M, Fett J, Guerinot ML (1996) A novel iron-regulated metal transporter from plants identified by functional expression in yeast. *PNAS USA* 93: 5624–5628.

Eide DJ (1998) The molecular biology of metal ion transport in *Saccharomyces cerevisiae*. *Ann Rev Nut* 18: 441-469.

Emery L, Whelan S, Hirschi KD, Pittman JK (2012) Phylogenetic analysis of Ca^{2+}/cation antiporter genes and insights into their evolution in plants. *Front Plant Sci*3:1.

Eren E, Arguello J (2004) *Arabidopsis* HMA2, a divalent heavy metal-transporting PIB-type ATPase, is involved in cytoplasmic Zn^{2+} homeostasis. *Plant Physiol* 136: 3712–3723.

Fitz WJ, Wenzel WW (2002) Arsenic transformations in the soil–rhizosphere–plant system: Fundamentals and potential application to phytoremediation. *J Biotechnol* 99: 259–278.

Fox TC, Guerinot ML (1998) Molecular biology of cation transport in plants. *Ann Rev Plant Physiol Plant Mol Biol* 49: 669–696.

Freeman JL, Zhang LH, Marcus MA, Fakra S, McGrath SP, Pilon-Smits EA (2006) Spatial imaging, speciation and quantification of Se in the hyperaccumulator plants *Astragalus bisulcatus* and *Stanleya pinnata*. *Plant Physiol* 142: 124–134.

Frietsch S, Wang YF, Sladek C, Poulsen LR, Romanowsky SM, Schroeder JI, Harper JF (2007) A cyclic nucleotide-gated channel is essential for polarized tip growth of pollen. *PNAS USA* 104: 14531–14536.

Gardea-Torresdey JL, de la Rosa G, Peralta-Videa JR, Montes M, Cruz-Jimenez G, Cano-Aguilera I (2005) Differential uptake and transport of trivalent and hexavalent chromium by tumbleweed (*Salsola kali*). *Arch Env Contam Toxicol* 48: 225–232.

Gendre D, Czernic P, Conejero G (2007) TcYSL3, a member of the YSL gene family from the hyperaccumulator *Thlaspi caerulescens*, encodes a nicotinamine–Ni/Fe transporter. *Plant J* 49: 1–15.

Gobert A, Park G, Amtmann A, Sanders D, Maathuis FJ (2006) *Arabidopsis thaliana* cyclic nucleotide gated channel 3 forms a non-selective ion transporter involved in germination and cation transport. *J Exp Bot* 57: 791–800.

Gonzaga MI, Ma LQ, Santos JA, Matias MI (2009) Rhizosphere characteristics of two arsenic hyperaccumulating *Pteris* ferns. *Sci Total Environ* 407: 4711–4716.

Gonzalez-Mendoza D, Zapata-Perez O (2008) Mechanism of plant tolerance to potentially toxic elements. *Bol Soc Bot Mex* 82: 53–61.

Govoni G, Gros P (1998) Macrophage NRAMP1 and its role in resistance to microbial infections. *Inflam Res* 47: 277–284.

Gratao PL, Prasad MNV, Cardoso PF, Lea PJ, Azevedo RA (2005) Phytoremediation: Green technology for the cleanup of toxic metals in the environment. *Braz J Plant Physiol* 17: 53–64.

Gravot A, LieutaudA, VerretF, AuroyP, Vavasseur A, Richaud P (2004) AtHMA3, a plant P1B-ATPase, functions as a Cd/Pb transporter in yeast. *FEBS Lett* 561: 22–28.

Gregor M (1999) Metal availability and bioconcentration in plants. In: Prasad MNV, Hagemeyer J (eds) *Heavy Metal Stress in Plants*. Springer-Verlag, Berlin Heidelberg pp 1–27.

Guerinot ML, Yi Y (1994) Iron: Nutritious, noxious and not readily available. *Plant Physiol* 104: 815–820.

Guerinot ML (2000) The ZIP family of metal transporters. *Biochim Biophys Acta* 1465: 190–198.

Gunshin H, Mackenzie B, Berger UV, Gunshin Y, Romero MF, Boron WF, Nussberger S, Gollan JL, Hediger MA (1997) Cloning and characterization of a mammalian proton-coupled metal-ion transporter. *Nature* 388: 482–488.

Gupta DK, Inouhe M, Rodríguez-Serrano M, Romero-Puerta MC, Sandalio LM (2013a) Oxidative stress and arsenic toxicity: Role of NADPH oxidases. *Chemosphere* 90: 1987–1996.

Gupta DK, Huang HG, Corpas FJ (2013b) Lead tolerance in plants: Strategies for phytoremediation. *Environ Sci Pollut Res* 20: 2150–2161.

Gustin JL, Loureiro ME, Kim D, Na G, Tikhonova M, Salt DE (2009) MTP1-dependent Zn sequestration into shoot vacuoles suggests dual roles in Zn tolerance and accumulation in Zn hyperaccumulating plants. *Plant J* 57: 1116–1127.

Hall JL, Williams LE (2003) Transition metal transporters in plants. *J Exp Bot* 54:2601–2613.

Hall JL (2002) Cellular mechanisms for heavy metal detoxification and tolerance. *J Exp Bot* 53: 1–11.

Hanikenne M, Talke Ina N, Haydon MJ, Lanz C, Nolte A, Motte P, Kroyman J, Weigel D, Kramer U (2008) Evolution of metal hyperaccumulation required cisregulatory changes and triplication of HMA4. *Nature* 453: 391–395.

Hasan SA, Fariduddin Q, Ali B, Hayat S, Ahmad A (2009) Cadmium: Toxicity and tolerance in plants. *J Environ Biol* 30: 165–174

Haydon MJ, Cobbett CS (2007) Transporters of ligands for essential metal ions in plants. *New Phytol* 174: 499–506.

HenikoffS, Greene EA, Pietrokovski S, BorkP, Attwood TK, Hood L (1997) Genome families: The taxonomy of protein prologs and chimeras. *Science* 279: 609–614.

Henriques R, Jaasik J, Klein M, Martinoia E, Feller U, Schell J, Pais MS, Koncz C (2002) Knock-out of *Arabidopsis* metal transporter gene IRT1 results in iron deficiency accompanied by cell differentiation defects. *Plant Mol Biol* 50: 587–597.

Hirayama T, Kieber JJ, Hirayama N, Kogan M, Guzman P, Nourizadeh S, Alonso JM, Dailey WP, Dancis A, Ecker JR (1999) Responsive-to-antagonist 1, a Menkes/Wilson disease related copper transporter, is required for ethylene signalling in *Arabidopsis*. *Cell* 97: 383–393.

Hirschi KD, Korenkov VD, Wilganowski NL, Wagner GJ (2000) Expression of *Arabidopsis* CAX2 in tobacco: Altered metal accumulation and increased manganese tolerance. *Plant Physiol* 124: 125–134.

Hirschi KD, Zhen RG, Cunningham KW, Rea PA, Fink GR (1996) CAX1, an H^+/Ca^{2+} antiporter from *Arabidopsis*. *PNAS USA* 93: 8782–8786.

Housecroft CE, Sharpe AG (2005)*Inorganic Chemistry*. Prentice Hall, Harlow.

Hua BG, Mercier RW, Leng Q, Berkowitz GA (2003a) Plants do it differently. A new basis for potassium/sodium selectivity in the pore of an ion channel. *Plant Physiol* 132: 1353–1361.

Hua BG, Mercier RW, Zielinski RE, Berkowitz GA (2003b) Functional interaction of calmodulin with a plant cyclic nucleotide gated cation channel. *Plant Physiol Biochem* 41: 945–954.

Huang JW, Cunningham SD (1996) Lead phytoextraction: Species variation in lead uptake and translocation. *New Phytol* 134: 73–84.

Huang JW, Shaff JE, Grunes DL, Kochian LV (1992) Aluminum effects on calcium fluxes at the root apex of aluminum-tolerant and aluminum-sensitive wheat cultivars. *Plant Physiol* 98: 230–237.

Hussain D, Haydon MJ, WangY, Wong E, Sherson SM, Young J, Camakaris J, Harper JF, Cobbett CS (2004) P-type ATPase heavy metal transporters with roles in essential zinc homeostasis in *Arabidopsis*. *Plant Cell* 16: 1327–1339.

Iram S, Ahmad I, Javed B, Yaqoob S, Akhtar K, Kazmi MR, Badar Z (2009) Fungal tolerance to heavy metals. *Pak J Bot* 41: 2583–2594.

James BR, Barlett RJ (1983) Behavior of chromium in soils VII. Adsorption and reduction of hexavalent forms. *J Env Qual* 12: 177–181.

Kamiya T, TanakaM, Mitani N, Ma JF, Maeshima M, Fujiwara T (2009) $NIP_{1;1}$, an aquaporin homolog, determines the arsenite sensitivity of *Arabidopsis thaliana*. *J Biol Chem* 284: 2114–2120.

Kampfenkel K, Kushnir S, Babiychuk E, Inzea D, Van Montagu M (1995) Molecular characterization of a putative *Arabidopsis thaliana* copper transporter and its yeast homologue. *J Biol Chem* 270: 28479–28486.

Kim D, Gustin JL, Lahner B, Persans MW, Baek D, Yun DJ, Salt DE (2004) The plant CDF family member TgMTP1 from the Ni/Zn hyperaccumulator *Thlaspi goesingense* acts to enhance efflux of Zn at the plasma membrane when expressed in *Saccharomyces cerevisiae*. *Plant J* 39: 237–251.

Kim YJ, Kim JH, Lee CE, Mok YG, Choi JS, Shin HS, Hwang S(2006) Expression of yeast transcriptional activator MSN1 promotes accumulation of chromium and sulfur by enhancing sulfate transporter level in plants. *FEBS Lett* 580: 206–210.

Koehler C, Neuhaus G (2000) Characterization of calmodulin binding to cyclic nucleotide-gated ion channels from *Arabidopsis thaliana*. *FEBS Lett* 471: 133–136.

Kohler C, Merkle T, Roby D, Neuhaus G (2001) Developmentally regulated expression of a cyclic nucleotide-gated channel from *Arabidopsis* indicates its involvement in programmed cell death. *Planta* 213: 327–332.

Korenkov V, Park SH, Cheng NH, Sreevidya C, Lachmansingh J, Morris J, Hirschi K, Wagner GJ (2007) Enhanced Cd^{2+} selective root-tonoplast-transport in tobaccos expressing *Arabidopsis* cation exchangers. *Planta* 225: 403–441.

Kramer U (2010) Metal hyperaccumulation in plants. *Ann Rev Plant Biol* 6: 517–534.

Kramer U, Talke IN, Hanikenne M (2007) Transition metal transport. *FEBS Lett* 581: 2263–2272.

Kupper H, Lombi E, Zhao FJ, McGrath SP (2000) Cellular compartmentation of cadmium and zinc in relation to other elements in the hyperaccumulator *Arabidopsis halleri*. *Planta* 212: 75–84.

Lang I, Wernitznig S (2011) Sequestration at the cell wall and plasma membrane facilitates zinctolerance in the moss *Pohlia drummondii*. *Environ Exp Bot* 74: 186–193.

Leea J, Reevesa RD, Brooksa RR, Jaffreb T (1977) Isolation and identification of a citrate complex of nickel from nickel-accumulating plants. *Phytochem* 16: 1503–1505.

Leng Q, Mercier RW, Hua BG, Fromm H, Berkowitz GA (2002) Electrophysiological analysis of cloned cyclic nucleotide-gated ion channels. *Plant Physiol* 128: 400–410.

Li ZS, Lu YP, Zhen RG, Szczypka M, Thiele DJ, Rea PA (1997) A new pathway for vacuolar cadmium sequestration in *Saccharomyces cerevisiae*: YCF1-catalyzed transport of bis(glutathionato) cadmium. *PNAS USA* 94: 42–47.

Lin AJ, Zhang XH, Wong MH, Ye ZH, Lou LQ, Wang YS, Zhu YG (2007) Increase ofmultimetal tolerance of three leguminous plants by arbuscular mycorrhizal fungi colonization. *Environ Geochem Heal* 29: 473–481.

Lombi E, Tearall KL, Howarth JR, Zhao FJ, Hawkesford MJ, McGrath SP (2002) Influence or iron status on cadmium and zinc uptake by different ecotypes of the hyperaccumulator *Thlaspi caerulescens*. *Plant Physiol* 128: 1359–1367.

Lutsenko S, Kaplan JH (1995) Organization of P-type ATPases: Significance of structural diversity. *Biochemistry* 34: 15607–15613.

Ma JF, Ueno D, Zhao FJ, McGrath SP (2005) Subcellular localisation of Cd and Zn in the leaves of a Cd-hyperaccumulating ecotype of *Thlaspi caerulescens*. *Planta* 220: 731–736.

Ma JF, Yamaji N, Mitani N, Xu XY, Su YH, McGrath SP, Fang-Jie Zhao (2008) Transporters of arsenite in rice and their role in arsenic accumulation in rice grain. *PNAS USA* 105: 9931–9935.

Ma LQ, Komar KM, Tu C, Zhang WH, Cai Y, Kennelley ED (2001) A fern that hyperaccumulates arsenic-a hardy, versatile, fast-growing plant helps to remove arsenic from contaminated soils. *Nature* 409: 579.

Ma W, Ali R, Berkowitz GA (2006) Characterization of plant phenotypes associated withloss of function of AtCNGC1, a plant cyclic nucleotide gated cation channel. *Plant Physiol Biochem* 44: 494–505.

Ma Wei, Smigel A, Verma R, Gerald AB (2009) Cyclic nucleotide gated channels and related signaling components in plant innate immunity. *Plant Signal Behav* 4: 277–282.

MacDiarmid CW, Gaither LA, Eide DJ (2000) Zinc transporters that regulate vacuolar zinc storage in Saccharomyces cerevisiae. *EMBO J* 19: 2845–2955.

Manara A (2012) Plants and Heavy Metals. In: Furini A (ed) *Springer Briefs in Molecular Sciences.* Springer-Verlag Berlin Heidelberg.

Marchiol L, Assolari S, Sacco P, Zerbi G (2004) Phytoextraction of heavy metals by canola (*Brassica napus*) and radish (*Raphanus sativus*) grown on multicontaminated soil. *Environ Pollut* 132: 21–27.

Maret W, Sandstead HH (2006) Zinc requirements and the risks and benefits of zinc supplementation. *J Trace Elem Med Biol* 20: 3–18.

Marschner H (1995) Mineral Nutrition of Higher Plants. 2nd edn, Academic Press, London.

Martinoia E, Klein M, Bovet L, Forestier C, Kolukisaoglu U, Muller-RoverB, Schulz B (2002) Multifunctionality of plant ABC transporters-more than just detoxifiers. *Planta* 214: 345–355.

Martins LL, Mourato MP, Cardoso AI, Pinto AP, Mota AM, Goncalves MDS, de Varennes A (2011) Oxidative stress induced by cadmium in *Nicotiana tabacum* L.: Effects on growth parameters, oxidative damage and antioxidant responses in different plant parts. *Acta Physiol Plant* 33: 1375–1383.

Maser P, Thomine S, Schroeder JI, Ward JM, Hirschi K, Sze H, Talke IN, Amtmann A, Maathuis FJM, Sanders D, Harper JF, Tchieu J, Gribskov M, Persans MW, Salt DE, Kim SA, Guerinot ML (2001) Phylogenetic relationships within cation transporter families of *Arabidopsis*. *Plant Physiol* 126: 1646–1667.

Meharg AA, Hartley-Whitaker J (2002) Arsenic uptake and metabolism in arsenic resistant and non-resistant plant species. *New Phytol* 154: 29–42.

Michalak A (2006) Phenolic compounds and their antioxidant activity in plants growing under heavy metal stress. *Pol J Environ Stud* 15: 523–530.

Mills RF, Krijger GC, Baccarini PJ, Hall JL, Williams LE (2003) Functional expression of AtHMA4, a P1B-type ATPase in the Zn/Co/Cd/Pb subclass. *Plant J* 35: 164–175.

Morel JL, Mench M, Guckert A (1986) Measurement of Pb^{2+}, Cu^{2+} and Cd^{2+} binding with mucilage exudates from maize (*Zea mays* L) roots. *Biol Fertil Soils* 2: 29–34.

Mortvedt JJ (1996) Heavy metal contaminants in inorganic and organic fertilizers. *Fert Res* 43: 55–61.

Naumann B, Eberius M, Appenroth (2007) Growth rate based dose–response relationships and EC-values of ten heavy metals using the duckweed growth inhibition test (ISO 20079) with *Lemna minor* L. clone St. *J Plant Physiol* 164: 1656–1664.

Navari-IzzoF, QuartacciMF, Pinzino C, Dalla VF, Sgherri C (1998) Thylakoid-bound and stromal antioxidative enzymes in wheat treated with excess of copper. *Physiol Planta* 104: 630–638.

Navari-Izzo F, Pinzino C, Quartacci MF, Sgherri C (1999) Superoxide and hydroxyl radical generation, and superoxide dismutase in PSII membrane fragments from wheat. *Free Radic Res* 31: S3–9.

Nelson N (1999) Metal ion transporters and homeostasis. *EMBO J* 18: 4361–4371.

Neumann D, Lichtenberger O, Gunther D, Tschiersch K, Nover L (1994) Heat-shock proteins induce heavy-metal tolerance in higher-plants. *Planta* 194: 360–367.

Nevo Y, Nelson N (2006) The NRAMP family of metal-ion transporters. *Biochim Biophys Acta* 1763: 609–620.

Nishida S, Tsuzuki C, Kato A, Aisu A, Yoshida J, Mizuno T (2011) AtIRT1, the primaryiron uptake transporter in the root, mediates excess nickel accumulation in *Arabidopsis thaliana*. *Plant Cell Physiol* 52: 1433–1442.

Ortiz DF, Kreppel L, Speiser DM, Scheel G, McDonald G, DW Ow (1992) Heavy metal tolerance in the fission yeast requires an ATP-binding cassette-type vacuolar membrane transporter. *EMBO J* 11: 3491–3499.

Ortiz DF, Ruscitti T, McCue KF, DW Ow (1995) Transport of metal-binding peptides by HMT1, fission yeast ABC-type vacuolar membrane protein. *J Biol Chem*270: 4721–4728.

Pagliano C, Raviolo M, Vecchia FD, Gabbrielli R, Gonneli C, Rascio N, Barbato R, Rocca N (2006) Evidence for PSII-donor-side damage and photo inhibition induced bycadmium treatment on rice (*Oryza sativa* L). *J Photochem Photobiol B: Biol* 84: 70–78.

Palmgren MG, Clemens S, Williams LE, Kramer U, Borg S, Schjorring JK (2008) Zinc biofortification ofcereals: Problems and solutions. *Trend Plant Sci* 13: 464–473.

Palmgren MG, Axelsen KB (1998) Evolution of P-type ATPases. *Biochim Biophys Acta* 1365: 37–45.

Park JY, Song WY,Wi KD,Jin EY, Hansen TH,Schiller M,Lee TG,Martinoia E, LeeYS (2012) The phytochelatin transporters AtABCC1 and AtABCC2 mediate tolerance to cadmium and mercury. *Plant J* 69: 278–288.

Paulsen IT, Saier Jr MH (1997) A novel family of ubiquitous heavy metal ion transport proteins. *J Mem Biol* 156: 99–103.

Peralta-Videaa JR, Lopeza ML, Narayana M, Saupea G, Gardea-TorresdeyaJ (2009) The biochemistry of environmental heavy metal uptake by plants: Implications for the food chain. *Int J Biochem Cell Biol* 41: 1665–1677.

Persans MW, Nieman K, Salt DE (2001) Functional activity and role of cation-efflux family members in Ni hyperaccumulation in *Thlaspi goesingense*. *PNAS USA* 98: 9995–10000.

Pickering IJ, Prince RC, George MJ, Smith RD, George GN, Salt DE (2000) Reduction andcoordination of arsenic in Indian mustard. *Plant Physiol* 122: 1171–1177.

Puig S, Penarrubia L (2009) Placing metal micronutrients in context: Transport and distribution in plants. *Curr Opin Plant Biol* 12: 299–306.

Puig S, Thiele DJ (2002) Molecular mechanisms of copper uptake and distribution. *Curr Opin Chem Biol* 6: 171–180.

Quartacci MF, Cosi E, Navari-Izzo F (2001) Lipids and NADPH-dependent superoxide production in plasma membrane vesicles from roots of wheat grown under copper deficiency or excess. *J Exp Bot* 52: 77–84.

Rakhshaee R, Giahi M, Pourahmad A (2009) Studying effect of cell wall's carboxyl-carboxylateratio change of *Lemna minor* to remove heavy metals from aqueous solution. *J Hazard Mater* 163: 165–173.

Ramos I, Esteban E, Lucena JJ, Garate A (2002) Cadmium uptake and subcellular distributionin plants of *Lactuca* sp. Cd–Mn interaction. *Plant Sci* 162: 761–767.

Rascio N, Navari-Izzo F (2011) Heavy metal hyperaccumulating plants: How and why do they do it? And what makes them so interesting? *Plant Sci* 180: 169–181.

Rastgoo L, Alemzadeh A, Afsharifar A (2011) Isolation of two novel isoforms encoding zinc- and copper-transporting P1B-ATPase from Gouan (*Aeluropus littoralis*). *Plant Omics* J 4: 377–383.

Rea PA (1999) MRP subfamily ABC transporters from plants and yeast. *J Exp Bot* 50: 895–913.

Rea PA, Li Z S, Lu YP, Drozdowicz YM (1998) From vacuolar GS-X pumps to multispeciffic ABC transporters. *Ann Rev Plant Physiol Plant Mol Biol* 49: 727–760.

Reeves RD (2006) Hyperaccumulation of trace elements by plants. In: Morel JL, Echevarria G, Goncharova N (eds) *Phytoremediation of Metal-Contaminated Soils, NATO Science Series IV: Earth and Environmental Sciences.* Springer, New York.

Robinson BH, Lombi E, Zhao FJ, McGrath SP (2003) Uptake and distribution of nickel and other metals in the hyperaccumulator *Berkheya coddii*. *New Phytol* 158: 279–285.

Robinson NJ, Proctor CM, Connolly EL, Guerinot M L (1999) A ferric chelate reductase for iron uptake from soil. *Nature* 397: 694–697.

Rocca N, La C, Andreoli G, Giacometti M, Rascio N, Moro I (2009) Responses of the Antarctic microalga *Koliella antartica* (Trebouxiophyceae, Chlorophyta) to cadmium contamination. *Photosynthetica* 47: 471–479.

Rodriguez-Serrano M, Romero-Puertas MC, Sparkes I, Hawes C, del Rio LA, Sandalio LM (2009) Peroxisome dynamics in *Arabidopsis* plants under oxidative stress induced by cadmium. *Free Radical Biol Med* 47: 1632–1639.

Sahi SV, Bryant NL, Nilesh CS, Singh SR (2002) Characterization of a lead hyperaccumulatorshrub, *Sesbania drummondii*. *Environ Sci Technol* 36: 4676–4680.

Saier MH (1999) Genome archeology leading to the characterization and classification of transport protein. *Curr Opin Microbiol* 2: 555–561.

Salt DE and Kramer U (2000) Mechanisms of metal hyperaccumulation in plants. In: Raskin I, Ensley BD (eds) *Phytoremediation of toxic metals: Using plants to clean up the environment.* Wiley, New York pp 231– 45.

Salt DE, Rauser WE (1995) Mg ATP-dependent transport of phytochelatins across the tonoplast of oat roots. *Plant Physiol* 107: 1293–1301.

Salt DE, Kato N, Kramer U, Smith RD, Raskin I (2000) The role of root exudates in nickelhyperaccumulation and tolerance in accumulator and nonaccumulator species of *Thlaspi*. In: Terry N, Banuelos G (eds) *Phytoremediation of Contaminated Soil and Water*. CRC Press LLC, Boca Raton.

Salt DE, Prince RC, Pickering IJ, Raskin I (1995) Mechanism of cadmium mobility and accumulation in Indian mustard. *Plant Physiol* 109: 1426–1433.

Salt DE, Wagner GJ (1993) Cadmium transport across tonoplast of vesicles from oat roots. Evidence for a Cd^{2+}/H^+ antiport activity. *J Biol Chem* 268: 12297–12302.

Sancenoan V, Puig S, Mira H, Thiele DJ, Penaarrubia L (2003) Identification of a coppertransporter family in *Arabidopsis thaliana*. *Plant Mol Biol* 51: 577–587.

Schuurink RC, Shartzer SF, Fath A, Jones RL (1998) Characterization of a calmodulin-binding transporter from the plasma membrane of barley aleurone. *PNAS USA* 95: 1944–1949.

Seigneurin-Berny D, Gravot A, Auroy P, Mazard C, Kraut A, Finazzi G, Grunwald D, Rappaport F, Vavasseur A, Joyard J, Richaud P, Rolland N (2006) HMA1, a New Cu-ATPase of the Chloroplast Envelope, is essential for growth under adverse light conditions. *J Biol Chem* 281: 2882–2892.

Sergio C, Figueira R, Crespo AMV (2000) Observations of heavy metal accumulation in the cellwalls of *Fontinalis antipyretica*, in a Portuguese stream affected by mine effluent. *J Bryol* 22: 251–255.

Shanker AK, Cervantes C, Loza-Tavera H, Avudainayagam S (2005) Chromium toxicity in plants. *Environ Int* 31: 739–753.

Sharma NC, Gardea-Torresdey JL, Parsons J, Sahi SV (2004a) Chemical speciation and cellular deposition of lead in *Sesbania drummondii*. *Environ Toxicol Chem* 23: 2068–2073.

Sharma P, Dubey RS (2005) Lead toxicity in plants. *Braz J Plant Physiol* 17: 35–52.

Sharma SS, Kaul S, Metwally A, Goyal KC, Finkemeier I, Dietz K J(2004b) Cadmium toxicityto barley (*Hordeum vulgare*) as affected by varying Fe nutritional status. *Plant Sci* 166: 1287–1295.

Shaul O, Hilgemann DW, de-Almeida-Engler JJ, Van Montagu M, Inze D, Galili G (1999) Cloningand characterization of a novel Mg^{2+}/H^+ exchanger. *EMBO J* 18: 3973–3980.

Shaw BP, Sahu SK, Mishra RK (2004) Heavy metal induced oxidative damage in terrestrial plants. In: Prasad MNV (ed) *Heavy Metal Stress in Plants*, 2nd edn, Springer-Verlag, New York pp 84–126.

Shigaki T, Pittman JK, Hirschi KD (2003) Manganese specificity determinants in the *Arabidopsis* metal/H^+ antiporter CAX2. *J Bio Chem* 278: 6610–6617.

Shikanai T, Muller-Moule P, Munekage Y, Niyogi KK, Pilon M (2003) PAA1, a P-type ATPase of *Arabidopsis*, functions in copper transport in chloroplasts. *Plant Cell* 15: 1333–1346.

Solioz M, Vulpe C (1996) CPx-type ATPases: a class of P-type ATPases that pump heavy metals. *Trend Biochem Sci* 21: 237–241.

Song WY, Sohn EJ, Martinoia E, Lee YJ, Yang YY, Jasinski M, Forestier C, Hwang I, Lee Y (2003) Engineering tolerance and accumulation oflead and cadmium in transgenic plants. *Nat Biotechnol*21: 914–919.

Sooksa-Nguan T, Yakubov B, Kozlovskyy VI, Barkume CM, Howe KJ, Thannhauser TW, Rutzke MA, Hart JJ, Kochian LV, Rea PA, Vatamaniuk OK (2009) Drosophila ABC transporter, DmHMT-1, confers tolerance to cadmium. DmHMT-1 and its yeast homolog, SpHMT-1, are not essential for vacuolar phytochelatin sequestration. *J Biol Chem* 284: 354–362.

Sunkar R, Kaplan B, Bouche N, Arazi T, Dolev D, Talke IN, Frans JM, Sanders D, Bouchez D, Fromm H (2000) Expression of a truncated tobacco NtCBP4 channel in transgenic plants and disruption of the homologous *Arabidopsis* CNGC1 gene confer Pb^{2+} tolerance. *Plant J* 24: 533–542.

Supek F, Supekova L, Nelson H, Nelson N (1997) Function of metal-ion homeostasis in the cell division cycle, mitochondrial protein processing, sensitivity to mycobacterial infection and brain function. *J Exp Biol* 200: 321–330.

Szczypka MS, Wemmie JA, Moye-Rowley WS, Thiele DJ (1994) A yeast metal resistance protein similar to human cystic fibrosis transmembrane conductance regulator (CFTR) and multidrug resistance-associated protein. *J Biol Chem* 269: 22853–22857.

Tabata Kashiwagi S, Mori H, Ueguchi C, Mizuno T (1997) Cloning of a cDNA encoding a putative metal-transporting P-type ATPase from *Arabidopsis thaliana*. *Biochim Biophys Acta* 1326: 1–6.

Talke IN, Blaudez D, Maathuis FJM, Sanders D (2003) CNGCs: Prime targets of plant cyclic nucleotide signalling? *Trends Plant Sci* 8: 286–293.

Theodoulou FL (2000) Plant ABC transporters. *Biochim Biophy Acta* 1465: 79–103.

Thomine S, Wang R, Ward JM, Crawford NM, Schroeder JI (2000) Cadmium and iron transportby members of a plant metal transporters family in *Arabidopsis* with homology to Nramp genes. *PNAS USA* 97: 4991–4996.

Tripathi RD, Srivastava S, Mishra S, Singh N, Tuli R, Gupta DK, Frans J, Maathuis M (2007) Arsenic hazards: strategies for tolerance and remediation by plants. *Trends Biotechnol* 25: 158–165.

Ueno D, Iwashita T, Zhao FJ, Ma JF (2008) Characterization of Cd translocation and identification of Cd form in xylem sap of the Cd-hyperaccumulator *Arabidopsis halleri*. *Plant Cell Physiol* 49: 540–548.

van der Zaal BJ, Neuteboom LW, Pinas JE, Chardonnens AN, Schat H, Verkleij JAC, Hooykaas PJJ (1999) Over-expression of a novel *Arabidopsis* gene related to putative zinc-transporter genes from animals can lead to enhanced zinc resistance and accumulation. *Plant Physiol* 119: 1047–1055.

Varotto C, Maiwald D, Pesaresi P, Jahns P, Salamini F, Leister D (2002) The metal ion transporter IRT1 is necessary for iron homeostasis and efficient photosynthesis in *Arabidopsis thaliana*. Plant J 31: 589–599.

Vatamaniuk OK, Bucher EA, Sundaram MV, Rea PA (2005) CeHMT-1, a putative phytochelatin transporter, is required for cadmium tolerance in *Caenorhabditis elegans*. *J Biol Chem* 280: 23684–23690.

Verret F, Gravot A, Auroy P, Leonhardt N, David P, Nussaume L, Vavasseur A, Richaud P (2004) Over-expression of AtHMA4 enhances root-to-shoot translocation of zinc and cadmium and plant metal tolerance, *FEBS Lett* 576: 306–312.

VertG, BarberonM, Zelazny E, Seguela M, BriatJF, CurieC (2009) *Arabidopsis* IRT2 cooperates with the high affinity iron uptake system to maintain iron homeostasis in root epidermal cells. *Planta* 229: 1171–1179.

Vert G, Grotz N, Dédaldéchamp F, Gaymard F, Guerinot ML, Briat JF, Curie C (2002) IRT1, an *Arabidopsis* transporter essential for iron uptake from the soil and for plant growth. *Plant Cell* 14: 1223–1233.

Wang MY, Glass ADM, Shaff JE, Kochian LV (1994) Ammonium uptake by rice roots. *Plant Physiol* 104: 899–906.

Wenzel WW, Bunkowski M, Puschenreiter M, Horak O (2003) Rhizosphere characteristics of indigenously growing nickel hyperaccumulator and excluder plants on serpentine soil. *Environ Pollut* 123: 131–138.

White PJ, Bowen HC, Demidchik V, Nichols C, Davies JM (2002) Genes for calcium-permeable channels in the plasma membrane of plant root cells. *Biochim Biophy Acta* 1564: 299—309.

Williams LE, Mills RF (2005) P_{1B}-ATPases--an ancient family of transition metal pumps with diverse functions in plants. *Trends Plant Sci* 10: 491–502.

Williams LE, Pittman JK, Hall JL (2000) Emerging mechanisms for heavy metal transport in plants. *Biochim Biophys Acta* 77: 1–23.

Woeste KE, Kieber JJ (2000) A strong loss-of-function mutation in RAN1 results in constitutive activation of the ethylene response pathway as well as a rosette-lethal phenotype. *Plant Cell* 12: 443–455.

Wollgiehn R, Neumann D (1999) Metal stress response and tolerance of cultured cells from *Silene vulgaris* and *Lycopersicon peruvianum*: Role of heat stress proteins. *J Plant Physiol* 154: 547–553.

Xiao S, Gao W, Chen QF, Ramalingam S, Chye ML (2008) Overexpression of membrane associated acyl-CoA-binding protein ACBP1 enhances lead tolerance in *Arabidopsis*. *Plant J* 54: 141–151.

Xiong ZT (1998) Lead uptake and effects on seed germination and plant growth in a Pb hyperaccumulator *Brassica pekinensis* Rupr. *Bull Environ Con Toxicol* 60: 285–291.

Yamaguchi H, Nishizawa NK, Nakanishi H, Mori S (2002) IDI7, a new iron regulated ABC transporter from barley roots, localizes to the tonoplast. *J Exp Bot* 53: 727–735.

Yang Z, Chu C (2011) Towards Understanding Plant Response to Heavy Metal Stress. In: Abiotic Stress in Plants - Mechanisms and Adaptations. In: Shanker A, Venkateswarlu B (eds) ISBN: 978-953-307-394-1 InTech China. *www.intechopen.com*

Yruela I (2005) Copper in plants. *Braz J Plant Physiol* 17: 145–156.

Zayed AM, Terry N (2003) Chromium in the environment: factors affecting biological remediation. *Plant Soil* 249: 139–156.

Zenk MH (1996) Heavy metal detoxification in higher plants - A review. *Gene* 179: 21–30.

Zhao FJ, Ma JF, Meharg AA, McGrath SP (2009) Arsenic uptake and metabolism in plants. *New Phytol* 181: 777–794.

Zhao H, Eide D (1996a) The yeast ZRT1 gene encodes the zinc transporter protein of a high affinity uptake system induced by zinc limitation. *PNAS USA* 93: 2454–2458.

Zhao H, Eide D (1996b) The ZRT2 gene encodes the low affinity zinc transporter in *Saccharomyces cerevisiae. J Biol Chem* 271: 23203–23210.

In: Heavy Metal Remediation   ISBN: 978-1-63321-568-9
Editors: Dharmendra Kumar Gupta and Soumya Chatterjee © 2014 Nova Science Publishers, Inc.

Chapter 2

METAL TRANSPORTERS FOR UPTAKE, SEQUESTRATION AND TRANSLOCATION

Sarra Arbaoui, Rym Ben Slimane, Salah Rezgui and Taoufik Bettaieb*

Horticultural Science laboratory
National Agronomic Institute of Tunisia,
Tunis Mahragene, Tunisia
University of Carthage, Carthage, Tunisia

ABSTRACT

Essential metals for normal plant development can be toxic when present in excess. So for plant growth, a range of metals are needed from the soil to be distributed (spread) into the plant with regulated concentrations into different cells. Metal transporter systems play an important role in these processes. The use of genetic and molecular techniques has identified a range of gene families that seemed to be involved in metal transport. This includes the ZIP family, the cation diffusion facilitator (CDF) family, the heavy metal ATPases (HMAs) and Nramps. This chapter aims to provide an overview of potential transport families involved in the uptake, homeostasis and the distribution of metals in plants.

Keywords: Heavy metal, Plant, Metal transporter families, Homeostasis, Detoxification, Accumulation

1. INTRODUCTION

Plants need metals such as zinc and iron for normal growth and development. The presence of one metal in short supply, deficiency symptoms can appear and the growth is

---

* Corresponding author: Dr. Sarra Arbaoui. National Agronomic Institute of Tunisia, 43 Charles Nicolle Street, 1082 Tunis Mahragene, Tunisia. Phone: 00216-71287110, fax: 00216-71799391, e-mail: saraharb@hotmail.fr.

reduced (Marschner 1995). Although they are essential, these metals can be toxic when they are present in excess with the production of reactive oxygen species and oxidative injury (Schutzendubel and Polle 2002). That's why their concentrations within cells must be controlled. Plants possess a range of potential mechanisms for metal ion homeostasis and tolerance, including membrane transport processes (Hall 2002).

Metal transporters play an important role in several functions such as the metal absorption, the sequestration and the storage. In metal polluted soil, plants have to deal with both toxic metals like lead, cadmium and mercury and toxic excess of essential metals such as zinc. Metal transporters are involved in metal detoxification by mediating the transport of metal cations or metal chelates from the cytosol to the vacuolar compartment. Since the trace metals are present in the soil solution in exceedingly low amounts, plants have to use high-affinity transporters to absorb these ions.

A large number of metal transporters and homologous genes involved in metal transport within plants have been identified thanks to genetic and molecular techniques, such as sequence comparison. Metal transporter families include the heavy metal ATPases, the natural resistance-associated macrophage proteins (NRAMPs) and the cation diffusion facilitators (CDFs) (Williams et al. 2000). The interest of these transporter classes includes their potential for genetic modification, to improve the plant nutrition or for the use of plant in phytoremediation, a technology that uses plants to remove heavy metals from polluted soil.

This chapter aims to provide an overview of the range of potential metal transporters involved in the uptake, homeostasis and distribution of metals in plants. It will focus on the general properties of transporter families, their function and location.

2. METAL UPTAKE TRANSPORTERS

2.1. ZIP Family

The ZIP family (Zinc-regulated transporter, Iron-regulated transporter) plays important roles in metal uptake. ZIP metal transporters have been identified in many organisms counting fungi, bacteria, humans and plants and are involved in the transport of Zn, Fe, Mn and Cd. Most ZIP proteins are predicted to include eight transmembrane domains. They have a similar membrane topology with the N- and C-termini exposed to the apoplast, and a variable region between transmembrane domains III and IV. This region contains a metal binding domain in histidine residues that is predicted to be cytoplasmic (Guerinot 2000).

The first ZIP metal transporter to be identified was the *Arabidopsis thaliana* IRT1, which is characterized as the principal transporter responsible for high-affinity iron uptake from the soil (Vert et al. 2002).

AtIRT1 encodes the main Fe transporter at the root surface in *A. thaliana* (Vert et al. 2002). Despite the IRT1 first identification as an iron transporter, it is known from the work of Cohen et al. (1998) and Korshunova et al. (1999) that IRT1 can also transport Mn^{2+} and heavy metal divalent cations such as Zn^{2+} and Cd^{2+} along with its ability to transport Ni^{2+} when expressed in yeast (Eide et al. 1996). Under iron deficiency conditions plants overexpressing *AtIRT1* accumulate higher amount of Zn and Cd than wild-type ones which proves that *AtIRT1* can also transport these metals (Connolly et al. 2002).

Some ZIP proteins are induced in *Arabidopsis thaliana* roots and shoots in response to Fe or Zn changing and suggesting that these proteins may contribute to stress response (Figure 1) (Manara 2012).

In hyperaccumulator plants, ZIP transporters are needed for the accumulation of metal ions and the accumulating capacity interacts with *ZIP* expression (Krämer et al. 2007). *Arabidopsis halleri* is a Zn/Cd hyperaccumulator species (Ernst 1974; Dahmani-Muller et al. 2001; Bert et al. 2002). The predominant expression of the ZIP transporters *AhIRT3*, *AhZIP3*, *AhZIP6* and *AhZIP12* in roots and shoots and *AhZIP9* in roots of *A. halleri* was indicated to be responsible for the Zn and Cd uptake capacity in this species (Becher et al. 2004; Weber et al. 2004; Chiang et al. 2006). Seven genes have been identified in *Medicago trancatula*, three of them *MtZIP1*, *MtZIP5*, and *MtZIP6* show through yeast complementation research the capacity of transporting Zn (Lopéz-Millán 2004). *ZRT3* gene has been identified by functional complementation in *Saccharomyces cerevisiae* but this appears to transport Zn out of the vacuole into the cytoplasm and not in the uptake from the soil (MacDiarmid et al. 2000).

2.2. NRAMP Family

The NRAMPs (Natural resistance associated macrophage proteins) represent a family of integral membrane proteinsidentified in fungi, bacteria, plants and animals and is involved in the transport of several metals, such as Zn^{2+}, Cd^{2+}, Cu^{2+}, Ni^{2+}, Mn^{2+}, Co^{2+} and Fe^{2+} (Cellier et al. 1995). The first Nramp gene identified in mouse, *NRAMP1*, was indicated to encode an integral membrane protein recruited in phagosomes of infected macrophages (Nelson 1999). Three membrane proteins belonging to NRAMP Family: SMF1, SMF2 and SMF3 , identified in yeast, appear to mediate the uptake of Mn^{2+}, Fe^{2+}, Cd^{2+}, Co^{2+}, and Cu^{2+} (Chen et al. 1999).

In plants, the NRAMP family was first identified in rice where OsNramp 1-3 were found (Belouchi et al. 1997). Members of this family expressed in roots and shoots (fig. 1) are responsible of metal ions transport through the plasma membrane and the tonoplast (Krämer et al. 2007). Six of the NRAMP transporters, *AtNRAMP1-6*, have been identified in *Arabidopsis* and classified into two subfamilies: the first contains *AtNRAMP1* and 6 and the second *AtNRAMP2* to 5 (Mäser et al. 2001). Among these NRAMP transporters *AtNRAMP1*, *3*, *4* and *6* have been shown to transport metals (Cailliatte et al. 2009). *AtNRAMPs* have been also suggested to contribute to iron homeostasis (Thomine et al. 2000, 2003; Nevo and Nelson 2006). In *A. thaliana AtNRAMP1* and *AtNRAMP2* have been shown to be inversely regulated in response to the iron status. In iron-starved *A. thaliana* plantlets, AtNramp1 expression is up regulated in roots whereas *AtNramp2* appears to be downregulated. In addition, *AtNramp1* gene complements the yeast *fet3- fet4* double mutant, and is induced under limiting Fe conditions. The overexpression of *AtNramp1* in transgenic *A. thaliana* plants results in an increase in plant's resistance to toxic iron concentration (Curie et al. 2000). From the work of Sano et al. (2012), it appears that *NtNRAMP1* over-expression in tobacco BY-2 cells suppressed cell death under the excess of Fe application. In tomato, *LeNRAMP1* is expressed in roots and up-regulated by Fe deficiency (Bereczky et al. 2003). Finkemeier et al. (2003) reported that *NRAMP* transcript from barley is down-regulated in the presence of Cd at adequate nitrogen supply, while, strongly up-regulated by Cd under N-deficiency.

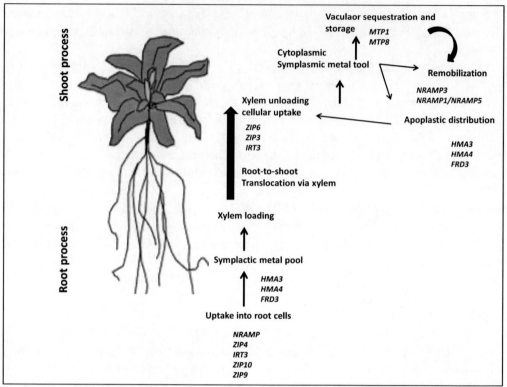

Modified from Krämer et al. (2007).

Figure 1. Examples of Plant proteins involved in the uptake translocation and sequestration of metal ions.

It is concluded from these research that the different NRAMP transporters may complete different physiological functions, and that at least some of them are involved in Fe and Cd uptake and homeostasis.

2.3. YSL Family

The YSL transporter family belongs to the superfamily of oligopeptide transporters (OPT) (Manara 2012). The *YSL* genes have been identified in *eubacteria*, *archaea*, plants, and fungi but not animals and their roles in plants seem to be the transport of metal-chelates (Roberts et al. 2004; Koike et al. 2004; Murata et al. 2006). YSL takes its name from the maize Yellow stripe 1 protein (ZmYS1) that mediates Fe uptake by transporting Fe(III)-phytosiderophore complexes (Curie et al. 2001). *YSL* proteins are considered to mediate the uptake of metals that are complexed with plant-derived phytosiderophores (PS) or a non-proteinogenic amino acid (NA) found in plants which plays the role of a precursor for PS synthesis in grasses (Roberts et al. 2004). The most studied member of this metal transporter family is YS1 from maize. The ZmYS1 transporter is able to translocate Fe, Cu, Ni, Zn, and to a lesser extent, Cd and Mn (Schaaf et al. 2004). On the basis of similarity to maize gene, eight predicted *YSL* proteins have been identified in *A. thaliana* (Colangelo and Guerinot 2006). The most studied ones, with details, among this family are *AtYSL1* and *AtYSL2*.

The former is a shoot-specific gene, that expressed in xylem parenchyma of leaves and whose transcript levels increase in response to excess Fe (LeJean et al. 2005). The latter is shown in shoot and root vascular tissues and is localized mostly in the lateral plasma membrane and involved in the lateral movement of metals (Schaaf et al. 2005).

AtYSL2 is modulated by Fe, Cu and Zn and can transport Fe and Cu as NA complexes (Di Donato et al. 2004; Schaaf et al. 2005). Conte et al. (2013) reported that *AtYSL4* and *AtYSL6*, the only genes in *Arabidopsis* belonging to YSL Group II, are localized to the internal membranes resembling endoplasmic reticulum and to the vacuole.

They also showed that plants with mutations in *YSL4* and *YSL6* and plants overexpressing GFP-tagged *YSL6* witnessed growth defects, in the presence of toxic levels of Mn and Ni, indicating a role for these transporters in heavy metal stress responses. Divol et al. (2013) concluded that the *Arabidopsis* AtYSL4 and AtYSL6 proteins are located in plastids by using immunofluorescence imaging. This localization information suggests that YSLs in the most basal clade may contribute in the intracellular transport of metal chelates.

3. HEAVY METALS SEQUESTRATION

Sequestration, which prevents high concentrations of heavy metals from persisting in metabolically active compartments of cells, is thought to be central in plants' tolerance to high levels of divalent cations metals. Vacuolar compartmentalization is the main way to ensure sequestration and detoxification of heavy metals (Hall 2002), while other compartments like endoplasmic reticulum or golgi can be involved but to a less extent (Williams and Pittman 2010). Hereafter, the three main heavy metals transporters families involved in sequestration: CDF, CAX and ABC transporters are detailed.

3.1. Transporters of CDF Family

Transporters of CDF family (Cation Diffusion Facilitator), also called MTP (Metal Tolerance Protein), first identified by Nies and Silver (1995), are ubiquitous transporters found in bacteria, *eucaryotes* and *saccharomyces* (Mäser et al. 2001).

Structural characteristics include six transmembrane domains and a long cytoplasmic C-terminal tail domain (Mäser et al. 2001). They are involved in the efflux of divalent cations such as Zn^{2+}, Co^{2+}, Cd^{2+}, Fe^{2+}, Mn^{2+} (Haney et al. 2005; Gustin et al. 2011) and their transport from the cytoplasm to the vacuole (Krämer et al. 2007), the apoplast and the endoplasmic reticulum (Peiter et al. 2007).

CDF proteins are classified into subgroups according to their respective major metal substrate: Zn-CDF, Fe/Zn-CDF and Mn-CDF (Gustin et al. 2011), however only the most characterized CDF transporters in plants which belong to Zn-CDF and Mn-CDF groups are considered in this chapter.

3.2. Specificity of Transporters to Metals

3.2.1. Zn-CDF

Genes encoding MTPs involved in Zn tolerance and homeostasis were detected in several plant species. For instance, *MTP1* was isolated in the metal hyperaccumulators *Thlaspi goesingense (TgMTP1)* (Kim et al. 2004) and *Arabidopsis halleri (AhMTP1)* (Dräger et al. 2004), and non-hyperacccumulators *Medicago truncatula (MtMTP1)* (Chen et al. 2009), rice (*OsMTP1*) (Yuan et al. 2011) and *Arabidopsis thaliana (AtMTP1)* (Kobae et al. 2004).

In *A. thaliana*, MTP1 and MTP3 are vacuolar Zn transporters (Arrivault et al. 2006; Kobae et al. 2004). Whereas MTP1 is more widely expressed in the plant, MTP3 expression is restricted to root epidermis and cortex (Arrivault et al. 2006). OsMTP1 which is closely related to *Arabidopsis thaliana* MTP1 is a member of the CDF/ MTP family in *Oryza sativa* that transports not only Zn but also Co, Fe, and Cd, possibly with lower affinity (Menguer et al. 2013). OsMTP1 is described as a plasma membrane Zn transporter based on onion epidermal cell transient expression or as tonoplast-localized when heterologously is expressed in yeast and *Arabidopsis* (Menguer et al. 2013). *OZT1*, another Zn transporter gene isolated from rice, was localized to vacuole and constitutively expressed in various rice tissues (Lan et al. 2013). This transporter was shown to confer tolerance to Zn^{2+} and Cd^{2+} stress (Lan et al. 2013).

3.2.2. Mn-CDF

In an attempt to classify CDF transporters, Gustin et al. (2011) divided the Mn-CDF group into 2 subgroups: group 8 including AtMTP8 and group 9 including AtMTP9/10/11.

Compared with Zn-CDFs, knowledge of the roles of Mn-CDFs is limited. In rice, one of the most Mn-tolerant crops, OsMTP8.1 (Mn-CDF) is a Mn-specific transporter that sequesters Mn into vacuoles and is required for Mn tolerance in shoots (Chen et al. 2013). In *Arabidopsis*, it was shown that AtMTP11 has a Mn^{2+}-specific transport activity, and that it localizes to the pre-vacuolar compartment, and is involved in maintaining Mn homeostasis (Delhaize et al. 2007).

3.2.3. CAX Transporters

CAX transporters refer to the tonoplast Ca^{2+}/H^+ antiporters. At first, CAX transporters designated Calcium Exchangers, but given that they displayed a broad specificity for a wide range of metals (Shigaki et al. 2003; Pittman et al. 2004; Korenkov et al. 2007), the name was changed to Cation Exchangers, so that the same abbreviation was kept (Shigaki and Hirschi 2006). CAX genes are not only present in plants but also in prokaryotes, fungi, invertebrates and lower vertebrates (Shigaki et al. 2006). Plant CAXs are characterized by 11 transmembrane domains and a central hydrophyle region (Maser et al. 2001). The specificity of CAXs depends on their amino acid sequence diversity (Shigaki and Hirschi 2006). In plants, CAXs belong to a multigene family (Shigaki and Hirschi 2006). They were first identified in *Arabidopsis* through the use of a yeast complementation screen (Hirschi et al. 1996) before their characterization in other species. In *Arabidopsis*, there are 11 CAX genes (Maser et al. 2001), five of which, originally named *CAX7–CAX11*, have been shown to be more similar to some animal *NCX* genes and then placed in a separate phylogenetic group called cation/Ca^{2+} exchanger (CCX) (Shigaki et al. 2006).

Among the CAXs, CAX1, CAX2, CAX3 and CAX4 have been the most studied. CAX members are involved in several physiological mechanisms, but in this chapter we only focus on the aspects of their involvement in heavy metals sequestration and the maintenance of metal ion homeostasis. Tissue and subcellular localization as well as the respective substrates and the functional characterization of each studied CAX will be given hereafter.

CAX1 is a high-capacity, low affinity Ca^{2+} transporter which localizes to the vacuolar membrane in *Arabidopsis* (Hirschi et al. 1996; Cheng et al. 2003). It is highly expressed in leaves, but modestly expressed in roots, stems, and flowers (Cheng et al. 2005). CAX1 is mostly involved in Ca^{2+} transport and homeostasis (Hirschi et al. 1996), but there is no indication on its role in other heavy metal sequestration. CAX3 is highly expressed in roots and to a less extent in leaves (Cheng et al. 2005). It is 77% identical at the amino acid level to CAX1 (Shigaki and Hirschi 2000; Shigaki et al. 2006) and like CAX1, it is also localized to the tonoplast and is induced by Ca^{2+} (Cheng et al. 2005). However there is no indication on its involvement in other heavy metal sequestration.

CAX2, which is a low-affinity Ca^{2+}/H^+ antiporter (Hirschi et al. 1996), localizes also to the plant vacuolar membrane (Hirschi et al. 2000). It has a broad range of substrates. Indeed, tobacco plants expressing *CAX2* accumulated more Ca^{2+}, Cd^{2+} and Mn^{2+} and this resulted in increased Cd^{2+} and Mn^{2+} transport in isolated root tonoplast vesicles (Hirschi et al. 2000). Other studies showed also that CAX2 is the only CAX transporter capable of vacuolar Mn^{2+} transport (Shigaki et al. 2003).

To assess the conservation of characteristics among CAX2-like transporters in higher plants, AtCAX2 orthologues were characterized in tomato (LeCAX2) and in barley (HvCAX2) (Edmond et al. 2009). It was suggested that in spite of the high sequence identity between plant CAX2 orthologues, their functional characteristics were different since each of them could transport Ca^{2+} and Mn^{2+} into the yeast vacuole but with different cation transport kinetics (Edmond et al. 2009).

CAX4 is expressed in the root apex and lateral root primordia, increasing by the elevation of Ni^{2+} or Mn^{2+} levels (Mei et al. 2009). The expression of full-length CAX4 in tobacco demonstrated that it can mediate proton coupled Cd^{2+}, Ca^{2+}, Zn^{2+} and Mn^{2+} transport, with highest transport activity for Cd^{2+} (Korenkov et al. 2007). Mei et al. (2009) hypothesized that CAX4 can efficiently transport Cd^{2+} when exposed to this metal. Thus it plays an important role in root growth under heavy metal stress conditions.

3.2.4. ABC Transporters (ATP Binding Cassette)

ABC transporters constitute a large family of transporters, whose members can be found in bacteria, fungi, animals and plants. Structurally, they possess one or two copies of two basic structural features: a highly hydrophobic transmembrane domain, each containing 4 or 6 transmembrane spans, and a peripheral (cytosolic) ATP-binding domain or nucleoside binding fold (Rea 1999; Theodoulou 2000). In Arabidopsis, their number exceeds 130, of which only 22 have been functionally characterized (Kang et al. 2011).

They can be found in most membranes of a plant cell: tonoplast, mitochondria, chloroplast, and plasma membrane, depending on their subfamilies (Kang et al. 2011).

They have a wide range of substrates such as xenobiotics, antibiotics, peptides, sugars, polysaccharides, lipids, alkaloids, and heavy metals (Theodoulou 2000). In plants, they were identified, at first, as transporters involved in the vacuolar deposition, the final detoxification process (Martinoia et al. 1993).

In spite of their varied functions in plant growth and development, plant nutrition, pathogen resistance, response to abiotic stress (Kang et al. 2011), the aim of this chapter is to give insight into the role of plant ABC transporters in heavy metal sequestration and detoxification.

Two main nomenclatures of ABC transporters subfamilies are used currently: the Sanchez-Fernandez nomenclature which was established after the naming of their human or microbial prototypes (e.g. pleiotropic drug resistance (PDR) and multidrug resistance associated protein (MRP), ATM (ABC Transporter of Mitochondria) and a new nomenclature approved by the Human Genome Organization (HUGO) to unify plant and animal ABC naming systems. According to this nomenclature, most eukaryotic ABC proteins are grouped into eight major subfamilies (A–H) regardless of the species of origin (Verrier et al. 2008).

Therefore, when we deal with ABC transporters involved in heavy metal sequestration and detoxification (mainly MRP, ATM and PDR), one should keep in mind that MRP transporter subfamily corresponds to ABCC while ATM corresponds to ABCB subfamily and PDR subfamily corresponds to ABCG (Verrier et al. 2008).

3.2.5. ABCC/MRP Transporters

Numbers of ABCC/MRP members vary among plant species. For instance, AtMRP consists of 15 members (wanke 2010; Kang et al. 2011) while OsABCC consists of 17 members (Wanke 2010). Most of ABCC transporters localize at the tonoplast (Kang et al. 2011).

Among the ABCC transporters, AtABCC3 (Bovet et al. 2003; Tommasini et al. 1998) and AtABCC6 (Gaillard et al. 2008) may function in cadmium tolerance as their expression levels were up-regulated after cadmium treatment (Bovet et al. 2003; Gaillard et al. 2008).

Also, AtABCC1 and AtABCC2 appear to confer tolerance to cadmium and mercury since the growth of *atabcc1* and *atabcc1 atabcc2* knockout plants was significantly more impaired in the presence of the two heavy metals than that of wild-type plants (Park et al. 2012).

3.2.6. ABCB/ATM Transporters

AtABCB25/AtATM3 (Kim et al. 2006), a mitochondrial protein, as well as its closest homolog in fission yeast localized at the tonoplast HMT1 (Ortiz et al. 1995) are involved in cadmium tolerance. Bovet et al. (2005) found, while using a microarray for ABC transporters, that AtABCB25 was highly induced in roots of cadmium treated plants.

In addition, HMT1 enhanced tolerance to copper, arsenic and zinc, when expressed in *Arabidopsis* (Huang et al. 2012). When overexpressed in *Brassica juncea*, AtATM3 enhanced tolerance to cadmium and lead (Bhuiyan et al. 2011).

3.2.7. ABCG/PDR Transporters

The PDR family is only found in fungi and plants (Crouzet et al. 2006). In *Arabidopsis* as well as in rice, 15 *PDR* genes were identified (Verrier et al. 2008), of which only few PDR transporters are involved in heavy metals detoxification. For instance, AtPDR8 was found to be involved in cadmium or lead resistance (Kim et al. 2007). AtPDR12 in lead detoxification (Lee et al. 2005) and OsPDR9 in zinc and cadmium stress (Moons 2003).

All of these PDR transporters localize to the plasma membrane (Kim et al. 2007; Lee et al. 2005; Moons 2003).

4. METAL TRANSLOCATION TRANSPORTERS

4.1. HMA Family

The *HMA2* and *HMA4* genes, which belong to the P1B-type ATPase family, control the translocation of the micronutrient Zn, and non-essential Cd to the shoots of *A. thaliana.* (Mills et al. 2012). *HMA4* is the first gene encoding for P-type ATPase cloned and characterized in *A. thaliana* (Mills et al. 2003). Overexpression of the *AtHMA4* protein increases Zn and Cd tolerance and also enhances the root to shoot translocation of both metals (figure 1). The tissue-specific expression of *HMA2* and *HMA4* genes was detected mostly in the vasculature (Hussain et al. 2004; Verret et al. 2004). The *HMA4* was used to transform tobacco, a plant suitable for phytoremediation due to its high biomass. Two *HMA4* genes have been expressed in tobacco: *AtHMA4* from *A. thaliana* under the constitutive *Cauliflower mosiac virus* (CaMV) 35S promoter (Siemianowski et al. 2013) and *AhHMA4* from *A. halleri* under its native promoter (Barabasz et al. 2010).

The *AtHMA5* is expressed in roots and induced by Cu in other plant organs. *hma5* mutants are hypersensitive to Cu and accumulate it in roots with a higher extent than wild-type plants which indicate their role in root-to-shoot translocation and Cu detoxification (Andrés-Colás et al. 2006).

4.2. MATE Family of Efflux Proteins

The MATE (multidrug and toxic compound extrusion) transporter family has been identified in bacteria (Morita et al. 2000). It is a family of membrane-localized efflux proteins involved in extrusion of multidrug and toxic compound from the cell. The MATE family seems to be a larger gene family of at least 56 members in *Arabidopsis*, than other sequenced organisms (Rogers and Guerinot 2002). *FRD3* (ferric reductase defective 3) has been cloned and thought to have an important role in iron homeostasis in *Arabidopsis*. It participates in iron-citrate efflux, i.e., the loading of Fe^{2+} and citrate into the vascular tissue in the roots (Fig. 1) (Durrett et al. 2007). Xylem exudates from *frd3* mutant plants has less citrate and Fe than wild-type plants, while the ones from transgenic plants overexpressing *FRD3* produce more citrate in root exudates. Ferric-citrate complexes are needed for the translocation of Fe to the leaves since Fe moves through the xylem in its chelated form (Durrett et al. 2007).

CONCLUSION

This chapter has focused on the main families of heavy metal transporters involved in the uptake, sequestration and translocation in plants. Understanding the uptake and the transport of metals in plants helps designing strategies to improve plant nutrition by increasing the essential metal uptake and decreasing the toxic metal uptake for food crops, as well as enhancing toxic metal tolerance in non-food crops such as industrial crops. The progress noticed in the studies of heavy metals uptake, translocation and sequestration in plants has a significant impact on human health by the remediation of polluted soils or water and preventing the entry of metals into the food chain. In order to improve plants for soil remediation, the identification and the isolation of involved genes in heavy metal transport are used as genetic and molecular techniques.

REFERENCES

Andrés-Colás N, Sancenón V, Rodríguez-Navarro S, Mayo S, Thiele DJ, Ecker JR, Puig S, Peñarrubia L (2006) The *Arabidopsis* heavy metal P-type ATPase HMA5 interacts with metallochaperones and functions in copper detoxification of roots. *Plant J* 45: 225–236.

Arrivault SP, Senger T, Krämer U (2006) The *Arabidopsis* metal tolerance protein AtMTP3 maintains metal homeostasis by mediating Zn exclusion from the shoot under Fe deficiency and Zn oversupply. *Plant J* 46: 861–879.

Barabasz A, Krämer U, Hanikenne M, Rudzka J, Antosiewicz DM (2010) Metal accumulation in tobacco expressing *Arabidopsis halleri* metal hyperaccumulation gene depends on external supply. *J Exp Bot* 61: 3057–3067.

Becher M, Talke IN, Krall L, Kramer U (2004) Cross-species microarray transcript profiling reveals high constitutive expression of metal homeostasis genes in shoots of the zinc hyperaccumulator *Arabidopsis halleri*. *Plant J* 37: 251–268.

Belouchi A, Kwan T, Gros P (1997) Cloning and characterization of the OsNramp family from *Oryza sativa*, a new family of membrane proteins possibly implicated in the transport of metal ions. *Plant Mol Biol* 33: 1085–1092.

Bereczky Z, Wang HY, Schubert V, Ganal M, Bauer P (2003) Differential regulation of nramp and irt metal transporter genes in wild type and iron uptake mutants of tomato. *J Biol Chem* 278: 24697–24704.

Bert V, Bonnin I, Saumitou-Laprade P, de Laguerie P, Petit D (2002) Do *Arabidopsis halleri* from nonmetallicolous populations accumulate zinc and cadmium more effectively than those from metallicolous populations? *New Phytol* 155: 47–57.

Bhuiyan MSU, Min SR, Jeong WJ, Sultana S, Choi KS, Lee Y, Liu JR (2011) Overexpression of AtATM3 in *Brassica juncea* confers enhanced heavy metal tolerance and accumulation. *Plant Cell Tiss Organ Cult* 107: 69–77.

Bovet L, Eggmann T, Meylan-Bettex M, Polier J, Kammer P, Marin E, Feller U, Martinoia E (2003) Transcript levels of AtMRPs after cadmium treatment: Induction of AtMRP3. *Plant Cell Environ* 26: 371–381.

Bovet L, Feller U, Martinoia E (2005) Possible involvement of plant ABC transporters in cadmium detoxification: A cDNA sub-microarray approach. *Environ Int* 31: 263–267.

Cailliatte R, Lapeyre B, Briat JF, Mari S, Curie C (2009) The NRAMP6 metal transporter contributes to cadmium toxicity. *Biochem J* 422:217–228.

Cellier M, Prive G, Belouchi A, Kwan T, Rodrigues V, Chia W, Gros P (1995) Nramp defines a family of membrane proteins. *PNAS USA* 92: 10089–10093.

Chen M, Shen X, Li D, Ma L, Dong J, Wang T (2009) Identification and characterization of MtMTP1, a Zn transporter of CDF family, in the *Medicago truncatula*. *Plant Physiol Biochem* 47: 1089–1094.

Chen XZ, Peng JB, Cohen A, Nelson H, Nelson N, Hediger MA (1999) Yeast SMF1 mediates H^+-coupled iron uptake with concomitant uncoupled cation currents. *J Biol Chem* 274: 35089–35094.

Chen Z, Fujii Y, Yamaji N, Masuda S, Takemoto Y, Kamiya T, Yusuyin Y, Iwasaki K, Kato SI, Maeshima M, Ma JF (2013) Mn tolerance in rice is mediated by MTP8.1, a member of the cation diffusion facilitator family. *J Exp Bot* 64: 4375-4387.

Cheng NH, Pittman JK, Barkla BJ, Shigaki T, Hirschi KD (2003) The *Arabidopsi scax1* mutant exhibits impaired ion homeostasis, development, and hormonal responses and reveals interplay among vacuolar transporters. *Plant Cell Online* 15: 347–364.

Cheng NH, Pittman JK, Shigaki T, Lachmansingh J, LeClere S, Lahner B, Salt DE, Hirschi KD (2005) Functional association of *Arabidopsis* CAX1 and CAX3 is required for normal growth and ion homeostasis. *Plant Physiol* 138: 2048–2060.

Chiang HC, Lo JC, Yeh KC (2006) Genes associated with heavy metal tolerance and accumulation in Zn/Cd hyperaccumulator *Arabidopsis halleri*: A genomic survey with cDNA microarray. *Environ Sci Techno* l40: 6792–6798.

Cohen CK, Fox TC, Garvin DF, Kochian LV (1998) The role of iron-deficiency stress responses in stimulating heavymetal transport in plants. *Plant Physiol* 116, 1063–1072.

Colangelo EP, Guerinot ML (2006) Put the metal to the petal: Metal uptake and transport throughout plants. *Curr Opin Plant Biol* 9: 322–330.

Connolly EL, Fett JP, Guerinot ML (2002) Expression of the irt1 metal transporter is controlled by metals at the levels of transcript and protein accumulation. *Plant Cell* 14: 1347–1357.

Conte SS, Chu HH, Chan-Rodriguez D, Punshon T, Vasques KA, Salt DE, Walker EL (2013) *Arabidopsis thaliana* Yellow Stripe1-Like4 and Yellow Stripe1-Like6 localize to internal cellular membranes and are involved in metal ion homeostasis. *Front Plant Sci* doi: 10.3389/fpls.2013.00283.

Crouzet JRM, Trombik T, Fraysse ÃS, Boutry M (2006) Organization and function of the plant pleiotropic drug resistance ABC transporter family. *FEBS Lett* 580: 1123–1130.

Curie C, Alonso JM, Le JM, Ecker R, Briat JF (2000) Involvement of NRAMP1 from *Arabidopsis thaliana* in iron transport. *Biochem J* 347: 749–755.

Curie C, Panaviene Z, Loulergue C, Dellaporta SL, Briat JF, Walker EL (2001) Maize yellow stripe1 encodes a membrane protein directly involved in Fe(III) uptake. *Nature* 409: 346–349.

Dahmani-Muller H, Van Oort F, Balabane M (2001).Metal extraction by *Arabidopsis halleri* grown on an unpolluted soil amended with various metal-bearing solids: A pot experiment. *Environl Pollut* 114: 77–84.

Delhaize E, Gruber BD, Pittman JK, White RG, Leung H, Miao Y, Jiang L, Ryan PR, Richardson AE (2007) A role for the *AtMTP11* gene of *Arabidopsis* in manganese transport and tolerance. *Plant J* 51: 198–210.

Di Donato RJ Jr, Roberts LA, Sanderson T, Eisley RB, Walker EL (2004) *Arabidopsis* Yellow Stripe-Like2 (YSL2): A metal-regulated gene encoding a plasma membrane transporter of nicotianamine–metal complexes. *Plant J* 39: 403–414.

Divol F, Couch D, Conejero G, Roschzttardtz H, Mari S, Curie C (2013) The *Arabidopsis* Yellow Stripe LIKE4 and 6 transporters control iron release from the chloroplast. *Plant Cell* 25: 1040–1055.

Dräger DB, Desbrosses-Fonrouge AG, Krach C, Chardonnens AN, Meyer RC, Saumitou-Laprade P, Krämer U (2004) Two genes encoding *Arabidopsis halleri* MTP1 metal transport proteins co-segregate with zinc tolerance and account for high *MTP1* transcript levels. *Plant J* 39: 425–439.

Durrett T P, Gassmann W, Rogers EE (2007) The FRD3-mediated efflux of citrate into the root vasculature is necessary for efficient iron translocation. *Plant Physiol* 144: 197–205.

Edmond C, Shigaki T, Ewert S, Nelson M, Connorton J, Chalova V, Noordally Z, Pittman J (2009) Comparative analysis of CAX2-like cation transporters indicates functional and regulatory diversity. *Biochem J* 418: 145-154.

Eide D, Broderius M, Fett J, Guerinot ML (1996) A novel iron-regulated metal transporter from plants identified by functional expression in yeast. *PNAS USA* 93:5624–5628.

Ernst WHO (1974) *Schwermetallvegetation der erde*. Stuttgart, Germany: G. Fischer Verlag.

Finkemeier I, Kluge C, Metwally A, Georgi M, Grotjohann N, Dietz KJ (2003) Alterations in Cd-induced gene expression under nitrogen deficiency in *Hordeum vulgare*. *Plant Cell Environ* 26: 821-833.

Gaillard SP, Jacquet HIN, Vavasseur A, Leonhardt N, Forestier C (2008) AtMRP6/AtABCC6, an ATP-binding cassette transporter gene expressed during early steps of seedling development and up-regulated by cadmium in *Arabidopsis thaliana*. *BMC Plant Biol* 8: 22.

Guerinot ML (2000) The ZIP family of metal transporters. *Biochem Biophys Acta* 1465: 190–198.

Gustin JL, Zanis MJ, Salt DE (2011) Structure and evolution of the plant cation diffusion facilitator family of ion transporters. *BMC Evoluty Biol* 11: 76.

Hall JL (2002) Cellular mechanisms for heavy metal detoxification and tolerance. *J Exp Bot* 53: 1-11.

Haney CJ, Grass G, Franke S, Rensing C (2005) New developments in the understanding of the cation diffusion facilitator family. *J Ind Microbiol Biotechnol* 32: 215–226.

Hirschi KD, Korenkov VD, Wilganowski NL, Wagner GJ (2000) Expression of *Arabidopsis* CAX2 in tobacco. Altered metal accumulation and increased manganese tolerance. *Plant Physiol* 124: 125–134.

Hirschi KD, Zhen RG, Cunningham KW, Rea PA, Fink GR (1996) CAX1, an H^+/Ca^{2+} antiporter from *Arabidopsis*. *PNAS USA* 93: 8782–8786.

Huang J, Zhang Y, Peng JS, Zhong C, Yi HY, Ow DW, Gong JM (2012) Fission yeast HMT1 lowers seed cadmium through phytochelatin-dependent vacuolar sequestration in *Arabidopsis*. *Plant Physiol* 158: 1779–1788.

Hussain D, Haydon MJ, Wang Y, Wong E, Sherson SM, Young J, Camakaris J, Harper JF, Cobbett CS (2004) P-Type ATPase heavy metal transporters with roles in essential zinc homeostasis in *Arabidopsis*. *Plant Cell* 16: 1327–1339.

Kang J, Park J, Choi H, Burla B, Kretzschmar T, Lee Y, Martinoia E (2011) Plant ABC transporters. *Arabidopsis book/American Society of Plant Biologists*. 9:e0153. doi: 10.1199/tab.0153.

Kim D, Gustin JL, Lahner B, Persans MW, Baek D, Yun DJ, Salt DE (2004) The plant CDF family member TgMTP1 from the Ni/Zn hyperaccumulator *Thlaspi goesingense* acts to enhance efflux of Zn at the plasma membrane when expressed in *Saccharomyces cerevisiae*. *Plant J* 39: 237–251.

Kim,DY, Bovet L, Kushnir S, Noh EW, Martinoia E, Lee Y (2006) AtATM3 is Involved in heavy metal resistance in *Arabidopsis*. *Plant Physiol* 140: 922–932.

Kim DY, Bovet L, Maeshima M, Martinoia E, Lee Y (2007) The ABC transporter AtPDR8 is a cadmium extrusion pump conferring heavy metal resistance. *Plant J* 50: 207–218.

Kobae Y, Uemura T, Sato MH, Ohnishi M, Mimura T, Nakagawa T, Maeshima M (2004) Zinc transporter of *Arabidopsis thaliana* AtMTP1 is localized to vacuolar membranes and implicated in zinc homeostasis. *Plant Cell Physio* l45: 1749–1758.

Koike S, Inoue H, Mizuno D, Takahashi M, Nakanishi H, Mori S, Nishizawa NK (2004) OsYSL2 is a rice metal–nicotianamine transporter that is regulated by iron and expressed in the phloem. *Plant J* 39: 415–424.

Korenkov V, Hirschi K, Crutchfield J D, Wagner GJ (2007) Enhancing tonoplast Cd/H antiport activity increases Cd, Zn, and Mn tolerance, and impacts root/shoot Cd partitioning in *Nicotiana tabacum L*. *Planta* 226: 1379–1387.

Korshunova YO, Eide D, Clark WG, Guerinot ML, Pakrasi HB (1999) The IRT1 protein from *Arabidopsis thaliana* is a metal transporter with a broad substrate range. *Plant Mol Biol* 40: 37–44.

Korshunova YO, Eide D, Clark WG, Guerinot Pakrasi HB (1999) *Arabidopsis thaliana* is a metal transporter with a broad substrate range. *Plant Mol Biol* 40: 37–44.

Krämer U, Talke IN, Hanikenne M (2007) Transition metal transport. *FEBS Lett* 581: 2263–2272.

Lan HX, Wang ZF, Wang QH, Wang MM, Bao YM, Huang J, Zhang HS (2013) Characterization of a vacuolar zinc transporter OZT1 in rice (*Oryza sativa L.*). *Mol Biol Rep* 40: 1201–1210.

Le Jean, M., Schikora, A., Mari, S., Briat, J. F., Curie, C. (2005) A loss-of function mutation in AtYSL1 reveals its role in iron and nicotianamine seed loading. *Plant J.* 44: 769–782.

Lee M, Lee K, Lee J, Noh E W, Lee Y (2005) AtPDR12 contributes to lead resistance in *Arabidopsis*. *Plant Physiol* 138: 827–836.

Lopéz-Millán AF, Ellis DR, Grusak MA (2004) Identification and characterization of several new members of the ZIP family of metal ion transporters in *Medicago truncatula*. *Plant Mol Biol* 54: 583–596.

MacDiarmid CW, Gaither L A, Eide D (2000) Zinc transporters that regulate vacuolar zinc storage in *Saccharomyces cerevisiae*. *EMBO J* 19: 2845–2855.

Manara A (2012) *Plants and Heavy Metals*. In: Furini A (ed.) Springer Briefs in Molecular Sciences. Springer-Verlag Berlin Heidelberg.

Marschner H (1995) *Mineral nutrition of higher plants* 2nd edn. Academic Press, London.

Martinoia E, Grill E, Tommasini R, Kreuz K, Amrhein N (1993) ATP-dependent glutathione S-conjugate 'export' pump in the vacuolar membrane of plants. *Nature* 364: 247–249.

Mäser P, Thomine S, Schroeder JI, Ward JM, Hirschi K, Sze H, Talke IN, Amtmann A, Maathuis FJ, Sanders D, Harper JF, Tchieu J, Gribskov M, Persans MW, Salt DE, Kim SA, Guerinot ML (2001) Phylogenetic relationships within cation transporter families of *Arabidopsis*. *Plant Physiol* 126: 1646–1667.

Mei H, Cheng NH, Zhao J, Park S, Escareno RA, Pittman JK, Hirschi KD (2009) Root development under metal stress in *Arabidopsis thaliana* requires the H^+/cation antiporter CAX4. *New Phytol* 183: 95–105.

Menguer PK, Farthing E, Peaston KA, Ricachenevsky FK, Fett JP, Williams LE (2013) Functional analysis of the rice vacuolar zinc transporter OsMTP1. *J Exp Bot* 64: 2871–2883.

Mills RF, Kerry A, Peaston JR, Williams LE (2012) HvHMA2, a P1BATPase from barley, is highly conserved among cereals and functions in Zn and Cd transport. *PLoS One* 7: e42640.

Mills R F, Krijger GC, Baccarini PJ, Hall JL, Williams LE (2003) Functional expression of AtHMA4, a P1B-type ATPase of the Zn/Co/Cd/Pb subclass. *Plant J* 35: 164–176.

Moons A (2003) *Ospdr9*, which encodes a PDR-type ABC transporter, is induced by heavy metals, hypoxic stress and redox perturbations in rice roots. *FEBS Lett* 553: 370–376.

Morita Y, Kataoka A, Shiota S, Mizushima T, Tsuchiya T (2000) NorM of *Vibrio parahaemolyticus* is an Na^+-driven multidrug efflux pump. *J Bacteriol* 182: 6694–6697.

Murata Y, Ma JF, Yamaji F, Ueno D, Nomoto K, Iwashita T (2006) A specific transporter for iron(III)–phytosiderophore in barley roots. *Plant J* 46: 563–572.

Nelson N (1999) Metal ion transporters and homeostasis. *EMBO J* 18: 4361–4371.

Nevo Y, Nelson N (2006) The NRAMP family of metal-ion transporters. *Biochim Biophys Acta* 1763: 609–620.

Nies DH, Silver S (1995) Ion efflux systems involved in bacterial metal resistances. *J Ind Microbiol* 14: 186–199.

Ortiz DF, Ruscitti T, McCue KF, Ow DW (1995) Transport of metal-binding peptides by HMT1, a fission yeast ABC-type vacuolar membrane protein. *J Biol Chem* 270: 4721–4728.

Park J, Song WY, Ko D, Eom Y, Hansen TH, Schiller M, Lee TG, Martinoia E, Lee Y (2012) The phytochelatin transporters AtABCC1 and AtABCC2 mediate tolerance to cadmium and mercury. *Plant J* 69: 278–288.

Peiter E, Montanini B, Gobert A, Pedas P, Husted SR, Maathuis FJM, Blaudez D, Chalot M, Sanders D (2007) A secretory pathway-localized cation diffusion facilitator confers plant manganese tolerance. *PNAS USA* 104: 8532–8537.

Pittman JK, Shigaki T, Marshall JL, Morris JL, Cheng NH, Hirschi KD (2004) Functional and regulatory analysis of the *Arabidopsis thaliana* CAX2 cation transporter. *Plant Mol Bio* 56: 959–971.

Rea PA (1999) MRP subfamily ABC transporters from plants and yeast. *J Exp Bot* 50: 895–913.

Roberts LA, Pierson AJ, Panavise Z, Walker EL (2004) Yellow Stripe1 expanded roles for the Maize iron–phytosiderophore transporter. *Plant Physiol* 135: 112–120.

Rogers EE, Eide DJ, Guerinot ML (2000) Altered selectivity in an *Arabidopsis* metal transporter. *PNAS USA* 97: 12356–12360.

Rogers EE, Guerinot ML (2002) FRD3, a member of the multidrug and toxin eflux family, controls iron deficiency responses in Arabidopsis. *Plant Cell* 14: 1787-1799.

Sano T, Yoshihara T, Handa K, Sato MH, Nagata T, Hasezawa S (2012) Metal ion homeostasis mediated by Nramp transporters in plant cells—focused on increased resistance to iron and cadmium ion. In: Weigert R (ed.) *Crosstalk and Integration of Membrane Trafficking Pathways*. INTECH, Rijeka, Shanghai pp. 214–228.

Schaaf G, Ludewig U, Erenoglu BE, Mori S, Kitahara T, von Wirén N (2004) ZmYS1 functions as a proton-coupled symporter for phytosiderophore- and nicotianamine-chelated metals. *J Biol Chem* 279: 9091–9096.

Schaaf G, Schikora A, Haberle J, Vert GA, Ludewig U, Briat JF. (2005) A putative function of the *Arabidopsis* Fe-Phytosiderophore transporter homolog AtYSL2 in Fe and Zn homeostasis. *Plant Cell Physiol* 46: 762-774.

Schützendübel A, Polle A (2002) Plant responses to abiotic stresses: heavy metal induced oxidative stress and protection by mycorrhization. *J Exp Bot* 53:1351-1365.

Shigaki T, Hirschi KD (2006) Diverse functions and molecular properties emerging for CAX cation/H$^+$ exchangers in plants. *Plant Biol* 8: 419–429.

Shigaki T, Pittman JK, Hirschi KD (2003) Manganese specificity determinants in the *Arabidopsis* metal/H$^+$ antiporter CAX2. *J Biol Chem* 278: 6610–6617.

Shigaki T, Rees I, Nakhleh L, Hirschi KD (2006) Identification of three distinct phylogenetic groups of CAX cation/proton antiporters. *J Mol Evolut* 63: 815–825.

Siemianowski O, Barabasz A, Weremczuk A, Ruszczyńska A, Bulska E, Williams L E, Antosiewicz DM (2013) Development of Zn-related necrosis in tobacco is enhanced by expressing AtHMA4 and depends on the apoplastic Zn levels. *Plant Cell Environ* 36: 1093–1104.

Sunkar R, Kaplan B, BoucheÂ N, Arazi T, Dolev D, Talke M, Frans JM, Sanders D, Bouchez D, Fromm H (2000) Expression of a truncated tobacco NtCBP4 channel in transgenic plants and disruption of the homologous *Arabidopsis* CNGC1 gene confer Pb^{2+} tolerance. *Plant J* 24: 533–542.

Theodoulou FL (2000) Plant ABC transporters. *Biochemica Biophysica Acta (BBA)-Biomemb* 1465: 79–103.

Thomine S, Lelie Ávre F, Debarbieux E, Schroeder JI, Barbier-Brygoo H (2003) AtNRAMP3, a multi specific vacuolar metal transporter involved in plant responses to iron deficiency. *Plant J* 34: 685–695.

Thomine S, Wang R, Ward JM, Crawford NM, Schroeder JI (2000) Cadmium and iron transport by members of a plant metal transporter family in *Arabidopsis* with homology to Nramp genes. *PNAS USA* 97: 4991–4996.

Tommasini R, Vogt E, Fromenteau M, Hortensteiner S, Matile P, Amrhein N, Martinoia E (1998) An ABC-transporter of *Arabidopsis thaliana* has both glutathione-conjugate and chlorophyll catabolite transport activity. *Plant J* 13: 773–780.

Verret F, Gravot A, Auroy P, Leonhardt N, David P, Nussaume L, Vavasseur A, Richaud P (2004) Overexpression of AtHMA4 enhances root-to-shoot translocation of zinc and cadmium and plant metal tolerance. *FEBS Lett* 576: 306–312.

Verrier PJ, Bird D, Burla B, Dassa E, Forestier C, Geisler M, Klein M. Kolukisaoglu Ã, Lee Y, Martinoia E (2008) Plant ABC proteins - a unified nomenclature and updated inventory. *Trends Plant Sci* 13: 151–159.

Vert G, Grotz N, Dédaldéchamp F, Gaymard F, Guerinot ML, Briat JF, Curie C (2002) IRT1, an *Arabidopsis* transporter essential for iron uptake from the soil and for plant growth. *Plant Cell* 14: 1223–1233.

Wanke D, Ãœner Kolukisaoglu H (2010) An update on the ABCC transporter family in plants: many genes, many proteins, but how many functions? *Plant Biol* 12: 15–25.

Weber M, Harada E, Vess C, von Roepenack-Lahaye E, Clemens S (2004)Comparative microarray analysis of *Arabidopsis thaliana* and *Arabidopsis halleri* roots identifies nicotianamine synthase, a zip transporter and other genes as potential metal hyperaccumulation factors. *Plant J* 37: 269–281.

Williams LE, Pittman JK (2010) Dissecting pathways involved in manganese homeostasis and stress in higher plant cells. In: Hell R, Mendel R (eds.) *Cell Biology of Metals and Nutrients, Plant Cell Monographs. Vol. 17.* Springer pp. 95–118.

Williams LE, Pittman JK, Hall JL (2000) Emerging mechanisms for heavy metal transport in plants. *Biochim Biophys Acta* 77:1–23.

Yuan L, Yang S, Liu B, Zhang M, Wu K (2011) Molecular characterization of a rice metal tolerance protein, OsMTP1. *Plant Cell Rep* 31: 67–79.

In: Heavy Metal Remediation   ISBN: 978-1-63321-568-9
Editors: Dharmendra Kumar Gupta and Soumya Chatterjee © 2014 Nova Science Publishers, Inc.

Chapter 3

UPDATE ON MECHANISMS INVOLVED IN ARSENIC AND CHROMIUM ACCUMULATION, TRANSLOCATION AND HOMEOSTASIS IN PLANTS

Paola S. González[1],*, *Melina A. Talano[1]*, *Ana L. Wevar Oller[1]*,
Sabrina G. Ibañez[1], *María I. Medina[1] and Elizabeth Agostini[1]*

[1]Departamento de Biología Molecular, Facultad de Ciencias Exactas,
Físico-Químicas y Naturales, Universidad Nacional de Río Cuarto,
Río Cuarto (Córdoba), Argentina

ABSTRACT

Arsenic (As) and chromium (Cr) are toxic heavy metals frequently found at high concentrations in polluted environments. The increasing interest in the study of these contaminants is related to the importance and urgency of their removal. Although different technologies have been developed for this purpose, phytoremediation has emerged as an attractive methodology due to its multiple advantages; it is environmentally friendly and potentially cost effective. In this sense, significant progress has been achieved in elucidating the mechanisms involved in As and Cr metabolism in hyperaccumulator, nonhyperaccumulator, land and aquatic plants. However, more advances regarding As than Cr have been obtained. In this chapter there is presented a review on physiological, biochemical and molecular mechanisms involved in As and Cr uptake, accumulation, translocation and homeostasis in plants. New reports in genetically modified plants for these heavy metals remediation are also mentioned. In this sense, the role of "omics" technology is discussed and suggested as an alternative for unraveling less explored aspects; mainly those related to Cr. Certainly, progress in knowledge will allow to assess the feasibility of more effective phytoremediation strategies as well as to develop more tolerant plants and/or heavy metals free-plants for safe consumption.

Keywords: Arsenic, Chromium, Toxicity, Hyperaccumulation

* Phone: 0054-358-4676537, Fax: 0054-358-4676232, E-Mail: psolangeg@hotmail.com.
All authors contributed equally to this chapter.

1. INTRODUCTION

In the recent years, the increasing environmental pollution caused by heavy metals has become a grave concern, since it implies important ecological, economical and health damages. Arsenic (As) and chromium (Cr) are elements abundantly found in the earth's crust, but they do not apparently have any known biological role in plants and are toxic even at low concentrations. In fact, As and Cr are listed as priority hazardous substances and considered among the top 20 contaminants by the United States Environmental Protection Agency (USEPA) (ATSDR 2012). Several anthropogenic activities release As and Cr and they may be accumulated to toxic levels into the environment (Sridhar et al. 2011). Arsenic is used in pesticides and wood preservatives, mining and melting operations (Wang and Mulligan 2006), whereas Cr is used in the manufacture of pigments, metal-finishing, Cr-plating, stainless steel production, leather tanning, and among other industrial uses (Kimbrough et al. 1999). Nowadays, the use of industrial effluents on agricultural land has become a common practice in some developing countries, resulting in the transference and concentration of these toxic metals into plant and animal tissues (Rogival et al. 2007). For this reason, the USEPA and several state regulatory agencies have suggested that soil As and Cr standard levels should be established based on potential health risks. In this context, an intensive search of new economic remediation technologies such as phytoremediation is being carried out (Danh et al. 2009).

Phytoremediation employs plants to extract, transfer, stabilize and remove toxic elements from polluted soils and water systems and it has received much attention because it is cost effective and environment-friendly (Schneider et al. 2012). The efficiency of phytoremediation approaches appears to be comparable to traditional cleanup methods. Besides, phytoremediation offers protection against erosion, maintains proper soil conditions and is less laborious. It is important to note that inorganic pollutants phytoremediation involves mechanisms, enzymes, and processes different from those concerning organic pollutants because heavy metals are not degradable. Thus, phytoextraction, phytostabilization, phytovolatilization, and rhizofiltration are suitable phytotechnologies for inorganic pollutants removal (Ibañez et al. 2014).

Some plants used in phytoextraction strategies are termed "hyperaccumulators". They have the ability to grow on metalliferous soils and accumulate extraordinarily high amounts of heavy metals in the aerial organs, far in excess of the levels found in the majority of species, without suffering phytotoxic effects. Ideally, hyperaccumulators should thrive in toxic (metal rich) environments, require little maintenance and produce high biomass, but few plants perform extremely well to fullfill these requirements (Salido et al. 2003). The discovery of hyperaccumulator plant species has attracted attention to understand the mechanisms involved in heavy metals tolerance and to evaluate phytoremediation potential. Several plant species such as *Pteris vittata, Pteris cretica, Agrostis cappillaris, Sarcosphaera coronaria* and *Pityrogramma calomelanos* are As hyperaccumulators (Srivastava et al. 2006; Xie et al. 2009), while *Eichhornia crassipes, Typha latifolia, Carex lurida, Prosopis* spp., *Allium sativum, Leptospermum scoparium*, and *Polypogon monspeliensis* have been identified as Cr hyperaccumulators (Sundaramoorthy et al. 2010).

Plants have several transport mechanisms to take up micronutrients from soil matrix. However, they do not possess specific transporter mechanisms for heavy metals, thus they are taken up by plants along with other micronutrients. Moreover, plants have developed defense mechanisms to minimize metal toxicity. For instance, plants can make metals insoluble mostly by the aid of chelating agents followed by vacuolar accumulation. Apart from that, some plants have enzymes that can change the redox state to a less toxic form; whereas others can transform heavy metals to make them more volatile (Ibañez et al. 2014). Consequently, the better understanding of these capabilities will allow improving the effectiveness of phytoremediation process through molecular biology and genetic engineering tools.

In this chapter, it is presented a description of physiological, biochemical and molecular mechanisms of As and Cr uptake, accumulation, translocation and homeostasis in plants, which are summarized in Figure 1. Finally, the new advances in genetically modified plants for As and Cr phytoremediation are also revised.

2. ARSENIC

Inorganic As is present mainly in the environment as arsenate [As(V)] and arsenite [As(III)] species, being the latter more toxic, soluble and mobile than As(V) (Finnegan and Chen 2012). In anaerobic soil environment, As(III) is the predominant species. However, part of this As(III) may be oxidized to As(V) in the rhizosphere by oxygen released from the aerenchyma tissue of wetland plants. It has been shown that Fe-plaque (Fe hydroxide/oxyhydroxide precipitate) formed on root surface of wetland plants allows As(V) adsorption and also increases As(III) uptake (Chen et al. 2005; Liu et al. 2006). Recently, Moore et al. (2011) showed that the Fe-plaque resulted in a high As accumulation on the epidermis of rice roots. On the other hand, in aerobic soils, As(V) is the main species, but there is evidence of the presence of As(III) under this condition that is likely a result of As(III) efflux from roots (Vetterlein et al. 2007; Logoteta et al. 2009).

Although monomethylarsenic acid, dimethylarsenic acid, and other organic forms have also been found in the rhizosphere (Zhao et al. 2013), this review will focus on As(V) and As(III) plant metabolism.

2.1. Arsenic Uptake

As(V) is taken up by plant roots via phosphate (Pi) transporters such as AtPht1;1 and AtPht1;4. This has been demonstrated through physiological and electrophysiological studies showing a potent inhibition by Pi (Abedin et al. 2002; Liu et al. 2004; Rosa et al. 2006). In fact, genes involved in Pi starvation response are repressed by As(V), suggesting that As(V) may mislead the Pi sensor and interferes with the Pi signaling mechanism (Catarecha et al. 2007). Some evidence came from *Arabidopsis thaliana* double mutant *pht1;1Δ4Δ* defective in Pi transport which showed more tolerance to As(V) (Shin et al. 2004; Catarecha et al. 2007). Overaccumulation of Pi in shoot is one of the mechanisms to increase As(V) resistance, even in rice in which rhizosphere As(III) is the main As species (Singh and Ma 2006; Wang and Duang 2009).

As(III), predominantly present as the neutral form $As(OH)_3$ enters root cells through aquaporins.

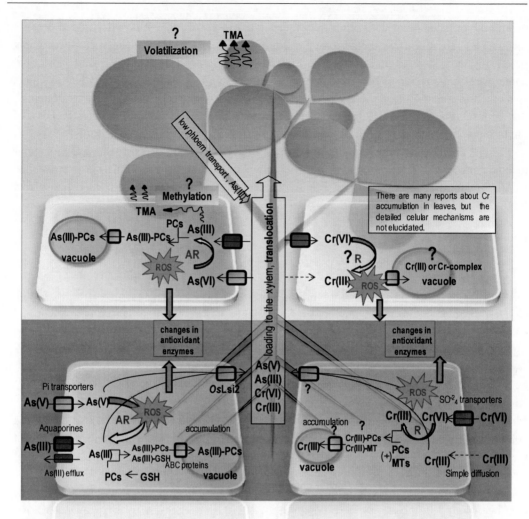

Figure 1. Scheme of the main mechanisms of arsenic (As) and chromium (Cr) uptake, accumulation, translocation and homeostasis in nonhyperaccumulators plants. Arsenate [As(V)] is taken up by roots via phosphate (Pi) transporters while arsenite [As(III)] enters into root cells through aquaporins. As(III) efflux from roots to soil can occurs. Trivalent chromium [Cr(III)] uptake is a passive process that implies simple diffusion and hexavalent chromium [Cr(VI)] uptake seems to be an active mechanism involving sulphate (SO_4^{-2}) transporters. Once As(V) enters the cells is reduced to As(III) by arsenate reductases (AR) and Cr(VI) is also reduced to Cr(III), probably by some ferric reductase enzymes (R). These reductions seem to increase reactive oxygen species (ROS) concentrations, which results in changes of the antioxidant system enzymes. Regarding accumulation of these heavy metals, As(III) forms complexes with reduced glutathione (GSH) or phytochelatins (PCs), and they are sequestered in vacuoles through ABC transporters. Similarly, after reduction, Cr(III) could form complexes with PCs and metallothioneins (MTs). Some uncomplexed As(III) and As(V) could be translocated to the xylem via *Os*Lsi2, and loaded to the aerial part, while Cr(III) and Cr(VI) xylem loading transporters remain unknown. In the aerial part, these heavy metals are probably reduced and accumulated in a similar way than in roots. However, Cr complexation and accumulation in leaves have not been fully elucidated as well as As and Cr transport in phloem. It is important to mention that As seems to be also methylated, being trimethylarsine (TMA), a volatile gas, the end product.

In rice, As(III) enters through Lsi1, a nodulin26-like intrinsic protein (NIP) aquaporin (*Os*NIP2;1), a major influx transporter for silicic acid (Ma et al. 2006; Li et al. 2009a). While Lsi1 transports As(III) into root cells, Lsi2, a protein initially identified as a silicon (Si) efflux transporter has been found to mediate As(III) efflux to the xylem. In rice mutants defective in Lsi2, As(III) transport to the xylem and accumulation in shoots and grain greatly decreased (Ma et al. 2008). The increased silicic acid concentration in the soil solution resulted in a decreased As accumulation in rice shoots and grain, probably through a competitive inhibition effect on As(III) transport via Lsi2 (Li et al. 2009b; Zhao et al. 2010a). Also, As uptake was affected by Si treatment in different tomato cultivars (Marmiroli et al. 2014).

2.2. Arsenic Metabolism and Accumulation

2.2.1. As(V) Reduction

Most plants have capacity to efficiently reduce As(V) to As(III). This was observed in *Brassica juncea*, *A. thaliana,* tomato and rice, where more than 90% of total As was present in their tissues as As(III), even though plants were exposed to As(V) (Pickering et al. 2000; Dhankher et al. 2002). In yeast and protozoa, Acr2p protein, a member of the tyrosine phosphatase (PTPase) superfamily, has been associated with As(V) reduction activity (Bhattacharjee and Rosen 2007). Plant homologues of ACR2, named also arsenate reductases (ARs) have been characterized in *A. thaliana*, *Holcus lanatus*, rice and the As hyperaccumulator *P. vittata* (Dhankher et al. 2006; Bleeker et al. 2006; Duan et al. 2007; Ellis et al. 2006), based on the sequence homology to Acr2p and enzymatic activity. However, some results with *A. thaliana* ACR2 knockout mutants in which As(III) was still the dominant species suggest the existence of other ARs or non-enzymatic As(V) reduction mechanisms in plants (Rathinasabapathi et al. 2006; Liu et al. 2012).

2.3. Arsenic Association with Thiol Compounds and Sequestration in Vacuoles

Following As(V) reduction to As(III), the latter forms complexes with sulphydryl (-SH) groups of thiol-rich peptides such as reduced glutathione (GSH) or phytochelatins (PCs), and then they are sequestered in vacuoles (Zhao et al. 2010b). The mechanism of As(III) complexation is an important aspect of As detoxification in nonhyperaccumulators plants. In this regard, *Arabidopsis* mutant lines deficient in PCs were more sensitive to As(V) than wild type plants (Ha et al. 1999), while transgenic plants overexpressing PC synthase genes or those involved in the synthesis of GSH showed enhanced As tolerance (Dhankher et al. 2002; Li et al. 2006a; Gasic and Korban 2007). An additional evidence about As and PCs relation has been the isolation of intact PCs-As complexes from plant tissues (Raab et al. 2005). Moreover, comparing two genotypes of rice contrasting in As tolerance, the tolerant variety showed a marked enhancement of enzymes activities particularly those related to thiol metabolism compared to the sensitive rice variety (Tripathi et al. 2012).

It is assumed that As(III)-thiol complexes formed in the cytoplasm are subsequently transported and sequestered into vacuoles, where the acidic pH maintains complexes stability. Based on studies with yeast the Ycf1p protein, a member of ATP-binding cassette (ABC) family, has been associated with the transport of As(III)-GSH complexes into the vacuole (Ghosh et al. 1999). Regarding plant cells, As(III)-GSH complexes have been incorporated in tonoplast vesicles prepared from *H. lanatus* roots in a Mg ATP-dependent manner and charge-neutral form, which is consistent with ABC-mediated transport (Bleeker et al. 2006). Song et al. (2010) showed that in the absence of two ABCC-type transporters (*At*ABCC1 and *At*ABCC2), *A. thaliana* was extremely sensitive to As. Heterologous expression of these ABCC transporters in PCs-producing *Saccharomyces cerevisiae* enhanced As tolerance and accumulation. Also, membrane vesicles isolated from this yeast exhibited a pronounced As(III)-PC transport activity. Furthermore, *A. thaliana* plants overexpressing PCS1 and ABCC1 resulted in increased As tolerance. These findings demonstrated that *At*ABCC1 and *At*ABCC2 are the major vacuolar PC transporters required for As resistance in *A. thaliana*.

It seems that plants could methylate As since some of the methylated forms of As have been found in plant extracts in hydroponic cultures, where no methylated As species were supplied. This would be achieved by a similar pathway as that of microorganisms, being trimethylarsine (TMA), a volatile gas, the end product (Bentley and Chasteen 2002). It is not yet known if plants can produce and volatilize TMA as microorganisms. However, if any potential volatilization of As occurs, it is likely to be small (Raab et al. 2007a). Recently, Zhang et al. (2013) demonstrated that *Ostreococcus tauri*, a marine green microalga was able to methylate and volatilize As; however, treatment with As(III) produced five times more volatile As compared to that with As(V). The authors explained that the reduction of As(V) would be the limiting step in As methylation and volatilization from seawater (Zhang et al. 2013).

2.4. Arsenic Translocation

Contrarily to hyperaccumulators, nonhyperaccumulator plants have low As translocation from roots to shoots (Raab et al. 2007b). Translocation is greatly affected by As uptake, reduction and complexation above-mentioned. Since As(V) reduction is a requirement for As(III) complexation and sequestration in root vacuoles, silencing of an AR (*At*ACR2) increased markedly As accumulation in *A. thaliana* shoots, probably due to that higher root As(V) concentrations were available for its transport to the shoots (Dhankher et al. 2006). Also, Liu et al. (2010) demonstrated that complexation with thiols decreases As(III) mobility from roots to shoots in *A. thaliana*.

In most plant species, As(III) is more abundant than As(V) in the xylem sap and it is not complexed with thiol compounds, suggesting that it is the main form loaded into the xylem, even when As(V) is supplied to plant roots (Raab et al. 2005; Zhao et al. 2009). However, plant species differ in xylem loading efficiency of As(III). In this sense, rice loads As(III) into xylem more efficiently than wheat, barley, cucumber and tomato (Su et al. 2010). It can be explained by the strong Si accumulation capability of rice allowing also an inadvertent passage of As(III) (Ma et al. 2007). *P. vittata* greatly exceeds As(III) loading efficiency of nonhyperaccumulator species, but the underpinning mechanism has not been elucidated (Su et al. 2008).

Regarding As transport in phloem, there is little knowledge of the extent and mechanisms involved. In rice and most plant species, As remobilization from stems and leaves to grain, if any, may be limited since As concentrations decrease markedly in the following order: roots > stems and leaves > husks > grain (Abedin et al. 2002; Xu et al. 2008). Ye et al. (2010) found As in phloem exudates of castor bean (*Ricinus communis*) mainly as As(III), and they also found high concentrations of reduced and oxidized GSH and some oxidized PCs but not As(III)-thiol complexes. It is thought that As(III)-thiol complexes would not be stable in the alkaline conditions of phloem sap. Some evidences suggest that cadmium would be transported as PCs and GSH complexes in the phloem of *Brassica napus* (Mendoza-Cózatl et al. 2008); however, As(III)-thiol complexes transport in phloem has not been demonstrated. It needs to be evaluated to elucidate the contribution of xylem-versus phloem-derived As to the accumulation specially in rice grains, since several reports warn about high As content in rice grains as well as in foods derived from it (Sun et al. 2009; Li et al. 2011).

2.5. Mechanisms Involved in As Hyperaccumulation

As it was already mentioned, the genus Pteris has several species, including *P. vittata* and *P. cretica* that hyperaccumulate As, despite not all are able to hyperaccumulate this metalloid (Zhao et al. 2009). For example, in *P. vittata* plants grown in As polluted areas, total As represented a high percentage of fronds dry weight (1-2 %) (Wang et al. 2002). Although hyperaccumulator and nonhyperaccumulator ferns take up As(V) by the same Pi transport system, hyperaccumulators have a high influx due to the higher affinity of this transport system for As(V) than that of nonhyperaccumulators (Caille et al. 2005).

Once As(V) is uptaken, its reduction occurs mainly in roots of *P. vittata*, being As(III) preferentially loaded into the xylem (Duan et al. 2005; Su et al. 2008). Then, As(III) is efficiently translocated to shoot and finally stored in frond vacuoles as free As(III), with small amount of As complexed with PCs (Zhao et al. 2003; Pickering et al. 2006). This As(III) vacuolar sequestration is therefore the key mechanism of As detoxification in the hyperaccumulator ferns, but the identity of the vacuolar transporters involved needs further investigation. In this sense, an important contribution is the recent report about quantitative proteomic analysis from *P. vittata* frond tonoplast that will allow clarifying the regulation of transport processes (Shen et al. 2014).

Also, hyperaccumulators differ from nonhyperaccumulators in the lower efflux of As(III) from the roots to the external medium (Su et al. 2008). This, along with little PC complexation of As(III) in *P. vittata* roots, may explain the highly efficient xylem loading (Zhao et al. 2003). It is also possible that transporters mediating As(III) efflux from cortical cells towards xylem are highly expressed in As hyperaccumulators, although their identities are not yet known.

Even though there has been a great advance in the elucidation of mechanisms involved in As metabolism in nonhyperaccumulators, mainly in rice, molecular understanding of As hyperaccumulation remains rudimentary. Future research should address these knowledge gaps, taking advantage of modern analytical tools for As speciation and the combination of physiological and molecular approaches.

2.6. Toxic Effects of Arsenic on Plants

Academic literature shows that As phytotoxicity varies greatly within plant species. Significant differences have been reported between hyperaccumulator and nonhyperaccumulator plants and also between land and aquatic plants. Current knowledge suggests that diverse mechanisms to preserve plant homeostasis have been developed. However, the mechanisms of As cell damage and toxicity are apparently common among plants, but they are still not fully understood. In this regard, modern "omics" technologies are clearly contributing in the elucidation of all the mechanisms involved in As stress response.

In the following paragraphs it is reviewed how As modulates metabolic pathways of various physiological processes necessary for growth and development on different plant species.

2.7. Arsenic Effects on Germination

Early stages of seedlings growth are very important indicators in determining phytotoxicity impact of heavy metals. Since seed germination is the first physiological process affected by pollutants, the ability of seeds to germinate in a medium containing As is indicative of their tolerance level. Thus, this parameter is a general and commonly used stress indicator, although it is highly variable among plant species. Even though there are several studies about As effect on germination, in this chapter some recent reports are presented. In wheat, low As concentrations (0-2.5 ppm) stimulated seed germination but higher concentrations (5-30 ppm) were progressively inhibitory (Li et al. 2007; Mahdieh et al. 2013), whereas in tobacco, total seed germination was not affected up to 15 ppm As (Talano et al. 2013).

Nevertheless, biochemical mechanisms involved in seed resistance to toxic metals remained unrevealed.

2.8. Arsenic Effects on Root and Shoot Growth and Plant Yield

Root growth quantified as root length, weight, surface and form, is also an important stress indicator since root is the plant organ in closest proximity to soil elements, including toxic contaminants. Decrease in root growth is a well documented As effect in several plant species like soybean (Talano et al. 2013).

Concerning studies related to detailed mechanisms involved in the inhibition of root growth in response to As, there are evidences that suggest an important role for oxidative stress.

Expression patterns of maize (*Zea mays*) root proteins showed that 10% of them were differentially regulated by As and that seven of the eleven proteins that were identified are involved in cellular homeostasis for redox perturbation, suggesting that oxidative stress is a major process underlying As toxicity (Requejo and Tena 2005).

Adverse effects of As on plant height and shoot growth have been extensively reported (Finnegan and Chen 2012 and references there in). The reduction in plant height is, in part, due to the reduced root growth and consequently to the reduced transport of nutrients and water to the above tissues. This could also be related to the fact that plants treated with As expend more energy and resources into immediate defense mechanisms than into normal growth requirements, as it was suggested in rice by genome wide transcriptome and miRNA analyses (Yu et al. 2012).

Finally, the effects of As on plant metabolism during growth and development culminates in yield and total dry matter reduction, as a consequence of poor production, translocation and partitioning of assimilates into grains or fruits. Yield reduction gains in importance when crops are affected, which has been well recognized as a threat to the sustainability of food production (Brammer and Ravenscroft 2009).

2.9. Arsenic Effects on Physiological Processes

2.9.1. Photosynthesis

Photosynthesis, in terms of pigments content, CO_2 fixation, electron transport, photophosphorylation and enzyme activities is adversely affected by As in most plants. In rice, both chlorophyll a and b contents decreased significantly with the increase of soil As concentration (Azizur Rahman et al. 2007). However, there are studies reporting increase of pigments content after exposure to low concentrations of the metalloid, for example in wheat and onion (Singh and Ghosh 2010; Mahdieh et al. 2013). In addition, Karimi et al. (2013) reported that photosynthesis efficiency in a hyperaccumulator (*Isatis cappadocica*) remained unaffected in the presence of As.

Aquatic plants are also affected by As, and many studies report a correlation with changes in reactive oxygen species (ROS) concentration. For instance, in *Hydrilla verticillata* As(V) concentration of 37 ppm led to a significant decline in chlorophyll a, chlorophyll b and carotenoids. This was correlated with a decrease in Photosystem II (PSII) and water use efficiency, as well as in net photosynthetic rate and electron transport (Srivastava et al. 2013). Similarly, in *Pistia stratiotes,* As treatment caused a decrease in pigments content, loss of PSII efficiency and reduction in CO_2 fixation (Farnese et al. 2014). Various As phytotoxicity mechanisms have been proposed, but most of them have not been experimentally proven. Recent studies in the rootless aquatic plant *Ceratophyllum demersum* L. exposed to As(V) suggest a different sequence of events induced by As than that previously reported. The first observed effect of As toxicity was a decrease in pigment concentration, then photosynthesis was inhibited and its malfunction caused oxidative stress. Thus photosynthesis inhibition occurred before any symptom of oxidative stress was observed (Mishra et al. 2014).

2.9.2. Antioxidant Enzymes

Biochemical evidence indicates that exposure to As has been generally correlated with increase of ROS in plant tissues, which induces oxidative stress and consequently lipid peroxidation, among others (Mishra et al. 2014 and references therein). In this sense, it was demonstrated that *P. vittata* possesses a higher antioxidant capacity and also maintains a lower concentration of ROS under As(V) treatment than the nonhyperaccumulator *Pteris ensiformis* (Srivastava et al. 2005; Singh et al. 2006). Exposure to As(III) also enhances enzymatic activity involved in the antioxidant response (Rai et al. 2011). Recently, the activities of As(V) reductase (AR), glutathione reductase (GR), superoxide dismutase (SOD), guaiacol peroxidase (GPX), ascorbate peroxidase (APX), and catalase (CAT) showed differential but coordinated stimulation in leaves and roots of the medicinal herb *Bacopa monnieri* after 50 μM As(V) exposure (Mishra et al. 2013).

Relative to the main role of GSH in antioxidant response, Norton et al. (2008) observed that a number of genes or enzymes involved in GSH synthesis or As sequestration are up-regulated in rice seedlings exposed to As(V). This probably explains the higher demand for GSH under As stress.

2.9.3. Mineral Nutrition

Two minerals can interfere in plant homeostasis under As stress: phosphorous (P) and sulfur (S). Arsenic and P seem to affect each other's uptake in a complex way depending on environmental and intracellular concentration, since a diversity of effects have been observed according to the plant species and the concentration of both elements. As it was mentioned before, P in addition drastically decreases As damages in plants not only by the known uptake competition but also by modifying uptake regulation and intracellular processes (Mishra et al. 2014). On the other hand, the strong positive correlation between As and S in plants points to the requirement of S in the biosynthesis of thiol containing ligands involved in As detoxification processes. In addition, some studies indicate that As(V) exposure can decrease cellular Cys pools (Sung et al. 2009). Thus, an increase in Cys biosynthesis to support GSH and PC production would contribute to the effectiveness of approaches designed to increase thiols within plants. Hence, the acquisition of S from the soil as sulfate (SO_4^{-2}) is determinant, and allows induction of SO_4^{-2} transporter genes in different plant species (Norton et al. 2008; Sung et al. 2009).

3. CHROMIUM

Chromium redox state considerably changes with rhizosphere conditions and their mobility is highly influenced by soil properties. The stable Cr forms are trivalent [Cr(III)] and hexavalent [Cr(VI)] (Dong et al. 2011). It has been reported that Cr(VI) is more watersoluble than Cr(III) and both chemical species are easily taken up by plants (Lopez-Luna et al. 2009). Furthermore, metal speciation is determinant for uptake, translocation and accumulation and it also affects Cr phytotoxicity.

3.1. Chromium Uptake

Even though it is well known that Cr uptake from media depends upon pH, Cr concentration and salinity, the uptake pathways in plants are not totally elucidated (Babula et al. 2008). Cr(III) uptake is a passive process that implies simple diffusion. On the contrary, Cr(VI) uptake seems to be an active mechanism involving transporters of essential elements. Because of the structural similarity between chromate (CrO_4^{-2}) and SO_4^{-2}, Cr(VI) may enter through SO_4^{-2} transporters of root cells, and also competes with Fe and P for transporter binding (Shanker et al. 2005). Hence, the presence of these elements in the growth medium reduces Cr uptake by plants. For example, Kleiman and Cogliatti (1997) showed that SO_4^{-2} strongly inhibited Cr uptake in wheat.

On the contrary, Cr(VI) uptake was stimulated after precultivation of these plants in SO_4^{-2} limited nutrient media. Regarding Cr and P competence, in *Raphanus sativus* L. a decrease in Cr accumulation was observed when Pi was supplied at low Cr concentrations (< 6.5 mM). However, at high Cr concentrations (6.5 mM and 8.0 mM), Pi amendments did not show any significant impact on the accumulation. It supports the fact that, at high concentrations, Cr acts as a stronger competitor than Pi for SO_4^{-2} transporters on the surface of root cells (Sayantan and Shardendu 2013).

It seems that Cr uptake is highly dependent upon the genus and species diversity. In this sense, two willow species showed significant differences in Cr removal rates although both were able to remove faster Cr(III) than Cr(VI) from hydroponic solution (Yu et al. 2008).

3.2. Chromium Metabolism

3.2.1. Chromium Association with Thiol Compounds

Once Cr(III) and Cr(VI) cross the endodermis of root cells via symplast, Cr(VI) within the cells is readily reduced to Cr(III), possibly by ferric reductase enzymes and then it can form complexes with thiols compounds (Kleiman and Cogliatti 1997). In this sense, PCs and metallothioneins (MTs) are commonly associated to tolerance mechanisms of plants induced by heavy metal stress. Diwan et al. (2010) detected PCs in canola plants after Cr exposure. Moreover, compounds with a similar retention time as PCs were obtained in rice seedlings; highlighting the need to identify them in future studies (Qiu et al. 2013). Induction of MTs synthesis was also described by some authors. MTs are low molecular mass proteins (from 2 to 16 kDa) with unique abundance of cysteine residues (more than 30% from all amino acids). Even though the role of MTs in plant protective mechanisms against metals is not fully understood, they are known as effective free radical regulators by binding metals. For instance, maize seeds exposed to Cr showed a MTs increase, which may confer tolerance by binding Cr ions (Labra et al. 2006). In addition, it has been reported that MTs-like proteins were expressed in sorghum under Cr stress (Shanker et al. 2004a). These examples show that the role of PCs and MTs in Cr detoxification has not been thoroughly studied compared to other heavy metals, thus it still remains a challenge for the future.

Currently, a study about physiological and proteomic alterations in roots of *Miscanthus sinensis* (a perennial C4 grass) exposed to Cr showed that in absence of PCs synthesis, a very important role could be reserved for a Cr antiporter dependent on V-ATPases activity. The antiporter activity depends on the presence of a proton gradient across the vacuolar membrane and thus, indirectly, on the V-ATPase.So far, vacuolar Cr-specific transporters have not been reported. Therefore, the large differential expression of several vacuolar and mitochondrial ATPases may provide important clues for further investigations (Sharmin et al. 2012).

3.2.2. Chromium Accumulation and Translocation

Chromium is mainly accumulated in plant roots, followed by the stems and a minor amount in leaves (Sundaramoorthy et al. 2010). The high root accumulation could be, in part, due to the presence of sites with high exchange capacity, such as the carboxylic groups of hemicelluloses, pectin and proteins, transforming the roots into an efficient cationic exchange barrier that can greatly reduce the movement of metals towards stem and leaves. On the other hand, the high root accumulation could also be related with the ability of roots to convert Cr(VI) to Cr(III), which is highly retained in root cortex cells as insoluble compounds such as Cr-EDTA, Cr-PCs and/or Cr-MTs. These complexes could be immobilized in the vacuoles of root cells, thus rendering them less toxic (Shanker et al. 2004a). In this sense, Qiu et al. (2013) demonstrated that root cell walls and vacuoles were the main plant subcellular compartments for Cr accumulation in rice seedlings.

After Cr uptake, it can be transported to the plant aerial parts by the xylem. Cr(VI) moves faster than Cr(III) in the xylem, presumably because there is an electrostatic interaction with the vessel walls (Cervantes et al. 2001). In this context, *Pluchea indica* and *Dyera costulata* presented high potential to accumulate high amounts of Cr in leaves, showing a good phytoremediation potential (Sampanpanish et al. 2006; Gafoori et al. 2011).

Among Cr hyperaccumulator species, several crops of interest are included, such as *Arachis hypogea, Cicer arietinum* L. and *Z. mays*, in which Cr accumulation was greater in the roots than in the aerial parts (Gheju et al. 2009; Rajalakshmi et al. 2010; Dasgupta et al. 2011).

Moreover, Yu et al. (2008) reported that Cr distribution was different in two willow species. Roots and lower stems were the major sites for accumulation in weeping willows exposed to Cr(VI) and Cr(III), respectively, while Cr was accumulated mostly in roots of hankow willow species, amended with either of the chemical forms. The author suggests that different uptake, assimilation and tissues distribution of Cr(VI) and Cr(III) exist in willow species, thus an effective Cr phytoextraction depends on an adequate selection of the plant species.

Several aquatic plants have also the capability of Cr accumulation. In this sense, *Alternanthera philoxeroides* (macrophyte) was able to accumulate high Cr concentrations, mainly in roots, with increasing Cr(VI) levels in the nutrient solution (Vajravel and Saravanan 2013). Contrarily, another Cr hyperaccumulator aquatic species (*Ipomoea aquatic*) accumulated 90% Cr(VI) in stems and leaves, similarly to what has been described for the model As hyperaccumulator *P. vittata* (Weerasinghe et al. 2008). Another work showed that submerged leaves of *Salvinia minima* exposed to Cr(VI) were capable of accumulating higher Cr concentrations than floating leaves, thus alleviating Cr toxicity in the last ones (Prado et al. 2010).

In addition, Duarte et al. (2012) showed that *Halimione portulacoides* could not only accumulate high Cr levels in roots, but also reduce large amounts of Cr(VI) in the external medium. This reduction capacity has also been shown in several aquatic macrophytes, such as *Salvinia auriculata, Pistia stratiotes* and *E. crassipes* (Espinoza-Quiñones et al. 2009).

Accumulation and reduction capabilities of aquatic plants, make them suitable species for Cr phytoremediation, both by phytoextraction and rhizo-transformation of the more toxic Cr form into the less harmful one. Recently, studies using another aquatic plant (*Lemna minor*) carried out in a pilot system with continuous wastewater flow showed that the highest Cr accumulation was achieved at pH 4 and that Cr(VI) was efficiently reduced (Uysal 2013).

In relation to both heavy metals addressed in this chapter, a recent study was presented by Oliveira et al. (2014), who investigated the effect of simultaneous exposure to As(V), Cr(VI) and SO_4^{-2} on As and Cr uptake and translocation in *P. vittata*. This plant was effective in taking large amounts of Cr and As, however As and Cr inhibited each other uptake and translocation. On the contrary, SO_4^{-2} may be used to enhance plant As and Cr uptake.

Although Cr uptake, translocation and accumulation mechanisms in plants are not yet fully understood in comparison with As and other heavy metals, the toxic effects produced by Cr have been extensively described and they will be presented below.

3.3. Toxic Effects of Chromium on Plants

Chromium induces toxicity in plants at morphological, physiological, biochemical and molecular levels (Singh et al. 2013). These toxic effects depend primarily on its redox state since both Cr(VI) and Cr(III) differ in terms of mobility and bioavailability (Hayat et al. 2012). In the soil, Cr(III) and Cr(VI) may interconvert and to be immobilized on soil particles, hence it is difficult to evaluate separately the effect of each one on plants.

3.3.1. Chromium Effects on Germination

It has been described that Cr(VI) significantly reduces the germination percentage in *Beta vulgaris, R. sativus, Daucus carota, Solanum melongena, Lycopersicon esculentum* and *Brassica oleracea* var. *acephala*, among others (Lakshmi and Sundaramoorthy 2010; Ozdener et al. 2011), whereas Cr(III) inhibits germination in *Triticum aestivum* (Vajpayee et al. 2011). This effect partially depends on plant species, since seed coats determine to what extent the heavy metal reaches embryo tissues, which is dependent on physical and chemical properties of the metal ions (Hayat et al. 2012). As it is well known, during germination, hydrolysis of protein and starch takes place providing amino acids and sugars. Under Cr treatment, a decrease in α and β amylase activities has been reported, resulting in an impaired supply of sugars to the developing embryo axis (Oliveira 2012; Singh et al. 2013). Besides, protease activity increases with Cr treatment, which could also contribute to the reduced seed germination (Hayat et al. 2012).

3.3.2. Chromium Effects on Root and Shoot Growth

Since root is the first organ to come in contact with contaminants, the decrease in its growth is a well documented effect in different plant species. Several studies have demonstrated the adverse effect of Cr(III) and Cr(VI) on root growth (Nematshahi et al. 2010; Sharmin et al. 2012; Texeira et al. 2013; Vajravel and Saravanan 2013). The general response of reduced root growth could be related to the inhibition of cell division and elongation, which might occur as a result of tissue collapse and consequent incapacity of the roots to absorb water and nutrients (Shanker et al. 2005; Oliveira 2012). Thus, the decreased water and nutrient transportation to aerial parts inhibit shoot growth as it was described in *Allium cepa, Solanum nigrum* and, *A. philoxeroides* (Nematshahi et al. 2010; Teixeira et al. 2013; Vajravel and Saravanan 2013). In addition, Cr transport to the aerial part of the plant can have a direct impact on cellular metabolism of shoots and leaves, contributing to the reduction in plant height and leaf area (Polti et al. 2011; Hayat et al. 2012). Leaf area is usually decreased in response to increased Cr concentrations as a consequence of the decrease in leaf cells number or size. Moreover, with a continued Cr supply the affected old leaves lamina became necrotic, permanently wilted, dry, and shed. It is noteworthy that leaf area decisively determines crops yield and serves as a suitable phytoindicator of heavy metal pollution (Oliveira 2012). For example, Nematshahi et al. (2010) described a reduction in dry matter as a consequence of root and shoot growth reduction in *A. cepa* plants treated with increasing Cr(III) concentrations. Similarly, Prado et al. (2010) observed a decrease in dry matter of *S. minima* plants when they were exposed to Cr(IV). This reduction under increasing Cr(VI) concentrations has been attributed to a decline in CO_2 assimilation due to a metal induced reduction of photosynthetic pigments.

3.4. Chromium Effects on Physiological Processes

3.4.1. Photosynthesis

In higher plants, the adverse effect of Cr on photosynthesis is well documented, although it is not well understood to what extent this is due to alteration of pigments biosynthetic pathways, disorganization of chloroplasts ultrastructure, inhibition of Calvin cycle enzymes, or inhibition of electron transport (Nagajyoti et al. 2010).

Changes in pigment contents are frequently observed in Cr stressed plants. Ghani (2011) observed a decrease in chlorophyll contents of *B. juncea* L. plants with increasing Cr(VI) concentrations, that might be caused by an inhibition of δ-aminolevulinic acid dehydratase and photochlorophyllide reductase, essential enzymes in chlorophyll biosynthesis (Ganesh et al. 2008; Singh et al. 2013). Pigment biosynthesis could also be affected because Cr competes with Mg and Fe (which are important components of chlorophyll molecule) for assimilation and transport to leaves (Oliveira 2012). In addition, the decrease in the chlorophyll *a*/*b* ratio indicates that Cr toxicity possibly reduces the size of the peripheral part of the antenna complex, which could be related to the destabilization and degradation of peripheral part proteins. The inactivation of enzymes involved in the chlorophyll biosynthesis could also contribute to the reduction in chlorophyll content in higher plants (Shanker et al. 2005). Another negative impact of Cr(VI) on photosynthesis is the decrease of malate dehydrogenase and RuBP carboxylase activities, which interferes with CO_2 assimilation and thus affecting net photosynthetic rate. Furthermore, Cr(VI) alters electron transport chain, since it inhibits uncoupled electron transport. This is possibly due to redox change in Cu and Fe tranporters, where Cr(VI) may be transferred by cytochrome to reduce it or the reduced heme group of cytochrome may act as a site for Cr(VI) binding, thereby interfering with electron transport. Cr(VI) may bind to cytochrome *a3* as well as complex IV of cytochrome oxidase, causing a severe inhibition of their activity (Dixit et al. 2002).

However, no significant differences regarding chlorophyll and carotenoid contents under Cr stress were found in both aquatic and terrestrial plants, such as floating leaves of *S. minima* and *S. nigrum*, respectively (Prado et al. 2010; Teixeira et al. 2013). Intriguingly, in the aquatic plant *E. crassipes*, Paiva et al. (2009) found that Cr(III) and Cr(VI) do not affect or even increase photosynthesis and chlorophyll content, whereas Cr(VI) increased the contents of chlorophyll *a*, chlorophyll *b* and carotenoids in *A. philoxeroides* (Vajravel and Saravanan 2013).

3.4.2. Antioxidant Enzymes

Chromium induces modifications in the activities of antioxidant enzymes since it interacts with GSH, NADH and H_2O_2, which results in hydroxyl radicals (OH^-) generation. In this sense, root tissues of *H. portulacoides* treated with Cr(VI) exhibited higher APX, GPX and SOD activities than control roots (Duarte et al. 2012). Similarly, Yadav et al. (2010) showed an increase of CAT, APX and glutathione S-transferase (GST) activities with increasing Cr concentration in *Jatropha curcas* L. Significantly higher activities of SOD, APX, CAT and GR were observed in *B. juncea* shoots compared with those activities of *Vigna radiata* at different Cr concentrations (Diwan et al. 2010). Vajravel and Saravanan (2013) also described an increase in CAT, peroxidase (POD) and APX activities in shoots and roots of *A. philoxeroides* Cr treated plants. On the other hand, a decrease in CAT activity and an increase in POD activity were observed in *P. stratiotes* L. and *Glycine max* plants with increasing Cr concentrations. POD induction is a general response of higher plants to toxic amounts of metals and it might be linked to a decline in growth rate and to an alteration of the cell wall. The decrease in CAT activity due to accumulated Cr could have an inhibitory effect on protein synthesis in seedlings.

This general induction of antioxidant defense system in response to Cr stress suggests the important role of antioxidants in conferring tolerance against accumulated Cr. Moreover, a marked decline in the GSH pool is usually observed under Cr stress conditions. This could be due to the interconversion of reduced and oxidized forms of GSH to maintain redox status of the cell as well as to contribute in the utilization of GSH to scavenge free radicals (Shanker et al. 2005 and references therein). Besides, the depletion of GSH under metal stress condition is related to the synthesis of PCs (Yadav et al. 2010).

Membrane damage, evaluated throughout the quantification of lipid peroxidation products such as malondialdehyde (MDA), is a common consequence of heavy metals exposure. However, MDA levels can increase or not after Cr treatment (Diwan et al. 2010; Sharmin et al. 2012; Duarte et al. 2012; Sayantan and Shardendu 2013).

3.5. Water Relations and Mineral Nutrition

It is known that water uptake and its movement through symplast and apoplast as well as stomatal functioning are affected by heavy metals. For instance, Cr decreased water potential and transpiration rate but increased diffusive resistance and relative water content in leaves of *B. oleracea* (Chatterjee and Chatterjee 2000). Besides, the high oxidative potential of Cr(VI) reduced stomatal conductance maybe by a damage in the stomatal guard cells membrane (Shanker et al. 2005; Hayat et al. 2012).

Nutrient uptake and biomass of plants are affected in a complex way under Cr stress. It has been suggested that both Cr(III) and Cr(VI) can interfere with the uptake of other ions, because of its structural similarity. For example, high Cr concentrations interfered with the uptake of N, K, P and Mg. Levels of Ca, Mn, Fe, Cu, Zn, Al and Mo could also be affected by this heavy metal (Singh et al. 2013). In this sense, it is known that P, Fe, S and Mn compete with Cr for surface sites and transport binding. Hence, it is possible that Cr effectively competes with these elements to gain rapid entry into the plant system. One of the reasons for the decreased uptake of most minerals in Cr stressed plants could be the inhibition of plasma membrane H^+ ATPase activity, causing a decrease in proton extrusion. This in turn may decrease transport activities of the root plasma membrane, thus reducing the uptake of most nutrient elements. It is possible that Cr interferes with the mechanism controlling the intracellular pH; this possibility is supported by the fact that Cr could be reduced in the cells, thereby utilizing the protons. Other alterations or even the inhibition of P, K, Zn, Cu, Ca and Fe translocation within the plant parts have also been described (Shanker et al. 2005).

It may be concluded that Cr stress affects the distribution and chemical forms of minerals in plant organs and cells, resulting in an imbalance between inorganic nutrients. The extent of this imbalance is related to genotype differences in Cr accumulation and tolerance levels (Hayat et al. 2012).

3.6. Other Biochemical Effects

Phytohormone synthesis is also affected under Cr stress. It has been mentioned that Cr(VI) inhibited ethylene biosynthesis from endogenous 1-aminocyclopropane-1-carboxylic acid (ACC) in *Phaseolus vulgaris,* due to the inhibition of ACC synthase activity or previous

ACC catalyzed reactions (Singh et al. 2013 and references therein). In addition, Cr(VI) caused a decrease in indole-3-acetic acid (IAA) and in indole-3-butyric acid (IBA) content of *T. aestivum* roots and shoots (Zhang et al. 2009).

Carbohydrate content and enzymes related to its metabolism are other parameters severely affected. For example, sucrose concentration was, in general, higher in Cr treated than in Cr untreated leaves of *S. minima* plants, while the glucose concentration showed an inverse pattern. Cr also affected soluble acid invertase activity and high enzymatic activities were observed in the Cr treated floating leaves (Prado et al. 2010). Starch phosphorylases activities were enhanced in *Solanum oleracea* and *P. sativum*, suggesting an increased utilization of retranslocated sugar in starch synthesis (Sinha et al. 2005; Tiwari et al. 2009).

Chromium toxicity also leads to alterations in various enzymes related to nitrogen metabolism. During transport, Cr can act at different sites to inhibit a large number of enzymes having functional sulphydryl groups, disrupting the protein synthesis pathways and consequently the normal protein form. Moreover, nitrogen content in plants gets reduced by Cr, thus reducing the amino acid content, as it was described for *P. stratiotes* L. and *G. max* plants (Ganesh et al. 2008).

3.6.1. Genotoxicity

Cr is highly mutagenic, because it reacts with DNA. Mitotic irregularities including C mitosis, anaphase bridges, chromosome stickiness, chromosome fragmentation, and lagging were reported in root tip cells of *A. cepa* under Cr(III) and Cr(VI) treatments (Singh et al. 2013 and references therein). In addition, Cr(VI) affected chromosome segregation as well as cytokinesis, leading to undivided nuclei and various chromosomal irregularities in *Lens culinaris* roots.

The above effects seem to result from the disturbance of the cell cycle specific microtubule arrays, which are a target of Cr(VI) toxicity (Eleftheriou et al. 2012). Other genotoxic effects include significant variations on cell cycle dynamics, ploidy level, hypermethylation of DNA and increase in DNA polymorphism (Oliveira 2012).

4. TRANSGENIC PLANTS FOR ENHANCING AS AND PHYTOREMEDIATION

Considerable progress in the elucidation of the mechanisms involved in As and Cr uptake and metabolism, as well as in tolerance and toxicity aspects, has allowed the development of genetically modified plants, to improve phytoremediation. In this sense, there are several studies regarding transgenic plants for As phytoremediation, but only a few describing the development of transgenic plants with enhanced Cr remediation capability. Some examples illustrating these advances are shown in Table 1.

The main target for genetic engineering directed to the improvement of As phytoremediation has been increasing sequestration of As within cells. Furthermore, increasing As translocation and volatilization have also been explored (Table 1). Concerning As sequestration, most research has focused in some of the three enzymes that constitute the PCs biosynthetic pathway: gamma-glutamylcysteine synthase (ECS), glutathione synthase (GS) and phytochelatin synthase (PCS).

Table 1. Examples of transgenic plants to enhance As and Cr phytoremediation

HM	Gene transferred	Gene function	Origin	Target plant species	Effect	Reference
Arsenic	arsC and γ-ECS	As(V) reduction and PC synthesis, respectively	E. coli	A. thaliana	Enhanced tolerance and accumulation	Dhankher et al. 2002
	A2::AtPCS1	PC synthesis	A. thaliana	A. thaliana	Enhanced tolerance	Li et al. 2004
	A2::ECS	PC synthesis	E. coli	A. thaliana	Enhanced tolerance	Li et al. 2005
	γ-ECS and GS	PC and GSH synthesis	E. coli	A. thaliana	Enhanced tolerance but no increase in As accumulation	Li et al. 2006b
	AtPCS1	PC synthesis	A. thaliana	B. juncea	Enhanced tolerance and accumulation	Gasic and Korban 2007
	AsPCS1 and GSH1	PC and GSH synthesis	A. sativum and S. cerevisiae	A. thaliana	Enhanced tolerance and accumulation	Guo et al. 2008
	AtMT2b	MTs synthesis	A. thaliana	N. tabacum	Enhanced sensitivity and translocation	Grispen et al. 2009
	AtPCS1	PC synthesis	A. thaliana	N. tabacum	Enhanced tolerance	Wojas et al. 2010
	CePCS	PC synthesis	Caenorhabditis elegans	N. tabacum	Enhanced tolerance	Wojas et al. 2010
	ECS	PC synthesis	E. coli	Populus spp.	Enhanced tolerance	LeBlanc et al. 2011
	arsM	As methylation	Rhodopseudomonas palustris	O. sativa	Enhanced volatilization	Meng et al. 2011
	CdPCS1	PC synthesis	Ceratophyllum demersum	N. tabacum	Enhanced PCs content and As accumulation	Shukla et al. 2012
	AsPCS1 and Ycf1	PC synthesis	A. sativum and S. cerevisiae	A. thaliana	Enhanced PCs content and As accumulation	Guo et al. 2012

Table 1. (Continued)

HM	Gene transferred	Gene function	Origin	Target plant species	Effect	Reference
	ScACR3	As(III) antiporter	*S. cerevisiae*	*O. sativa*	Increase As efflux and decreased accumulation	Duan et al. 2012
	PvACR3	As(III) antiporter	*P. vittata*	*A. thaliana*	Enhanced accumulation and translocation	Chen et al. 2013
	A putative yeast transcriptional activator (MSNI)	Multi-functional protein	yeast	*N. tabacum*	Enhanced tolerance and accumulation	Kim et al. 2006
Chromium	Glucocorticoid receptor (GR)	Increase the auxin/cytokinin ratio, ABA and AIA contents	rat	*N. langsdorffii*	Increased resistance	del Bubba et al. 2013

MTs are also targets of genetic engineering. All current publications seem to indicate that multigene approach directed to increase sequestration of As within cells led to better results than simple gene transformation.

Despite Cr toxicity has been thoroughly studied, its molecular mechanisms are poorly documented in plants compared to other heavy metals. Moreover, the events underlying Cr perception and the defense signal transduction have been only partially elucidated. Consequently, the development of transgenic plants improved for Cr remediation has been delayed, which is reflected in the few examples showed in Table 1.

CONCLUSION

Arsenic and chromium are toxic heavy metals present in the environment in different chemical forms. Phytoremediation technology seems to be a successful approach to remediate these heavy metals from polluted sites. Nevertheless, several factors must be considered in order to accomplish a high performance in remediation, since each plant-heavy metal-soil system presents specific characteristics. Moreover, a thorough knowledge is essential to know the metabolism and accumulation mechanisms of these heavy metals. Even though important advances have been made to elucidate As and Cr metabolism in plants, it is necessary to integrate these outcomes in terms of "omics" technologies. In this way, it has been recently compiled and analyzed transcriptome, proteome, and metabolome alterations in plants under As stress, named as "Arsenomics". The interesting findings obtained in that study highlight the need to investigate integrative biochemical networks in other less investigated heavy metals, such as Cr. In this context, one important aspect to understand Cr toxicity would be to unravel the interconversion of Cr species within the plant. Thus, further research would help to build up tools required to develop more tolerant plants for effective phytoremediation strategies, as well as achieving heavy metal free-plants for safe consumption.

REFERENCES

Abedin MJ, Feldmann J, Meharg AA (2002) Uptake kinetics of arsenic species in rice plants. *Plant Physiol* 128: 1120–1128.

Agency for Toxic Substances and Disease Registry (ATSDR) (2012) Health and Human Services. Atlanta, GA.

Azizur Rahman M, Hasegawa H, Mahfuzur Rahman M, Nazrul Islam M, Majid Miah MA, Tasmin A (2007) Effect of arsenic on photosynthesis, growth and yield of five widely cultivated rice (*Oryza sativa* L) varieties in Bangladesh. *Chemosphere* 67: 1072–1079.

Babula P, Adam V, Opatrilova R, Zehnalek J, Havel L, Kizek R (2008) Uncommon heavy metals, metalloids and their plant toxicity: A review. *Environ Chem Lett* 6: 189–213.

Bentley R, Chasteen TG (2002) Microbial methylation of metalloids: Arsenic, antimony, and bismuth. *Microbiol Mol Biol Rev* 66: 250–271.

Bhattacharjee H, Rosen BP (2007) Arsenic metabolism in prokaryotic and eukaryotic microbes. In: Nies DH, Silver S (eds) Molecular microbiology of heavy metals. Springer-Verlag, Berlin, Germany pp 371–406.

Bleeker PM, Hakvoort HWJ, Bliek M, Souer E, Schat H (2006) Enhanced arsenate reduction by a CDC25-like tyrosine phosphatase explains increased phytochelatin accumulation in arsenate-tolerant *Holcus lanatus*. *Plant J* 45: 917–929.

Brammer H, Ravenscroft P (2009) Arsenic in groundwater: A threat to sustainable agriculture in South and South-East Asia. *Environ Int* 35: 647–654.

Caille N, Zhao F J, McGrath SP (2005) Comparison of root absorption, translocation and tolerance of arsenic in the hyperaccumulator *Pteris vittata* and the nonhyperaccumulator *Pteris tremula*. *New Phytol* 165:755–761.

Catarecha P, Segura MD, Franco-Zorrilla JM, Garcia-Ponce B, Lanza M, Solano R, Paz-Ares J, Leyva A (2007) A mutant of the *Arabidopsis* phosphate transporter PHT1;1 displays enhanced arsenic accumulation. *Plant Cell* 19: 1123–1133.

Cervantes C, Garcia JC, Devars S, Corona FG, Tavera HL, Torres-Guzman JC, Moreno-Sanchez R (2001) Interactions of chromium with micro-organisms and plants. *FEMS Microbiol Rev* 25: 335–347.

Chatterjee J, Chatterjee C (2000) Phytotoxicity of cobalt, chromium and copper in cauliflower. *Environ Pollut* 109: 69–74.

Chen Y, Xu W, Shen H, Yan H, Xu W, He Z, Ma M (2013) Engineering arsenic tolerance and hyperaccumulation in plants for phytoremediation by a PvACR3 transgenic approach. *Environ Sci Technol* 47: 9355–9362.

Chen Z, Zhu YG, Liu WJ, Meharg AA (2005) Direct evidence showing the effect of root surface iron plaque on arsenite and arsenate uptake into rice (*Oryza sativa*) roots. *New Phytol* 165: 91–97.

Danh LT, Truong P, Mammucari R, Tran T, Foster N (2009) Vativer grass, *Vetiveria zizanioides*: A choice plant for phytoremediation of heavy matals and organis wastes. *Int J Phytorem* 11: 664–691.

Dasgupta S, Satvat S, Mahindrakar AB (2011) Ability of *Cicer arietinum* (L.) for bioremoval of lead and chromium from soil. *Int J Technol Eng Syst* l: 338–341.

del Bubbaa M, Ancillottia C, Checchinia L, Ciofia L, Fibbia D, Gonnelli C, Mosti S (2013) Chromium accumulation and changes in plant growth, selected phenolics and sugars of wild type and genetically modified *Nicotiana langsdorffii*. *J Hazard Mater* 262: 394–403.

Dhankher OP, Li YJ, Rosen BP, Shi J, Salt D, Senecoff JF, Sashti NA, Meagher RB (2002) Engineering tolerance and hyperaccumulation of arsenic in plants by combining arsenate reductase and gammaglutamylcysteine synthetase expression. *Nature Biotechnol* 20: 1140–1145.

Dhankher O P, Rosen BP, McKinney EC, Meagher RB (2006) Hyperaccumulation of arsenic in the shoots of *Arabidopsis* silenced for arsenate reductase (ACR2). *PNAS USA,* 103: 5413-5418.

Diwan H, Khan I, Ahmad A, Iqbal M (2010) Induction of phytochelatins and antioxidant defence system in *Brassica juncea* and *Vigna radiata* in response to chromium treatments. *Plant Gro Regul* 67: 97–107.

Dixit V, Pandey V, Shyam R (2002) Chromium ions inactivate electron transport and enhance superoxide generation in vivo in pea (*Pisum sativum* L. cv. Azad) root mitochondria. *Plant Cell Environ* 25: 687–693.

Dong X Ma LQ, Li Y (2011) Characteristics and mechanisms of hexavalent chromium removal by biochar from sugar beet tailing. *J Hazard Mater* 190: 909–915.

Duan G, Kamiya T, Ishikawa S, Arao T, Fujiwara T (2012) Expressing ScACR3 in rice enhanced arsenite efflux and reduced arsenic accumulation in rice grains. *Plant Cell Physiol* 53: 154–163.

Duan GL, Zhou Y, Tong YP, Mukhopadhyay R, Rosen BP, Zhu YG (2007) A CDC25 homologue from rice functions as an arsenate reductase. *New Phytol* 174: 311–321.

Duan GL, Zhu YG, Tong YP, Cai C, Kneer R (2005) Characterization of arsenate reductase in the extract of roots and fronds of Chinese brake fern, an arsenic hyperaccumulator. *Plant Physiol* 138: 461–469.

Duarte BN, Silva V, Cacador I (2012) Hexavalent chromium reduction, uptake and oxidative biomarkers in *Halimione portulacoides*. *Ecotoxicol Environ Saf* 83: 1–7.

Eleftheriou EP, Adamakis IDS, Fatsiou M, Panteris E (2012) Hexavalent chromium disrupts mitosis by stabilizing microtubules in *Lens culinaris* root tip cells. *Physiol Plant* 147: 169–180.

Ellis DR, Gumaelius L, Indriolo E, Pickering IJ, Banks JA, Salt DE (2006) A novel arsenate reductase from the arsenic hyperaccumulating fern *Pteris vittata*. *Plant Physiol* 141: 1544–1554.

Espinoza-Quiñones FR, Martin N, Stutz G, Tirao G, Palácio SM, Rizzutto MA, Módenes AN, Silva FG, Szymanski N, Kroumov AD (2009) Root uptake and reduction of hexavalent chromium by aquatic macrophytes as assessed by high-resolution X-ray emission. *Water Res* 43: 4159–4166.

Farnese FS, Oliveira JA, Gusman GS, Leão GA, Silveira NM, Silva PM, Ribeiro C, Cambraia J (2014) Effects of adding nitroprusside on arsenic stressed response of *Pistia stratiotes* L. under hydroponic conditions. *Int J Phytorem* 16: 123–137.

Finnegan PM, Chen W (2012) Arsenic toxicity: The effects on plant metabolism. *Front Physiol* 3: 1–18.

Gafoori M Majid NM, Islam MM, Luhat S (2011) Bioaccumulation of heavy metals by *Dyera costulata* cultivated in sewage sludge contaminated soil. *Afr J Biotechnol* 10: 10674–10682.

Ganesh KS, Baskaran L, Rajasekaran S, Sumathi K, Chidambaram ALA, Sundaramoorthy P (2008) Chromium stress induced alterations in biochemical and enzyme metabolism in aquatic and terrestrial plants. *Coll Surf B: Biointer* 63:159-163.

Gasic K, Korban SS (2007) Transgenic Indian mustard (*Brassica juncea*) plants expressing an *Arabidopsis* phytochelatin synthase (AtPCS1) exhibit enhanced As and Cd tolerance. *Plant Mol Biol* 64: 361–369.

Ghani A (2011) Effect of chromium toxicity on growth, chlorophyll and some mineral nutrients of *Brassica juncea* L. *Egypt. Acad J Biol Sci* 2: 9–15.

Gheju M, Balcu I, Ciopec M (2009) Analysis of hexavalent chromium uptake by plants in polluted soils. *Ovidius University Ann Chem* 20: 127–131.

Ghosh M, Shen J, Rosen BP (1999) Pathways of As(III) detoxification in *Saccharomyces cerevisiae*. *PNAS USA* 96: 5001–5006.

Grispen VMJ, Irtelli B, Hakvoort HWJ, Vooijs R, Bliek T, Bookum WM, Verkleij JAC, Schat H (2009) Expression of the *Arabidopsis* metallothione in 2b enhances arsenite sensitivity and root to shoot translocation in tobacco. *Environ Exp Bot* 66: 69–73.

Guo J, Dai X, Xu W, Ma M (2008) Overexpressing gsh1 and AsPCS1 simultaneously increase the tolerance and accumulation of cadmium and arsenic in *Arabidopsis thaliana*. *Chemosphere* 72: 1020–1026.

Guo J, Xu W, Ma M (2012) The assembly of metals chelation by thiols and vacuolar compartmentalization conferred increased tolerance to and accumulation of cadmium and arsenic in transgenic *Arabidopsis thaliana*. *J Hazard Mater* 199: 309–313.

Ha SB, Smith AP, Howden R, Dietrich WM, Bugg S, O'Connell MJ, Goldsbrough PB, Cobbett CS (1999) Phytochelatin synthase genes from *Arabidopsis* and the yeast *Schizosaccharomyces pombe*. *Plant Cell* 11: 1153–1163.

Hayat SS, Khalique G, Irfan M, Wani AS, Tripathi BN, Ahmad A (2012) Physiological changes induced by chromium stress in plants: An overview. *Protoplasma* 249: 599–611.

Ibañez SG, Paisio CE, Wevar Oller AL, Talano MA, González PS, Medina MI, Agostini E (2014) Overview and new insights of genetically engineered plants for improving phytoremediation. In: Phytoremediation: Management of Environment Contaminants. Springer-Verlag, Berlin, Germany. (In press).

Karimi N, Siyahat Shayesteh L, Ghasmpour H, Alavi M (2013) Effects of arsenic on growth, photosynthetic activity, and accumulation in two new hyperaccumulating populations of *Isatis cappadocica* Desv. *J Plant Gro Regul* 32: 823–830.

Kim YJ, Kima JH, Leea CE, Moka YG, Choib JS, Shinb HS, Hwang S (2006) Expression of yeast transcriptional activator MSN1 promotes accumulation of chromium and sulfur by enhancing sulfate transporter level in plants. *FEBS Lett* 580: 206–210.

Kimbrough DE, Cohen Y, Winer AM, Creelman L, Mabuni C (1999) A critical assessment of chromium in the environment. *Environ Sci Technol* 29: 1–46.

Kleiman ID, Cogliatti D H (1997) Uptake of chromate in sulfate deprived wheat plants. *Environ Pollut* 97: 131–135.

Labra M, Gianazza E, Waitt R, Eberini I, Sozzi A, Regondi S, Grassi F, Agradi E (2006) *Zea mays* L. protein changes in response to potassium dichromate treatments. *Chemosphere* 62: 1234–1244.

Lakshmi S, Sundaramoorthy P (2010) Effect of chromium on germination and seedling growth of vegetable crops. *Asian J Sci Technol* 1: 28–31.

LeBlanc MS, Lima A, Montello P, Kim T, Meagher RB, Merkle S (2011) Enhanced arsenic tolerance of transgenic eastern cottonwood plants expressing gamma-glutamylcysteine synthetase. *Int J Phytorem* 13: 657–673.

Li C, Feng S, Shao Y, Jiang L, Lu X, Hou X (2007) Effects of arsenic on seed germination and physiological activities of wheat seedlings. *J Environ Sci*, 19: 725–732.

Li G, Sun GX, Williams PN, Nunes L, Zhu YG (2011) Inorganic arsenic in Chinese food and its cancer risk. *Environ Int* 37: 1219–1225.

Li RY, Ago Y, Liu WJ, Mitani N, Feldmann J, McGrath SP, Ma JF, Zhao FJ (2009a) The rice aquaporin Lsi1 mediates uptake of methylated arsenic species. *Plant Physiol* 150: 2071–2080.

Li RY, Stroud JL, Ma JF, McGrath SP, Zhao FJ (2009b) Mitigation of arsenic accumulation in rice with water management and silicon fertilization. *Environ Sci Technol* 43: 3778–3783.

Li Y, Dhankher OP, Carreira L, Balish RS, Meagher RB (2005) Arsenic and mercury tolerance and cadmium sensitivity in *Arabidopsis* plants expressing bacterial gamma-glutamylcysteine synthetase. *Environ Toxicol Chem* 24: 1376–1386.

Li Y, Dhankher OP, Carreira L, Lee D, Chen A, Schroeder JI, Balish RS, Meagher RB (2004) Overexpression of phytochelatin synthase in *Arabidopsis* leads to enhanced arsenic tolerance and cadmium hypersensitivity. *Plant Cell Physiol* 45: 1787–1797.

Li Y, Heaton ACP, Carreira L, Meagher RB (2006b) Enhanced tolerance to and accumulation of mercury, but not arsenic, in plants overexpressing two enzymes required for thiol peptide synthesis. *Physiol Plant* 128: 48–57.

Li YJ, Dankher OP, Carreira L, Smith AP, Meagher RB (2006a) The shoot-specific expression of gammaglutamylcysteine synthetase directs the long-distance transport of thiol-peptides to roots conferring tolerance to mercury and arsenic. *Plant Physiol* 141: 288–298.

Liu W, Schat H, Bliek M, Chen Y, McGrath SP, George G, Salt DE, Zhao FJ, Zhao FJ (2012) Knocking out ACR2 does not affect arsenic redox status in *Arabidopsis thaliana*: Implications for As detoxification and accumulation in plants. *PLoS ONE* 7: e42408.

Liu WJ, Wood BA, Raab A, McGrath SP, Zhao FJ, Feldmann J (2010) Complexation of arsenite with phytochelatins reduces arsenite efflux and translocation from roots to shoots in Arabidopsis. *Plant Physiol* 152: 2211–2221.

Liu WJ., Zhu YG, Hu Y, Williams PN, Gault AG, Meharg AA, Charnock JM, Smith FA (2006) Arsenic sequestration in iron plaque, its accumulation and speciation in mature rice plants (*Oryza sativa* L.). *Environ Sci Technol* 40: 5730–5736.

Liu WJ, Zhu YG, Smith FA, Smith SE (2004) Do phosphorus nutrition and iron plaque alter arsenate (As) uptake by rice seedlings in hydroponic culture? *New Phytol* 162: 481–488.

Logoteta B, Xu XY, Macnair MR, McGrath SP, Zhao FJ (2009) Arsenite efflux is not enhanced in the arsenate-tolerant phenotype of *Holcus lanatus*. *New Phytol* 183: 340–348.

Lopez-Luna J, Gonzalez-Chavez MC, Esparza-García FJ, Rodrıguez-Vazquez R (2009) Toxicity assessment of soil amended with tannery sludge, trivalent chromium and hexavalent chromium, using wheat, oat and sorghum plants. *J Hazard Mater* 163: 829–834.

Ma JF, Tamai K, Yamaji N, Mitani N, Konishi S, Katsuhara M, Ishiguro M, Murata Y, Yano M (2006) A silicon transporter in rice. *Nature* 440: 688–691.

Ma JF, Yamaji N, Mitani N, Tamai K, Konishi S, Fujiwara T, Katsuhara M, Yano M (2007) An efflux transporter of silicon in rice. *Nature* 448: 209–212.

Ma JF, Yamaji N, Mitani N, Xu XY, Su YH, McGrath SP, Zhao FJ (2008) Transporters of arsenite in rice and their role in arsenic accumulation in rice grain. *PNAS USA,* 105: 9931–9935.

Mahdieh S, Ghaderian SM, Karimi N (2013) Effect of arsenic on germination, photosynthesis and growth parameters of two winter wheat varieties in Iran. *J Plant Nut* 36: 655–664.

Marmiroli M, Pigoni V, Savo-Sardaro ML, Marmiroli N (2014) The effect of silicon on the uptake and translocation of arsenic intomato (*Solanum lycopersicum* L.). *Environ Exp Bot* 99: 9–17.

Mendoza-Cózatl DG, Butko E, Springer F, Torpey JW, Komives EA, Kehr J, Schroeder JI (2008) Identification of high levels of phytochelatins, glutathione and cadmium in the phloem sap of *Brassica napus*: A role for thiol-peptides in the long-distance transport of cadmium and the effect of cadmium on iron translocation. *Plant J* 54: 249–259.

Meng XY, Qin J, Wang LH, Duan GL, Sun GX, Wu HL, Chu CC, Ling HQ, Rosen BP, Zhu YG (2011) Arsenic biotransformation and volatilization in transgenic rice. *New Phytol* 191: 49–56.

Mishra S, Srivastava S, Dwivedi S, Tripathi RD (2013) Investigation of biochemical responses of *Bacopa monnieri* L. upon exposure to arsenate. *Environ Toxicol* 28: 419–430.

Mishra S, Stärk HJ, Küpper H (2014) A different sequence of events than previously reported leads to arsenic-induced damage in *Ceratophyllum demersum* L. *Metallomics* 6: 444–454.

Moore KL, Schroder M, Wu Z, Martin BGH, Hawes CR, McGrath SP, Hawkesford MJ, Ma JF, Zhao FJ, Grovenor CRM (2011) High-resolution secondary ion mass spectrometry reveals the contrasting subcellular distribution of arsenic and silicon in rice roots. *Plant Physiol* 156: 913–924.

Nagajyoti PC, Lee PC, Sreekanth KD (2010) Heavy metals, occurrence and toxicity for plants: A review. *Environ Chem Lett* 8: 199–216.

Nematshahi N, Lahouti M, Ganjeali A (2012) Accumulation of chromium and its effect on growth of (*Allium cepa* cv. Hybrid). *Europ J Exp Biol* 2: 969–974.

Norton GJ, Meher NM, Williams PN, Dasgupta T, Meharg AA, Price AH (2008) Rice-arsenate interactions in hydroponics: A three-gene model for tolerance. *J Exp Bot* 59: 2277–2284.

Oliveira H (2012) Chromium as an environmental pollutant: insights on induced plant toxicity. *J Bot ID* 375843.

Oliveira LM, Ma LQ, Santos JAG, Guilherme LRG, Lessl JT (2014) Effects of arsenate, chromate, and sulfate on arsenic and chromium uptake and translocation by arsenic hyperaccumulator *Pteris vittata* L. *Environ Pollut* 184: 187–192.

Ozdener Y, Aydin BK, Aygün SF, Yürekli F (2011) Effect of hexavalent chromium on the growth and physiological and biochemical parameters on *Brassica oleracea* L. var. acephala DC. *Acta Biol Hung* 62: 463–476.

Paiva L B, Gonçalves de Oliveira J, Azevedoc RA, Rodrigues Ribeiro D, Gomes da Silva M, Vitória AP (2009) Ecophysiological responses of water hyacinth exposed to Cr^{3+} and Cr^{6+}. *Environ Exp Bot* 65: 403–409.

Pickering IJ, Gumaelius L, Harris HH, Prince RC, Hirsch G, Banks Ja, Salt DE, George GN (2006) Localizing the biochemical transformations of arsenate in a hyperaccumulating fern. *Environ Sci Technol* 40: 5010–5014.

Pickering IJ, Prince RC, George MJ, Smith RD, George GN, Salt DE (2000) Reduction and coordination of arsenic in Indian mustard. *Plant Physiol* 122: 1171–1177.

Polti MA, Atjiána MC, Amoroso MJ, Abate CM (2011) Soil chromium bioremediation: Synergic activity of actinobacteria and plants. *Int Biodeter Biodegrad* 65: 1175–1181.

Prado C, Rodríguez-Montelongob L, González JA, Paganod EA, Hilal M, Prado FE (2010) Uptake of chromium by *Salvinia minima*: Effect on plant growth, leaf respiration and carbohydrate metabolism. *J Hazard Mater* 177: 546–553.

Qiu B, Zeng F, Cai S, Wu X, Haider SI, Wu F, Zhang G (2013) Alleviation of chromium toxicity in rice seedlings by applying exogenous glutathione. *J Plant Physiol* 170: 772–779.

Raab A, Ferreira K, Meharg AA, Feldmann J (2007b) Can arsenic phytochelatin complex formation be used as an indicator for toxicity in *Helianthus annuus*? *J Exp Bot* 58: 1333–1338.

Raab A, Schat H, Meharg AA, Feldmann J (2005) Uptake, translocation and transformation of arsenate and arsenite in sunflower (*Helianthus annuus*): Formation of arsenic-phytochelatin complexes during exposure to high arsenic concentrations. *New Phytol* 168: 551–558.

Raab A, Williams PN, Meharg A, Feldmann J (2007a) Uptake and translocation of inorganic and methylated arsenic species by plants. *Environ Chem* 4: 197–203.

Rai R, Pandey S, Rai SP (2011) Arsenic-induced changes in morphological, physiological, and biochemical attributes and artemisinin biosynthesis in *Artemisia annua*, an antimalarial plant. *Ecotoxicology* 20: 1900–1913.

Rajalakshmi K, Kumar P, Saravanakumar A, Aslam A, Shahjahan A, Ravikumar R (2010) Arachis bioassay for soil contaminated with hexavalent chromium. *Recent Res Sci Technol* 2: 110–115.

Rathinasabapathi B, Wu S, Sundaram S, Rivoal J, Srivastava M, Ma LQ (2006)Arsenic resistance in *Pteris vittata* L.: Identification of a cytosolic triosephosphate isomerase based on cDNA expression cloning in *Escherichia coli*. *Plant Mol Biol*, 62: 845–857.

Requejo R, Tena M (2005) Proteome analysis of maize roots reveals that oxidative stress is a main contributing factor to plant arsenic toxicity. *Phytochemistry* 66: 1519–1528.

Rogival D, Scheirs J, Blust R (2007) Transfer and accumulation of metals in a soil diet-wood mouse food chain along a metal pollution gradient. *Environ Pollut* 145: 516–528.

Rosa GDL, Parsons JG, Martinez-Martinez A, Peralta-Videa JR, Gardea-Torresdey JL (2006) Spectroscopic study of the impact of arsenic speciation on arsenic/phosphorus uptake and plant growth in tumbleweed (*Salsola kali*). *Environ Sci Technol* 40: 1991–1996.

Salido AL, Hasty KL, Lim JM, Butcher DJ (2003) Phytoremediation of arsenic and lead in contaminated soil using Chinese Brake ferns (*Pteris vittata*) and Indian mustard (*Brassica juncea*). *Int J Phytorem* 5: 89–103.

Sampanpanish P, Pongsapich W, Khaodhiar S, Khan E (2006) Chromium removal from soil by phytoremediation with weed plant species in Thailand. *Water Air Soil Pollut* 6: 191–206.

Sayantan D, Shardendu N (2013) Amendment in phosphorus levels moderates the chromium toxicity in *Raphanus sativus* L. as assayed by antioxidant enzymes activities. *Ecotoxicol Environ Saf* 95: 161–170.

Schneider J, Oliveira LM, Guilherme LRG, Stürmer SL, Soares CRFS (2012) Espécies tropicais de pteridófitas em associação com fungos micorrízicos arbusculares em solo contaminado com arsênio. *Quím Nova* 35: 709–714.

Shanker AK, Cervantes C, Loza-Tavera H, Avudainayagam S (2005) Chromium toxicity in plants. *Environ Int* 31: 739–753.

Shanker AK, Djanaguiraman M, Sudhagar R, Chandrashekar CN, Pathmanabhan G (2004a) Differential antioxidative response of ascorbate glutathione pathway enzymes and metabolites to chromium speciation stress in green gram (*Vigna radiata* (L) R Wilczek, cv CO 4) roots. *Plant Sci* 166: 1035–1043.

Sharmin SA, Alam I, Kim KH, Kim YG, Kim PJ, Bahk JD, Lee BH (2012) Chromium-induced physiological and proteomic alterations in roots of *Miscanthus sinensis*. *Plant Sci* 187: 113–126.

Shen H, He Z, Yan H, Xing Z, Chen Y, Xu W, Xu W, Ma M (2014) The fronds tonoplast quantitative proteomic analysis in arsenic hyperaccumulator *Pteris vittata* L. *J. Proteomics (In press)*, doi: 10.1016/j.jprot.2014.01.029.

Shin H, Shin HS, Dewbre GR, Harrison MJ (2004) Phosphate transport in Arabidopsis: Pht1;1 and Pht1;4 play a major role in phosphate acquisition from both low- and high-phosphate environments. *Plant J* 39: 629–642.

Shukla D, Kesari R, Mishra S, Dwivedi S, Tripathi RD, Nath P, Trivedi PK (2012) Expression of phytochelatin synthase from aquatic macrophyte *Ceratophyllum demersum* L. enhances cadmium and arsenic accumulation in tobacco. *Plant Cell Rep* 31: 1687–1699.

Singh SK, Ghosh AK (2010) Effect of arsenic on photosynthesis, growth and its accumulation in the tissues of *Allium cepa* (Onion). Int J Environ Eng Manag 1: 39–50.

Singh HP, Mahajan P, Kaur S, Batish DR, Kohli RK (2013) Chromium toxicity and tolerance in plants. *Environ Chem Lett* 11: 229–254.

Singh N, Ma LQ (2006) Arsenic speciation, and arsenic and phosphate distribution in arsenic hyperaccumulator *Pteris vittata* L. and non-hyperaccumulator *Pteris ensiformis* L. *Environ Pollut* 141: 238–246.

Singh N, Ma LQ, Srivastava M, Rathinasabapathi B (2006) Metabolic adaptations to arsenic-induced oxidative stress in *Pteris vittata* L and *Pteris ensiformis* L. *Plant Sci* 170: 274–282.

Sinha S, Saxena R, Singh S (2005) Chromium induced lipid peroxidation in the plants of *Pistia stratiotes* L: role of antioxidants and antioxidant enzymes. *Chemosphere* 58: 595–604.

Song WY, Parka J, Mendoza-Cózatl DG, SuterGrotemeyerd M, Shima D, Hörtensteiner S, Geisler M, Weder B, Rea PA, Rentsch D, Schroeder JI, Lee Y, Martinoia E (2010) Arsenic tolerance in *Arabidopsis* is mediated by two ABCC-type phytochelatin transporters. *PNAS USA* 107: 21187–21192.

Sridhar BBM, Han FX, Diehl SV, Monts DL, Su Y (2011) Effect of phytoaccumulation of arsenic and chromium on structural and ultrastructural changes of brake fern (*Pteris vittata*). *Braz Soc Plant Physiol* 23: 285–293.

Srivastava M, Ma LQ, Gonzaga Santos JA (2006) Three new arsenic hyperaccumulating ferns. *Sci Total Environ* 364: 24–31.

Srivastava M, Ma LQ, Singh N, Singh S (2005) Antioxidant responses of hyper-accumulator and sensitive fern species to arsenic. *J Exp Bot* 56: 1335–1342.

Srivastava S, Srivastava AK, Singh B, Suprasanna P, D'souza SF (2013) The effect of arsenic on pigment composition and photosynthesis in *Hydrilla verticillata*. *Biol Plant* 57: 385–389.

Su YH, McGrath SP, Zhao FJ (2010) Rice is more efficient in arsenite uptake and translocation than wheat and barley. *Plant Soil*, 328: 27–34.

Su YH, McGrath SP. Zhu YG, Zhao FJ (2008) Highly efficient xylem transport of arsenite in the arsenic hyperaccumulator *Pteris vittata*. *New Phytol* 180: 434–441.

Sun GX, Williams PN, Zhu YG, Deacon C, Carey AM, Raab A, Feldmann J, Meharg AA (2009) Survey of arsenic and its speciation in rice products such as breakfast cereals, rice crackers and Japanese rice condiments. *Environ Int* 35: 473–475.

Sundaramoorthy P, Chidambaram A, Ganesh KS, Unnikannan P, Baskaran L (2010) Chromium stress in paddy: (i) nutrient status of paddy under chromium stress; (ii) phytoremediation of chromium by aquatic and terrestrial weeds. *Com Rend Biol* 333: 597–607.

Sung DY, Kim TH, Komives EA, Mendoza-Cózatl DG, Schroeder JI (2009) ARS5 is a component of the 26S proteasome complex, and negatively regulates thiol biosynthesis and arsenic tolerance in Arabidopsis. *Plant J* 59: 802–812.

Talano MA, Wevar Oller AL, González P, Oliva González S, Agostini E (2013) Effects of arsenate on tobacco hairy root and seedling growth, and its removal. *Vitro Cell Develop Biol Plant*

Teixeira J, Ferraz P, Almeida A, Verde N, Fidalgo F (2013) Metallothionein multigene family expression is differentially affected by Chromium (III) and (VI) in *Solanum nigrum* L. plants. *Food Energy Sec* 2: 130–140.

Tiwari KK, Dwivedi S, Singh NK, Rai UN, Tripathi RD (2009) Chromium (VI) induced phytotoxicity and oxidative stress in pea (*Pisum sativum* L.): Biochemical changes and translocation of essential nutrients. *J Environ Biol* 30: 389–394.

Tripathi P, Mishra A, Dwivedi S, Chakrabarty D, Trivedi PK, Singh RP, Tripathi RD (2012) Differential response of oxidative stress and thiol metabolism in contrasting rice genotypes for arsenic tolerance. *Ecotoxicol Environ Saf* 79: 189–198.

Uysal Y (2013) Removal of chromium ions from wastewater by duckweed, *Lemna minor* L. by using a pilot system with continuous flow. *J Hazard Mater* 263: 486–492.

Vajpayee P, Khatoon I, Patel CB, Singh G, Gupta KC, Shanker R (2011) Adverse effects of chromium oxide nano-particles on seed germination and growth in *Triticum aestivum* L. *J Biomed Nanotechnol* 7: 205–206.

Vajravel S, Saravanan P (2013) Accumulation of chromium and its effects on physiological and biochemical parameters of *Alternanthera philoxeroides* seedlings. *J Pharmacy Res* 7: 633–639.

Vetterlein D, Szegedi K, Neackermann J, Mattusch J, Neue HU (2007) Competitive mobilization of phosphate and arsenate associated with goethite by root activity. *J Environ Qual* 36: 1811–1820.

Wang J, Zhao FJ, Meharg AA, Raab A, Feldman J, McGrath SP (2002) Mechanisms of arsenic hyperaccumulation in *Pteris vittata*: Uptake kinetics, interactions with phosphate, and arsenic speciation. *Plant Physiol* 130: 1552–1561.

Wang L, Duan G (2009) Effect of external and internal phosphate status on arsenic toxicity and accumulation in rice seedlings. *J Environ Sci* 21: 346–351.

Wang S, Mulligan CN (2006) Occurrence of arsenic contamination in Canada: Sources, behavior and distribution. *Sci Total Environ* 366: 701–721.

Weerasinghe A, Ariyawnasa S, Weerasooriya R (2008) Phytoremediation potential of *Ipomoea aquatica* for Cr(VI) mitigation. *Chemosphere* 70: 521–524.

Wojas S, Clemens S, Sklodowska A, Antosiewicz DA (2010) Arsenic response of AtPCS1- and CePCS-expressing plants-Effects of external As(V) concentration on As-accumulation pattern and NPT metabolism. *J Plant Physiol* 167: 169–175.

Xie QE, Yan XL, Liao XY, Li X (2009) The arsenic hyperaccumulator fern *Pteris vittata* L. Environ *Sci Technol* 43: 8488–8495.

Xu XY, McGrath SP, Meharg A, Zhao FJ (2008) Growing rice aerobically markedly decreases arsenic accumulation. *Environ Sci Technol* 42: 5574–5579.

Yadav SK, Dhote M, Kumar P, Sharma J, Chakrabarti T, Juwarkar AA (2010) Differential antioxidative enzyme responses of *Jatropha curcas* L. to chromium stress. *J Hazard Mater* 180: 609–615.

Ye WL, Wood BA, Stroud JL, Andralojc PJ, Raab A, McGrath SP, Feldmann J, Zhao FJ (2010) Arsenic speciation in phloem and xylem exudates of castor bean. *Plant Physiol* 154: 1505–1513.

Yu LJ, Luo YF, Liao B, Xie LJ, Chen L, Xiao S, Li JT, Hu SN, Shu WS (2012) Comparative transcriptome analysis of transporters, phytohormone and lipid metabolism pathways in response to arsenic stress in rice (*Oryza sativa*). *New Phytol* 195: 97–112.

Yu XZ, Gu JD, Xing LQ (2008) Differences in uptake and translocation of hexavalent and trivalent chromium by two species of willows. *Ecotoxicology* 17: 747–755.

Zhang D, Jiang L, Shao Y, Chai B, Li C (2009) Variations in germination and endogenous hormone contents of wheat cultivars under Cr stress. *Chin J Appl Environ Biol* 15: 602–605.

Zhang SY, Sun GX, Yin XX, Rensing C, Zhu YG (2013) Biomethylation and volatilization of arsenic by the marine microalgae *Ostreococcus tauri*. *Chemosphere* 93: 47–53.

Zhao FJ, Ma JF, Meharg AA, McGrath SP (2009) Arsenic uptake and metabolism in plants. *New Phytol* 181: 777–794.

Zhao FJ, McGrath SP, Meharg AA (2010b) Arsenic as a food chain contaminant: mechanisms of plant uptake and metabolism and mitigation strategies. *Ann Rev Plant Biol* 61: 535–559.

Zhao FJ, Wang JR, Barker JHA, Schat H, Bleeker PM, McGrath SP (2003) The role of phytochelatins in arsenic tolerance in the hyperaccumulator *Pteris vittata*. *New Phytol* 159: 403–410.

Zhao FJ, Zhu YG, Meharg AA (2013) Methylated arsenic species in rice: Geographical variation, origin, and uptake mechanisms. *Environ Sci Technol* 47: 3957–3966.

Zhao XQ, Mitani N, Yamaji N, Shen RF, Ma JF (2010a) Involvement of silicon influx transporter OsNIP2;1 in selenite uptake in rice. *Plant Physiol* 153: 1871–1877.

In: Heavy Metal Remediation   ISBN: 978-1-63321-568-9
Editors: Dharmendra Kumar Gupta and Soumya Chatterjee © 2014 Nova Science Publishers, Inc.

Chapter 4

MECHANISMS AND ENGINEERING PLANT METAL ACCUMULATION AND TRANSPORT

*Rajeev Kumar Sarma[1#^], Varghese Inchakalody[1#], Hema Jagadeesan[2] and Sathishkumar Ramalingam[*1]*
[1]Plant Genetic Engineering Laboratory, Department of Biotechnology, Bharathiar University, Coimbatore, Tamil Nadu, India
[2]Department of Biotechnology, PSG College of Technology, Coimbatore, Tamil Nadu, India

ABSTRACT

Environmental pollution has increased significantly since the beginning of industrial revolution due to the accumulation of trace elements, metals and organic wastes. The primary source of pollutants are due to excessive burning of fossil fuels, mining and smelting of metalliferous ores, wastes from industrial process associated with production of fertilizers, pesticides, etc. Among this, heavy metals are the most dangerous environmental contaminant because of its high toxicity. As most of these heavy metals are not metabolised naturally, they threaten directly the health of animals and human beings and poses more serious risk to the community, especially when it enters the food chain. Therefore, heavy metal pollution research has attracted more attention across the World, with an aim to remove these pollutants completely from the environment. Phytoremediation is one of the well-known approaches where the use of plants to remediate the contaminated soils, sediments and groundwater, making it both a cost-effective and environmentally friendly process. There are different plant processes and mechanisms in different plant species that includes accumulation, complexation, volatilization and degradation of pollutants. Some of the plants are natural hyperaccumulators that have the capability of accumulating higher concentration of heavy metals. Reports also proved that phytoremediation efficiency of these natural

* Corresponding author: Dr. Sathishkumar Ramalingam, Plant Genetic Engineering Laboratory, Department of Biotechnology, Bharathiar University, Coimbatore- 641046, Tamil Nadu, India, Phone: 0091-9360151669, Fax: 0091-422 2422387, E. Mail: rsathish@buc.edu.in.
# Both authors contributed equally ^ Present address: Biotechnology Division, Central Institute of Medicinal and Aromatic Plants (CSIR-CIMAP), Lucknow, India.

plants could be substantially improved using genetic engineering technologies. Towards this, research is on for past two decades for further understanding of the resistant mechanism of plants to various heavy metals at cellular as well as at molecular levels. It includes, identification of genes using recently emerged functional genomic approaches. Recent reports on over-expression of genes involved in metal uptake, transport and sequestration, have opened up new avenues in phytoremediation research. Hence, in this review, we have summarised the recent developments related to the mechanisms of metal transport and accumulation in plants as well as application of genetic engineering to improve the efficiency of phytoremediation process.

Keywords: Biotransformation, Genetic Engineering, Hyperaccumulators, Metal transporters, Vacuolar targeting

1. INTRODUCTION

Heavy metals are introduced into the environment as contaminants mainly due to anthropogenic activities, namely excessive use of pesticides, paints, fertilizers including application of sludge on agricultural fields, emissions from incinerators, residues from mines, etc., (Lombi et al. 2001; Garbisu and Alkorta 2003; Halim et al. 2003). Metals are naturally occurring and many are essential for living organisms at lower concentrations for physiological functions of organisms as they act as co-factors, (like Cu^{2+}, $Fe^{2+/3+}$, Mn^{2+}, Ni^{2+}, Co^{2+}, Zn^{2+}, etc.), but at higher concentrations, it is toxic. Some metals like Cd^{2+} could interfere with physiological activities by replacing Ca^{2+}. Any metal may be considered as a contaminant if it is present, where it is unwanted or at concentration that is detrimental to humans or pose environmental threat (McIntyre 2003). The main problem with metals unlike many other contaminants is due to their persistence, as they cannot be further degraded but could only be removed, which leads to a process called bioaccumulation that occurs along the food chain (Gisbert et al. 2003). Irrespective of the origin of the metal contaminants in the soil, excessive levels of these can lead to degradation in soil quality; alter the yield and quality of agricultural products (Long et al. 2002; Shanmugaraj et al. 2013). Thus, the presence of higher level of metal affects living organisms and hence eco-friendly remediation technology is the need of the hour to restore the desirable quality of the environment.

Currently, clean up of metal contaminated soil is by excavation and burial of the soil at the hazardous waste disposal sites, which is a very expensive method. In USA, the cost goes up to several billion dollars for cleaning up sites contaminated with toxic and radioactive metals (Salt et al. 1995). The problem is even more serious in developing countries where large areas are contaminated with heavy metals. Microbial-based bioremediation has proven to be effective in the degradation of certain organic pollutants but it is not proved to be successful in metal removal from contaminated sites. Phytoremediation of metals using metal accumulating plants is being projected as a cost-effective 'green' technology exploiting the plants inherent ability to remove toxic metals, from soil and water and sequester them in the above ground parts. This has recently become a subject of intense research with lot of public and scientific interest. This method takes advantage that a living plant acts as pump driven by solar energy, which can accumulate certain heavy metals from the environment (Raskin et al. 1997). This remediation method maintains the biological properties and physical structure of the soil. The technique is environmentally friendly, potentially cheap and visually unobtrusive offering the possibility of bio-recovery of the heavy metals (Yang et al. 2002).

2. POTENTIAL TARGETS FOR ENGINEERING METAL TOLERANCE IN PLANTS

Plant based phytoremediation is considered a cost effective as well as ecofriendly approach and have gained considerable attention over the past few years, but all plants do not have this ability. The characteristic features of plants suitable for phytoremediation are (a) ability to tolerate and accumulate high amount of metals in the harvestable parts without showing alteration in physiological properties, (b) Rapid growth rate and high biomass (c) easily harvestable (d) environmental friendly. At present around 400 plant species have been identified as potential candidates for phytoremediation. Hyper-accumulators are capable of accumulating potentially phytotoxic elements to a concentration up to 500 times higher than average plants accumulate (Cherian and Oliveira 2005). Hyper-accumulating plants can be found in naturally occurring metal contaminated sites. Some of the typical representatives of hyper accumulators are listed in Table 1. Hyper-accumulating plants may not be ideal for phytoremediation as they have low biomass, specific metal accumulation capacity and limited geographical distribution. On the other hand improving the plants, which are known to have a higher biomass, broader growth conditions, ability to tolerate and accumulate wider range of metals will be better host for phytoremediation. Genetic engineering has paved a way to improve the efficiency of these plants for phytoremediation by over expression of genes, whose protein products are involved in various processes like metal uptake, transport, and sequestration (Song et al. 2003).

Table 1. List of typical metal hyper-accumulators and its reference

Plant	Metal	Reference
Berkheya coddii	Ni	Robinson et al. 1997
Astragalus racemosus	Se	Beath et al. 1937
Pteris vittata	As	Dong et al. 2005
Ipomoea alpine	Cu	Baker and Walker 1989
Iberis intermedia	Ti	Leblanc et al. 1999
Alyssum sp	Ni	Reeves and Brooks 1983
Eichornia crassipes	Cr	Lytle et al. 1998
Sesbania drummondi	Cd	Israr et al. 2006
T.caerulescens	Zn, Cd	Banasova and Horak 2008
Phytolacca Americana	Mn	Pollard et al. 2009

Adapted with permission from Cherian and Oliveira, American Chemical Society, Copyright (2005).

Genetic engineering includes the delivery of desired genes into the chosen plants, [which is done either by a direct (e.g., particle gene gun method) or indirect method (*Agrobacterium* mediated method)]. The gene product used for remediation approach can be targeted to specific cellular compartments like plastids, vacuole, mitochondrion, etc., by fusing specific transit peptide along with the candidate gene. The ideal plant to engineer for metal uptake should have properties like high biomass, fast growth and should not be used for food or feed, or a contaminant by itself. Ideally, there should be an existing genetic transformation protocol or the system should be easy to engineer. To engineer plants with enhanced phytoremediation potential, one possible approach is to enhance the biomass production of plants, which can accumulate more metals. As multiple genes control plant productivity, it is difficult to alter such property by single gene transfer. Alternate strategy is to engineer metal tolerance and/or accumulation ability of plants. To enhance plant metal tolerance, transport and accumulation or in combinations from an existing plant process, which is limiting the remediation could be engineered. This includes plant processes like root uptake, root-shoot translocation and sequestration in specific compartments, biotransformation, volatilisation etc. The over-expression of a specific gene having a role in metal uptake/transport in a pathway has been proved to increase the efficiency of the phytoremediation. Hence, genes involved in different metal transporter proteins, metal chelation, metal-modifying enzymes and different kinds of regulatory proteins, especially transcription factors are of specific interest for transgenic approach. These genes either alone or in combination could be the ideal targets for engineering the phytoremediation process. Depending on the application, genetic engineering strategies may be designed to generate transgenic plants that can accumulate metals in harvestable plant parts (a process known as phytoextraction), or adsorb metals at their root surface (rhizofiltration) or releasing small metal binding proteins through roots (rhizosecretion). Enhanced metal tolerance can also be achieved by reducing the uptake, by efficient sequestration to storage compartments, overproduction of metal chelating molecules. The over-expression of transporter gene leads to enhanced uptake, translocation, and sequestration of metals in specific cell types or tissues. It is also equally important to identify the regulatory genes that can simultaneously induce many metal-related responses to enhance the phytoremediation capacity.

3. METAL UPTAKE

The bioavailability of metal is the basic prerequisite for its uptake by plants. Roots compete with soil particles for metal uptake. Plants have evolved diverse mechanisms to make metal ions more bioavailable. Some plants excrete organic acids, which act as metal chelators thereby reducing the rhizosphere pH, making ions available for uptake (Ross 1994). Microbial consortia in the rhizosphere can also affect the uptake of metals by root and host plant genes are also implicated in this plant-microbe interaction. Plants can also affect pH of rhizosphere by operating proton pumps in membranes of root cell. Metals are absorbed to create an electrochemical gradient and later it is transported to symplast by specific membrane transporter proteins. Metal transporters aid in the transport of metals into cells as well as membrane bound organelles and they play a major role in metal uptake and sequestration, and are therefore very important in the context of phytoremediation. In most organisms studied so far, different kinds of transporters exist and multiple transporters with varying affinities for the same metal are reported (Nelson 1999). Sequestration of metals in the vacuoles is one of the strategies adopted by plants to avoid metal toxicity. Transporters may be specific for a certain cell type or can aid in transport of more than one metal ion like Iron Regulated Transporter (IRT) proteins helps in transports of both Iron and Cadmium (Thomimine 2000).

The metal uptake ability of a plant is directly proportional to the biomass of the root. The root biomass of plants grown in metal contaminated areas is hindered due to the accelerated ethylene production and it is a major obstacle for phytoremediation (Kawahigashi 2009). Over-expression of regulators of ethylene production like bacterial 1-aminocyclopropane-1-carboxylate (ACC) deaminase has reduced ethylene production and enhanced root biomass leading to an improved metal uptake ability (Arshad et al. 2008). Over-expression of metal binding ligands in root is another approach for enhancing the metal uptake ability. The enhanced metal uptake process has to be complemented by other methods to reduce the toxicity of metals.

4. METAL TRANSLOCATION AND SEQUESTRATION

It has been reported that there are various transporters to mediate metal transport within the plant system. Translocation from root to shoot is through the transpiration stream (Salt 1995). Specific transporters as well as metal chelators have been implicated in this process. The metals are translocated from root symplast to shoot apoplast by specific transporters. Many chelators are also reported to be involved in the process of translocation to xylem. Later, these metals from xylem apoplast are transferred to shoot symplast by diverse metal transporters present in the cell membrane. These metals are then translocated to their final destination by membrane transporters and metal-binding proteins like metallothioneins or phytochelatins.

The role of the metal binding proteins and their over-expression has been well studied. Metallothioneins (MTs) are a low molecular weight (500-14000Da) cystein rich protein, which are commonly present in animals, plants, and microbes (Vallee 1991). In plants, MT's are located in the membrane of Golgi apparatus and this protein has the ability to bind with metals like zinc, copper, cadmium, lead, and mercury, through the thiol group of its cysteine residues (Sigel and Sigel 2009). The studies revealed that, the MTs in plants are transcriptionally regulated by metals (Cobbett and Goldsbrough 2002; Hall 2002) and play an essential role in the metal detoxification. Transgenic plants expressing metallothioneins have been generated and these plants showed enhanced tolerance to high metal concentrations as shown in Table 2.

Table 2. List of transgenic plants expressing Metallothionein genes

Target plant	Gene (s)	Source	Transgene effects	Reference
Tobacco	CUP1	Yeast	Enhanced metal tolerance against Cu and Cd	Thomas et al. 2003
Arabidopsis	Class II MT's	*Arabidopsis*	Enhanced metal tolerance against cd and Cu	Guo et al. 2008
Brassica campestris	Class II MT's	Chinese hamster	Enhanced tolerance against Cd	Lefevebre et al. 1987
Tobacco	Alpha domain of MT's 1	Mouse	Enhanced Cd tolerance	Pan et al. 1993
Tobacco	MT gene	*Nicotiana plumbaginifolia*	Enhanced Cd tolerance	Thomas et al. 2003

Metal chaperones are another class of proteins that transports metals to specific sites in the cell. Toxic levels of essential or non-essential metals are stored in vacuole by means of specialized transporters where the metal exerts least damage to vital cellular processes. For storage in sites like vacuole, metals may form complexes with phytochelatins, which are expressed during metal stress in order to enhance the toxic metal tolerance levels (Goldsbrough 2000; Cobbett and Goldsbrough 2000). Phytochelatins (PC's) are a group of cysteine-rich non ribosomal peptides synthesized from glutathione by the action of phytochelatin synthase commonly present in plant species and in some microorganisms, and have also been reported in nematode *Caenorhabditis elegans* (Vatamaniuk et al. 2001). Accumulation of PC in plants is regulated by the presence of various metal ions such as Cu^{2+}, Zn^{2+}, Pb^{2+} and Ag^{2+}, however, Cd^{2+} (Grill et al. 1989). PCs have high metal binding capacity and have been implicated not only in intracellular transport and sequestration of metals but also in metal translocation from root to shoot (Gong et al. 2003). These characteristic features have made the enzymes involved in the phytochelatins pathway, a reliable candidate for developing transgenic plants for phytoremediation. Transgenic plants over-expressing glutamyl cysteine synthetase and phytochelatins synthase genes have shown higher tolerance and accumulation ability towards heavy metals (Zhu et al. 1999; Brunetti et al. 2011)

5. BIOTRANSFORMATION

Metal-modifying enzymes play a crucial role in converting toxic metals ions to less harmful ions or compounds. Selenate is converted to dimethylselenide, which can be metabolized by plants (de Souza et al. 1998). The change in oxidation state of metals are aided by different reductase, e.g., toxic Cr^{4+} is reduced to nontoxic Cr^{3+} in *Eichhornia crassipes* reported by Lytle et al. (1998) and in dicots Fe and Cu are reduced by reductase at the root cell membrane before uptake (Robinson et al. 1999).

6. HYPERACCUMULATION MECHANISMS

Metal hyperaccumulators are defined as plants that accumulate ~500 fold higher metal ions than the normal plants naturally. Over 500 different species across 75 families have been identified so far and it has been shown that they probably evolved independently (Pollard et al. 2002). Hyperaccumulators are mostly slow growing with low biomass. At the root membrane level, metal uptake is very high in hyperaccumulators, which are later translocated to shoots. This could be due to high expression of metal transporter in the plasma membrane, which were characterised in *Thlaspi caerulescens*, for the Zn^{2+} and Cd^{2+} hyperaccumulator (Pence et al. 2000; Lombi et al. 2001). The uptake of metals in such plants is enhanced by the excretion of metal chelators, by rhizospheric microbes. The translocation of metals in this plants are rapid and shows high concentration in shoots and leaf cells. The high metal tolerance thus attained can be attributed to the highly efficient mechanism of intracellular compartmentalization.

7. GENETIC ENGINEERING OF MEMBRANE TRANSPORTERS

Development of transgenic plants with the ability to tolerate and accumulate heavy metals in the harvestable parts requires a clear understanding of the diverse processes involved in metal acquisition from soil to plant roots, its translocation to shoots, and accumulation of high concentrations of metals in sites like vacuoles. Hence, a clear knowledge of different transport mechanisms in cells are essential for formulating effective strategies to develop transgenic plants in order to transport different metal ions (Thomine et al. 2000). Diverse metal transporter proteins with high-affinity intracellular binding sites mediate uptake of metal ions across the plasma membrane in root. In order to increase the metal uptake through transporters, there are number of approaches followed, which are as follows, the number of uptake sites per area could be increased, altering the specificity of the uptake proteins and metal sequestration capacity can also be enhanced by engineering the intracellular high-affinity binding sites or the rate of transport across organelles. In this scenario, several transporter proteins have been implicated for heavy metal transport in plants and its engineering strategies are as follows,

Three different classes of membrane transporters have been characterized, which are involved in transport of heavy metals are, (a) Heavy metal (CPx-type) ATPases, (b) Natural resistance-associated macrophage protein (Nramp) family, and (c) Members of the cation diffusion facilitator (CDF) or cation efflux family (CEF) family (Maser et al. 1998; Williams et al. 2000). ZIP gene family proteins are also capable of transporting a variety of cations, like Cd, Fe, Mn and Zn (Guerinot 2000). Table 3 lists some of the metal transport proteins.

Table 3. Transporter genes involved in heavy metal uptake

Gene	Plant	Metal	Reference
Cpx-type heavy metal ATPases	*Arabidopsis*	Cu, Zn, Cd, Pb	Tabata et al. 1997 Williams et al. 2000 Belouchi et al. 1997
Nramp	*Arabidopsis*	Cd	Belouchi et al. 1997 Thomine et al. 2000
OsNramp1/ OsNramp2	*O. sativa*	Mn	Belouchi et al. 1997
CDF family proteins	*Arabidopsis*	Zn, Co, Mn	Maser et al. 1998
ZIP family (ZAT1, ZAT2, ZAT3)	*Arabidopsis, T. caerulescens*	Zn, Co, Mn	Van der Zaal et al. 1999; Pence et al. 2000; Assuncao et al. 2001; Lombi et al. 2002
YCF1	*S. cerevisiae*	Cd, Hg, Ar	Gueldry et al. 2003

CPx-type heavy metal ATPases are involved in maintaining metal-ion homeostasis in plants (Williams et al. 2000). These types of ATPases have been identified in a wide range of organisms and have been implicated with specific role in transport of toxic metal ions like Cd and Pb across the cell membranes (Williams et al. 2000). These proteins use ATP to pump charged substrates (metal ions) across cell membranes (Lombi et al. 2002). Heavy metal transporters are classified as CPx-ATPases based on conserved CPx motif, which is thought to function in metal transport across the membrane (Thomine et al. 2000). P_{IB}-type ATPases, a class of CPx type transporters are involved in regulating Zinc homeostasis in *Arabidopsis* and Yeast (Eren and Arguello 2004). This is also reported to be involved in transport of other metals like Cadmium, Copper, etc. Heterologous expression of this class of transporters will be a promising approach to enhance transport of heavy metals like Zn, Cd and Cu.

Nramp is another novel family of proteins that play an important role in transport of divalent metal ions. The genes that code for these proteins are called *Nramp* genes and three classes of *Nramp* homologs have been identified in rice (Belouchi et al. 1997). Later, two classes of *Arabidopsis* genes showing similarity to *Nramp* were characterized (Alonso et al. 1999). *Oryza Nramps (OsNrampl, OsNramp2,* and *OsNramp3)* show tissue specific expression. *OsNrampl* is primarily expressed in roots, *OsNramp2* in leaves and *OsNramp3* in both tissues of rice (Belouchi et al. 1997; Thomine et al. 2000). These distinct patterns of expression could mean that they are regulated differentially and may have unique functions in different tissues, or they may be involved in transport of distinct but related ions in different parts of the plant. Transgenic lines expressing *AtNramp*1 metal transporter showed enhanced Iron tolerance (Curie et al. 2000), over- expression of *AtNramp3* another metal transporter led to reduced cadmium tolerance without affecting its accumulation (Thomine et al. 2000). *PgIREG1* a class of IREG transporters that confer tolerance to nickel in *Psychotria gabriellae* when expressed in *A. thaliana,* transgenic plants showed similar ability of tolerance (Merlot et al. 2014). In *A. halleri* and *N. caerulescens,* Zinc/Cadmium tolerance and its accumulation are linked to the high and constitutive expression of specific genes coding for metal transporters (Hanikenne et al. 2008; Ueno et al. 2011; Craciun et al. 2012).

Members of the ubiquitous CDF protein family catalyse the efflux of metal ions, like Zinc, Cobalt, Cadmium, Manganese or Nickel, from cytoplasm or into sub-cellular compartments (Gaither and Eide 2001; Palmiter and Huang 2004). *Schizosaccharomyces pombe* CDF protein member *Znf1*p transport Zn and other transition metal to endoplasmatic reticulum (Borrelly et al. 2002). *A. thaliana* over-expressing *ZAT1,* a putative zinc transporter in the CDF family, accumulated higher Zinc concentrations in roots. Root growth of control plants was severely inhibited (~85%), whereas in transgenic plants there was a 15% inhibition (Van der Zaal et al. 1999). *A. halleri MTP1,* a class of CDF mediates the detoxification of zinc in the cell vacuole (Drager et al. 2004).

A Zn transporter (*ZAT1*) from *Arabidopsis* belongs to another important super family of metal-ion transporters known as the ZIP gene family (Williams et al. 2000; Pollard et al. 2002). Various members of ZIP are known to transport Iron, Manganese and Cadmium apart from Zinc (Pence et al. 2000). One of the ZIP genes *ZNT1*, characterized in hyperaccumulator *T. caerulescens* is involved in transport of Zn (Williams et al. 2000). Two ZIP genes (*ZNT1* and *ZNT2*) were reported to be highly expressed in roots of *T. caerulescens*. Over-expression of metal transporters also altered the metal specificity in transgenic lines. *AtIRT1* iron transporter can transport metals like Iron, Zinc, Manganese and Cadmium. Alteration of a single amino acid in IRT1 resulted in loss of Zinc, Iron or Manganese transport capacity (Rogers et al. 2000). These transgenic lines capable of accumulating specific metals will be of special interest to remove areas contaminated with single metal contaminant. All the above reports indicates the potential role of these transporter genes and/or proteins in metal accumulation and further detailed studies are required to fine tune the expression of these genes and/or proteins in hyperaccumulator plants.

A summary of the common metal transporters and genetic manipulation for enhanced tolerance in plants are listed in table 4.

Table 4. Transgenic plants over expressing different transporters

Gene	Product	Source	Transgenic host	Function	Reference
NtCBP4	Cation channel	Tobacco	Tobacco	Enhanced to Ni^{2+} and Pb^{2+} tolerance	Arazi et al. 1999; Sunkar et al. 2000
AtMHX1	Vacuolar transporter	Arabidopsis	Tobacco	Reduced tolerance to Mg^{2+} and Zn^{2+}	Shaul et al. 1999
AtCAX2	Vacuolar transporter	A. thaliana	Tobacco	Mn^{2+} tolerance in transgenic lines	Hirschi et al. 2000
ZAT1	Zn transporter	A. thaliana	Arabidopsis	Enhanced Zn^{2+} accumulation in roots	Van der Zaal et al. 1999
ZntA	Heavy-metal transporter	E. coli	Arabidopsis	Enhanced tolerance to Pb^{2+} and Cd^{2+}	Lee et al. 2003
YCF1	Transport protein	Yeast	Arabidopsis	Enhanced tolerance to Pb^{2+} and Cd^{2+}	Song et al. 2003
FRE1 and FRE2	Ferric reductase	Yeast	Tobacco	Elevated Fe^{3+} reduction in transgenic lines	Samuelsen et al. 1998
AtNramp1	Fe transporter	Arabidopsis	Arabidopsis	Enhanced Iron tolerance	Curie et al. 2000
AtNramp3	Fe transporter	Arabidopsis	Arabidopsis	Increased accumulation of Iron and Cd^{2+} hypersensitity	Thomine et al. 2000

Adapted with permission from Cherian and Oliveira. Copyright (2005) American Chemical Society.

8. VACUOLAR COMPARTMENTALIZATION OF METALS- A NEW APPROACH TO ENGINEER PLANTS

Vacuole is generally considered to be the main storage site for metals in yeast as well as in plant cells (Tong et al. 2004; Yang et al. 2005). The Ni^{2+} hyperaccumulator *Thlaspi goesingense* enhances Nickel tolerance by transporting the intracellular leaf Ni to vacuole (Kramer et al. 2000). A vacuolar-targeted transporter *TgMTP1* in *T. goesingense* aids the accumulation of metal ions within shoot vacuoles (Persans et al. 2001). *Saccharomyces cerevisiae*, *YCF1* is an Mg^{2+} -ATP dependent glutathione S-conjugate transporter involved in transport of Cadmium, Mercury and Arsenic (Gueldry et al. 2003). Over- expression of *YCF1* in *A. thaliana* resulted in 4-fold higher uptake of Cd^{2+} -GS2 conjugate. Transgenic lines also exhibited an increased tolerance to Pb^{2+} suggesting it could be an alternate substrate for YCF1 (Song et al. 2003).

CONCLUSION

Phytoremediation is a promising approach that has gained wide acceptance and is currently an area of intense research. Many plants have been identified as potential candidates for use in phytoremediation applications. The genetic and biochemical processes involved in metal uptake, transport, and storage by hyperaccumulating plants have been already reported for many plants. The knowledge gained from these studies with advanced tools in plant molecular biology has helped substantially to improve the phytoremediation capacity of plants. Genetic engineering technology in phytoremediation process enhanced the heavy metal tolerance in plants dramatically (Tong et al. 2004). Real breakthrough using genetic engineering require a thorough understanding of biological mechanisms involved in metal uptake, transport, translocation and accumulation processes on a molecular basis especially in natural metal hyperaccumulators. A number of transgenic plants have been raised with novel traits like enhanced metal uptake, transport, and accumulation proving the potential of this technology. Nevertheless, there are many gaps still exists in understanding the mechanisms of metal accumulation, transport and ion homeostasis. Hence, future research should focus on (a) Engineering of metal transporters to target metals to specific cell types like vacuoles for safe compartmentalization (b) Plastid engineering is another important area to ensure transgene containment and biosafety aspects of transgenic plants (c) Identification of novel plants having higher metal tolerance (d) Development of transgenic plants with enhanced plant-microbe interaction or rhizosecretion to increase the remediation approach. (e) Transgenic research for gene pyramiding to address the problem of mixed contamination occurring in many of the polluted sites.

The trafficking of metals at the cellular level and their enhanced uptake by hyperaccumulating plants are well characterized, however many steps of the pathway remain enigmatic. Many transport mechanism are yet to be understood completely with respect to localization, function, etc., the technique of phytoremediation was proposed few decades back but still not reached to the field application stage. The development of transgenic plants with higher biomass and better metal extracting and sequestering abilities would pave way for the use of this technique widely in future clean-up strategies.

REFERENCES

Alonso JM, Hirayama T, Roman G, Nourizadeh S, Ecker JR (1999) EIN2, a bifunctional transducer of ethylene and stress responses in Arabidopsis. *Science* 284: 2148–2152.

Arazi T, Sunkar R, Kaplan B, Fromm HA (1999) Tobacco plasma membrane calmodulin-binding transporter confers Ni^{2+} tolerance and Pb^{2+} hypersensitivity in transgenic plants. *Plant J* 20: 171–182.

Arshad M, Silvestre J, Pinelli E, Kallerhoff J, Kaemmerer M, Tarigo A, Shahid M, Guiresse M, Pradere P, Dumat C (2008) A field study of lead phytoextraction by various scented Pelargonium cultivars. *Chemosphere* 71: 2187–2192.

Assuncao AGL, Martins PD, De Folter S, Vooijs R, Schat H, Aarts MGM (2001) Elevated expression of metal transporter genes in three accessions of the metal hyperaccumulator *Thlaspi caerulescens. Plant Cell Environ* 24: 217–226.

Baker AJM, Walker PL (1989) Ecophysiology of metal uptake by tolerant plants. In: Shaw AJ (ed) *Heavy Metal Tolerance in Plants: Evolutionary Aspects*. CRC Publication, Boca Raton, FL pp 155–177.

Banasova V, Horak O (2008) Heavy metal content in *Thlaspi caerulescens* J. et C. Presl growing on metalliferous and non-metalliferous soils in Central Slovakia. *Int J Environ Pollut* 33: 133–145.

Beath OA, Eppsom HF, Gilbert GS (1937) Selenium distribution in and seasonal variation of vegetation type occurring on seleniferous soils. *J Amer Pharm Assocn* 26: 394–405.

Belouchi A, Kwan T, Gros P (1997) Cloning and characterization of the OsNramp family from *Oryza sativa*, a new family of membrane proteins possibly implicated in the transport of metal ions. *Plant Mol Biol* 33: 1085–1092.

Borrelly GP, Harrison MD, Robinson AK, Co SG, Robinson NJ, Whitehall SK (2002) Surplus zinc is handled by Zym1 metallothionein and Zhf endoplasmic reticulum transporter in *Schizosaccharomyces pombe*. *J Biol Chem* 277: 30394–30400.

Brunetti P, Zanella L, Proia A, De Paolis A, Falasca G, Altamura MM, Sanità di Toppi L, Costantino P, Cardarelli M (2011) Cadmium tolerance and phytochelatin content of *Arabidopsis* seedlings over-expressing the phytochelatin synthase gene AtPCS1. *J Exp Bot* 62: 5509–5519.

Cherian S, Oliveira MM (2005) Transgenic plants in phytoremediation: Recent advances and new possibilities. *Environ Sci Technol* 39: 9377–9390.

Cobbett C, Goldsbrough P (2002) Phytochelatins and metallothioneins: Roles in heavy metal detoxification and homeostasis. *Ann Rev Plant Biol* 53: 159–182.

Cobbett CS, Goldsbrough PB (2000) Mechanisms of metal resistance: Phytochelatins and metallothioneins. In: Raskin I, Ensley BD (eds) *Phytoremediation of Toxic Metals: Using Plants to Clean up the Environment*. Wiley, New York pp 247–271.

Craciun AR, Meyer CL, Chen J, Roosens N, De Groodt R, Hilson P, Verbruggen N (2012) Variation in HMA4 gene copy number and expression among *Noccaea caerulescens* populations presenting different levels of Cd tolerance and accumulation. *J Exp Bot* 63: 4179–4189.

Curie C, Alonso JM, Le Jean M, Ecker JR, Briat JF (2000) Involvement of NRAMP1 from *Arabidopsis thaliana* in iron transport. *Biochem J* 347: 749–755.

Dong R (2005) Molecular cloning and characterization of a phytochelatin synthase gene, PvPCS1, from *Pteris vittata* L. *J Indust Microbiol Biotechnol* 32: 527–533.

Dräger DB, Desbrosses-Fonrouge A-G, Krach C, Chardonnens AN, Meyer, RC, Saumitou-Laprade P, Krämer U (2004) Two genes encoding *Arabidopsis halleri* metal transport proteins 1 (MTP1) co-segregate with zinc tolerance and account for high MTP1 transcript levels. *Plant J* 39: 425–439.

Eren E, Arguello JM (2004) *Arabidopsis* HMA2, a divalent heavy metal-transporting PIB-type ATPase, is involved in cytoplasmic Zn21 homeostasis. Plant Physiol 136: 1–12.

Gaither LA, Eide DJ (2001) Eukaryotic zinc transporters and their regulation. *Biometals* 14: 251–270.

Garbisu C, Alkorta I (2003) Basic concepts on heavy metal soil bioremediation. *Eur J Min Proc Environ Protect* 13: 58–66.

Gisbert C, Ros R, De Haro A, Walker DJ, Bernal MP, Serrano R, Navarro-Avino J (2003) A plant genetically modified that accumulates Pb is especially promising for phytoremediation. *Biochem Biophy Res Comm* 303: 440–445.

Goldsbrough P (2000) Metal tolerance in plants: The role of phytochelatins and metallothioneins. In: Terry N, Banuelos G (eds) *Phytoremediation of Contaminated Soil and Water. Lewis*, Boca Raton, Florida pp 221–234.

Gong JM, Lee DA, Schroeder JI (2003) Long-distance root -to- shoot transport of phytochelatins and cadmium in Arabidopsis. *PNAS USA* 100: 10118–10123.

Grill E, Loffler S, Winnacker EL, Zenk MH (1989) Phytochelatins, the heavy-metal-binding peptides of plants, are synthesized from glutathione by a specific γglutamylcysteine dipeptidyl transpeptidase (phytochelatin synthase). *PNAS USA* 86: 6838–6842.

Gueldry O, Lazard M, Delort F, Dauplais M, Grigoras I, Blanquet S, Plateau P (2003) Ycf1p-dependent Hg(II) detoxification in *Saccharomyces cerevisiae*. *Europ J Biochem* 270: 2486–2496.

Guerinot ML (2000) The ZIP family of metal transporters. *Biochim Biophy Acta* 1465: 190-198.

Guo JB, Dai XJ, Xu WZ, Ma M (2008) Overexpressing GSH1 and AsPCS1 simultaneously increases the tolerance and accumulation of cadmium and arsenic in *Arabidopsis thaliana*. *Chemosphere* 72: 1020–1026.

Halim M, Conte P, Piccolo A (2003) Potential availability of heavy metals to phytoextraction from contaminated soils induced by exogenous humic substances. *Chemosphere* 52: 265–275.

Hall JL (2002) Cellular mechanisms for heavy metal detoxification and tolerance. *J Exp Bot* 53: 1–11.

Hanikenne M, Talke IN, Haydon MJ, Lanz C, Nolte A, Motte P, Kroymann J, Weigel D, Kramer U (2008) Evolution of metal hyperaccumulation required cis-regulatory changes and triplication of HMA4. *Nature* 453: 391–395.

Hirschi KD, Korenkov VD, Wilganowski NL, Wagner GJ (2000) Expression of *Arabidopsis* CAX2 in tobacco. Altered metal accumulation and increased manganese tolerance. *Plant Physiol* 124: 125–133.

Israr M, Sahi SV, Jain J (2006) Cadmium accumulation and antioxidative responses in the *Sesbania drummondii* callus. *Arch Environ Cont Toxicol* 50: 121–127.

Kawahigashi H (2009) Transgenic plants for phytoremediation of herbicides. *Curr Opi Biotechnol* 20: 225–230.

Krämer U, Pickering IJ, Prince RC, Raskin I, Salt DE (2000) Subcellular localization and speciation of nickel in hyperaccumulator and non-accumulator Thlaspi species.   *Plant Physiol* 122: 1343–1353.

Leblanc M, Petit D, Deram A, Robinson B, Brooks RR (1999) The hytomining and environmental significance of hyperaccumulation of thallium by *Iberis intermedia* from Southern France. *Econ Geol* 94: 109–113.

Lee J, Bae H, Jeong J, Lee JY, Yang YY, Hwang I, Martinoia ELY (2003) Functional expression of a bacterial heavy metal transporter in Arabidopsis enhance resistance to and decreases. *Plant Physiol* 133: 589–596.

Lefebvre DD, Miki BL, LaliberteÂ JF (1987) Mammalian metal- lothionein functions in plants. *Biotechnology* 5: 1053–1056.

Lombi EI, Zhao FJ, Dunham SJ, McGrath SP (2001) Phytoremediation of heavy metal-contaminated soils: Natural hyperaccumulation versus chemically enhanced phytoextraction. *J Environ Qual* 30: 1919–1926.

Lombi E, Zhao FJ, McGrath SP, Young SD, Sacchi GA (2001) Physiological evidence for a high affinity cadmium transporter highly expressed in a *Thlaspi caerulescens* ecotype. *New Phytol* 149: 53–60.

Long XX, Yang XE, Ni WZ (2002) Current status and perspective on phytoremediation of heavy metal polluted soils. *J App Ecol* 13: 757–762.

Lytle CM, Lytle FW, Yang N, JinHong Q, Hansen D, Zayed A, Terry N (1998) Reduction of Cr (VI) to Cr (III) by wetland plants: Potential for in situ heavy metal detoxification. *Environ Sci Technol* 32: 3087–3093.

Maser P, Thomine S, Schroeder JI, Ward JM, Hirschi KH, Sze IN, Talke A, Amtmann FJ, Maathuis M, Sanders D, Harper JE, Tchieu JM, Gribskov MW, Persans DE, Salt S, Kim A, Guerinot ML (1998) Phylogenetic relationships within cation transporter families of Arabidopsis. *PNAS USA* 95: 12049–12054.

McIntyre T (2003) Phytoremediation of heavy metals from soils. *Adv Biochem Engg/Biotechnol* 78: 97–123.

Merlot S, Hannibal L, Martins S, Martinelli L, Amir H, Lebrun M, Thomine S (2014) The metal transporter PgIREG1 from the hyperaccumulator *Psychotria gabriellae* is a candidate gene for nickeltolerance and accumulation. *J Exp Bot* doi:10.1093/jxb/eru025.

Nelson N (1999) Metal ion transporters and homeostasis. EMBO J 18: 4361–4371.

Palmiter RD, Huang L (2004) Efflux and compartmentalization of zinc by members of the SLC30 family of solute carriers. *Europ J Physiol* 447: 744–751.

Pence NS, Larsen PB, Ebbs SD, Letham DLD, Lasat MM, Garvin DF, Eide D, Kochian LV (2000) The molecular physiology of heavy metal transport in the Zn/Cd hyperaccumulator *Thlaspi caerulescens*. *PNAS USA* 97: 4956–4960.

Persans MW, Nieman K, Salt DE (2001) Functional activity and role of cation-efflux family members in Ni hyperaccumulation in *Thlaspi goesingense*. PNAS USA 98: 9995–10000.

Pollard AJ, Stewart HL, Roberson CB (2009) Manganese hyperaccumulation in *Phytolacca americana* L. from the South Eastern United States. *Nature* 16: 155–162.

Pollard JA, Powell KD, Harper FA, Smith JAC (2002) The genetic basis of metal hyperaccumulation in plant. Crit Rev Plant Sci 21: 539–566.

Raskin I, Smith RD, Salt DE (1997) Phytoremediation of metals: Using plants to remove pollutants from the environment. *Curr Opi Biotechnol* 1997: 221–226.

Reeves RD, Brooks RR (1983) Hyperaccumulation of lead and zinc by two metallophytes from a mining area of central Europe. *Environ Pollut* 31: 277–287.

Robinson BH, Brooks RR, Howes AW, Kirkman JH, Gregg PEH (1997) The potential of the high biomass nickel hyperaccumulator *Berkheya coddii* for phytoremediation and phytomining. *J Geochem Explor* 60: 115–126.

Robinson NJ, Procter CM, Connolly EL, Guerinot ML (1999) A ferric-chelate reductase for iron uptake from soils. *Nature* 397: 694–697

Rogers EE, Eide DJ, Guerinot ML (2000) Altered selectivity in an *Arabidopsis* metal transporter. *PNAS USA* 97: 12356–12360.

Ross SM (1994) Sources and forms of potentially toxic metals in soil-plant systems. In: Ross SM (ed) *Toxic Metals in soil – Plant Systems*. John Wiley & Sons, Chichester pp 63–52.

Salt DE, Blaylock M, kumar PBAN, Dushenkov V, Ensley BD, Chet L, Raskin L. Phytoremediation (1995) A novel strategy for the removal of toxic metals from the environment using plants. *Nat Biotechnol* 13: 468–474.

Samuelsen AI, Martin RC, Mok DWS, Machteld CM (1998) Expression of the yeast FRE genes in transgenic tobacco. *Plant Physiol* 118: 51–58.

Shanmugaraj BM, Chandra HM, Srinivasan B, Ramalingam S (2013) Cadmium induced physio-biochemical and molecular response in *Brassica juncea*. *Int J Phytorem* 15: 206–218.

Shaul O, Hilgemann DW, de Almeida-Engler J, van Montagu M, Inze D, Galili G (1999) Cloning and characterization of a novel Mg^{2+}/H^+ exchanger. *EMBO J* 18: 3973–3980.

Sigel H, Sigel A, Sigel RKO (2009) Metallothioneins and related chelators. In: *Metal Ions in Life Sciences,* Vol. 5. Royal Society of Chemistry Publishing, Cambridge, England.

Song WY, Sohn EJ, Martinoia E, Lee YJ, Yang YY, Jasinski M, Forestier C, Hwang I, Lee Y (2003) Engineering tolerance and accumulation of lead and cadmium in transgenic plants. *Nat Biotechnol* 21: 914–919.

Sunkar R, Kaplan B, Bouche N, Arazi T, Dolev D, Talke IN, Maathuis FJM, Sanders D, Bouchez D, Fromm H (2000) Expression of a truncated tobacco NtCBP4 channel in transgenic plants and disruption of the homologous *Arabidopsis* CNGC1 gene confer Pb^{2+} tolerance. *Plant J* 24: 533–542.

Tabata K, Kashiwagi S, Mori H, Ueguchi C, Mizuno T (1997) Cloning of a cDNA encoding a putative metal-transporting P-type ATPase from *Arabidopsis thaliana. Biochem Biophy Acta* 1326: 1–6.

Thomine S, Wang R, Ward JM, Crawford NM, Schroeder JI (2000) Cadmium and iron transport by members of a plant metal transporter family in *Arabidopsis* with homology to Nramp genes. *PNAS USA* 97: 4991–4996.

Thomas JC, Davies EC, Malick FK, Endreszl C, Williams CR, Abbas M, Petrella S, Swisher K, Perron M, Edwards R, Ostenkowski P, Urbanczyk N, Wiesend WN, Murray KS (2003) Yeast metallothionein in transgenic tobacco promotes copper uptake from contaminated soils. *Biotechnol Prog* 19: 273–280.

Tong YP, Kneer R, Zhu YG (2004) Vacuolar compartmentalization: A second-generation approach to engineering plants for phytoremediation. *Trends Plant Sci* 9: 7–9.

Ueno D, Milner MJ, Yamaji N, Yokosho K, Koyama E, Clemencia Zambrano M, Kaskie M, Ebbs S, Kochian LV, Ma JF (2011) Elevated expression of TcHMA3 plays a key role in the extreme Cd tolerance in a Cd-hyperaccumulating ecotype of *Thlaspi caerulescens. Plant J* 66: 852–862.

Vallee BL (1991) Introduction to metallothionein. *Method Enzymol* 205: 3–7.

Van der Zaal BJ, Neuteboom LW, Pinas JE, Chardonnens AN, Schat H, Verkleij JAC, Hooykaas PJJ (1999) Overexpression of a novel *Arabidopsis* gene related to putative zinc-transporter genes from animals can lead to enhanced zinc resistance and accumulation. *Plant Physiol* 119: 1047–1055.

Vatamaniuk OK, Bucher EA, Ward JT, Rea PA (2001) A new pathway for heavy metal detoxification in animals phytochelatin synthase is required for cadmium tolerance in *Caenorhabditis elegans. J Biol Chem* 276: 20817–20820.

Williams LE, Pittman JK, Hall JL (2000) Emerging mechanisms for heavy metal transport in plants. *Biochim Biophy Acta* 1465: 104–126.

Williams LE, Pittman JK, Hall JL (2000) Emerging mechanisms for heavy metal transport in plants. *Biochim Biophy Acta* 1465: 104–126.

Yang XE, Feng Y, He Z, Stoffella PJ (2005) Molecular mechanisms of heavy metal hyperaccumulation and phytoremediation. *J Trace Elem Med Biol* 18: 339–353.

Zhu YL, Pilon-Smits EA, Tarun AS, Weber SU, Jouanin L, Terry N (1999) Cadmium tolerance and accumulation in Indian mustard is enhanced by overexpressing gamma-glutamylcysteine synthetase. *Plant Physiol* 121: 1169–1178.

In: Heavy Metal Remediation   ISBN: 978-1-63321-568-9
Editors: Dharmendra Kumar Gupta and Soumya Chatterjee © 2014 Nova Science Publishers, Inc.

Chapter 5

PLANT METABOLOMICS AND ITS APPLICATION TO EXPLORE METAL TOXICITY MECHANISM

*Xiangfeng Zeng[1,2], Alexandra Lynn[3], Shuhe Wei[*1] and Jun Wang[3]*

[1] Key Laboratory of Pollution Ecology and Environment Engineering,
Institute of Applied Ecology, Chinese Academy of Sciences, Shenyang, P.R. China
[2] University of Chinese Academy of Sciences, Beijing, P.R. China
[3] Center for Environmental Biotechnology, The University of Tennessee,
Knoxville, TN, US

ABSTRACT

Understanding the plant mechanisms underlying metal toxicity is challenging because of the vast and complex effects that metals have on plant cells and tissue. However, plant metabolomics has the potential to significantly contribute to the stress biology field through the identification of low molecular weight metabolites. This chapter is an introduction to key techniques for plant metabolomics research as well as to general applications for exploring the mechanism of metal toxicity. Alone or in combination with techniques from other 'omics,' such as genomics, transcriptomics and proteomics, plant metabolomics provides a systems biology view of plant metabolism. The following techniques and strategies associated with plant metabolomics were summarized and described: the collection of organisms, metabolism quenching and sample collection, metabolite extraction, the direct detection or chromatographic separation coupled to detection, and data analysis. Finally, the application of plant metabolomics in elucidating the metal toxicity mechanism in plants was reviewed. Although plant metabolomics is still a relatively new approach, it is rapidly becoming one of the primary tools used for revealing the characteristic features of cellular metal toxicity.

Keywords: Plant metabolomics, Heavy metals, Toxicity mechanism, Omics, Systems biology

---

[*] Corresponding Author: Dr. Shuhe Wei, Key Laboratory of Pollution Ecology and Environment Engineering, Institute of Applied Ecology, Chinese Academy of Sciences, Shenyang 110016, P.R. China, Phone: 0086-2483970373, Fax: 0086-2483970436, E. Mail: shuhewei@iae.ac.cn

1. INTRODUCTION

Environmental pollution, particularly with a high metal concentration, presents a major challenge for plants worldwide. Depending on their oxidation states, metals can be highly reactive, subsequently resulting in numerous avenues for plant cell toxicity. At the cellular and molecular level, metals can alter a plant's metabolism, inhibit photosynthesis and respiration, and alert the activities of several key enzymes (Hossain et al. 2012). Furthermore, metals are known to disturb redox homeostasis by stimulating the formation of free radicals and reactive oxygen species (ROS). Consequently, plants have evolved different mechanisms that serve to maintain physiological concentrations of essential metal ions and to minimize any exposure to non-essential heavy metals. Some of these mechanisms are ubiquitous because they are additionally required to maintain general metal homeostasis, and therefore, they minimized the damage caused by high heavy metal concentrations in plants through detoxification, thereby conferring tolerance to heavy metal stress (Sytar et al. 2013). Other mechanisms target individual metal ions; these processes may involve in exclusion of particular metals from the intracellular environment or the sequestration of toxic ions within compartments to isolate them from sensitive cellular components (Clemens 2006; Hong et al. 2010). However, as effects of metals on plant cells and tissue are varied and complicated, it is a challenging task to understand the plant mechanisms involved in metal toxicity.

New technologies that permit the simultaneous monitoring of several hundreds or thousands of macro- and small molecules are keys to the simultaneous functional monitoring of multiple key cellular pathways. These new "global" methods of measuring families of cellular molecules, such as RNA, proteins, and intermediary metabolites, have been termed as "omic" technologies based upon their ability to characterize all or most of the members of a family of molecules in a single analysis (Aardema et al. 2002; Debnath et al. 2010). Accordingly, omics has become the new mantra of molecular biology encompassing the technological fields of genomics, transcriptomics, proteomics and metabolomics. These technologies generate enormous amounts of information, boosting the bioinformatics field through the yearly publication of thousands of new algorithms and software (Schneider et al. 2011). With these new tools, it is now possible to obtain the previously unattainable complete assessments of the functional activity of biochemical pathways and of the structural genetic (sequence) differences among individuals and species. Omics analyses were crucial to understanding the complete processes underlying molecular networks' responses to metal toxicity stress (Gehlenborg et al. 2010). Metabolomics is, therefore, a newer yet more useful approach in which there is great potential for advancing the study of metal toxicity in addition to its ability to provide a unique perspective concerning metal-induced changes in cellular metabolic architecture (Rochfort et al. 2005).

2. PLANT METABOLOMICS: A SYSTEMS BIOLOGY VIEW OF PLANT METABOLISM

As previously mentioned, metabolomics is defined as the qualitative and quantitative identification of low molecular weight metabolites (usually < 1000 Da) present in a cell under a given set of physiological conditions (Kell et al. 2004; Nielsen et al. 2005; Weckwerth

2010). As a result of gene deletion or environmental stress being amplified through the hierarchy of the transcriptome and the proteome, the cell's physiology changes are more easily measured through the metabolome due to the metabolomics' 'downstream' – amplified changes in the metabolome relative to changes in the transcriptome and proteome– and are arguably more tractable numerically (Quanbeck et al. 2012). Normally, although the changes in the expression level of individual proteins might only have minimal influence on fluxes, they can and do have large effects on the concentrations of intermediary metabolites (Schuster et al. 2000; terKuile et al. 2001). Because the metabolic pathways' activities were more accurately reflected in the metabolite pools' concentrations than in the relevant enzymes' concentrations (or indeed the concentrations of the mRNAs encoding them), the metabolome was expected to be more sensitive to perturbations than either the transcriptome or the proteome (Oksman-Caldentey et al. 2005). Thus, the metabolome represents the ultimate phenotype of cells that are deduced by the perturbation of gene expression and the modulation of protein functions (Kell et al. 2012). In addition, the metabolome can also influence gene expression and protein function. Therefore, metabolomics has played a key role in understanding cellular systems and decoding gene functions (Bino et al. 2004; Hagel and Facchini 2008).

Although the primary focus of metabolomics is not just the simultaneous detection of 'every' metabolite in a cell, community efforts to improve this aspect have dramatically increased the number of identifiable compounds (Tohge and Fernie 2009). To understand the cellular metabolic systems of plants, identifying the functions of enzymatic genes is no longer satisfactory. Rather, we need to decipher the coordination and interaction among the various metabolic pathways. In this context, other high-throughput experiments, including both transcriptomics and proteomics, provide the complementary information to elucidate such coordination (Kopka et al. 2005; Fukushima et al. 2009; Yuan et al. 2008). As for the field of metal toxicity, there exists substantial evidence that suggests that certain toxic metals, such as aluminum, evoke significant metabolic shifts in the cell (Vaidyanathan 2005). Transcriptomic and proteomic studies on metal-exposed plants demonstrated significant changes in the cell physiology including their metabolic pathways, which indicates that metal stress induces significant metabolic changes in plant cells (Booth et al. 2011).

3. PLANT METABOLOMICS TECHNIQUES AND STRATEGIES

Metabolomic experiments consist of a series of well-established steps, as summarized in fig. 1: the collection of organisms, metabolism quenching and sample collection, metabolite extraction, direct detection or chromatographic separation coupled to detection, and finally, data analysis. Just as important as the choice of analytical technique is the selection of suitable pre-analysis procedures for the samples, involving both the collection of plants and the sample treatment. Likewise, data analysis requires sophisticated techniques, in which multivariate statistical analysis and bioinformatics tools play fundamental roles. Hines et al. (2008) provided an excellent assessment of metabolomes obtained in the field versus those obtained from laboratory samples. Additionally, various metabolite harvesting and extraction techniques have been further described by Kim and Verpoorte (2010). Soon after, introductory books on metabolome analysis, written by Villas-Bôas et al. (2007), and the plant metabolomics methods and protocols, by Hardy et al. (2012), gave a comprehensive overview of the analytical techniques that are suitable for plant metabolomics-based studies. The metabolomics Standards Initiative has provided guidelines for reporting metabolomic experiments, standardizing the various techniques and detailing experimental designs (Morrison et al. 2007). The consensus in the above reviews is that it is essential to consider the samples purity, to quench metabolism quickly, to use the most appropriate analytical equipment, and to be able to sensibly interpret large datasets (Brunetti et al. 2013).

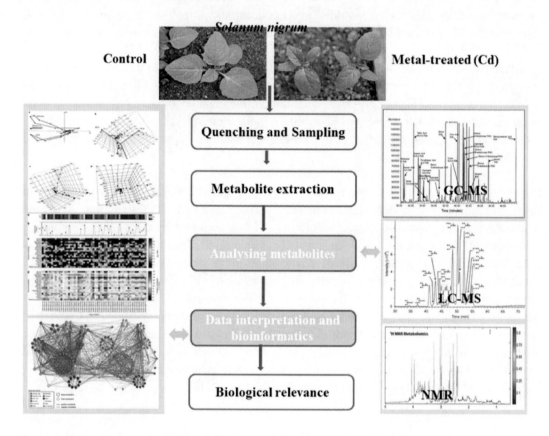

Figure 1. Schematic overview of metabolomics workflow on metal toxicity experiments.

3.1. Pre-Analysis Procedures

The ability to identify and quantify a whole range of metabolites has become progressively simpler and increasingly cost-effective over the past two decades. However, pre-analysis procedures, such as experimental design, controlled cessation of metabolism and the subsequent extraction of metabolites from plant tissue, remained the most crucial steps in carrying out a meaningful metabolomics study of the organism(s) in question (Saito and Matsuda 2010).

Two critical pre-analysis parameters to be considered are both tissue availability and sample purity. Tissue availability should be considered from the very start of the experiment. The necessary amount will be dependent upon the analysis pipeline, but typically 10-100 mg of fresh tissue is required for most analytical applications. The number of samples required for a correct biological interpretation must also be considered (Brunetti et al. 2013). This number, however, could potentially be determined for the researcher based upon the number of samples that are within access; this is especially true if rare or difficult to obtain plants are being analyzed. It is also important to consider the purity of the samples being harvested for metabolite analyses because plant tissue that has been contaminated with bacteria, fungi, or pests, such as aphids, may interfere with the results, especially if the samples were derived from natural habitats and not from controlled growth room facilities. However, even if the samples are from controlled growth rooms, it is necessary to take into consideration the application of chemicals to control pests, such as aphid and sciarid flies, in these facilities when studying the metabolome of plants exposed to such chemicals (Broadhurst and Kell 2013).

As the highest level of functionality within the cell, metabolism is subject to extremely rapid turnover rates (some metabolite turnover rates are less than 1s), which makes sample handling an important concern (Reaves and Rabinowitz 2011). As such, metabolism must be quenched as quickly as possible, thus eliminating the opportunity for the cells to react to the sampling procedure in addition to preventing any chemical change to the metabolites or any leakage of the metabolites from the cell. This process was generally achieved by flash-freezing either whole organisms or a dissected tissue in liquid nitrogen or cold organic solvents in the laboratory and field environment and then, subsequently grinding the samples for metabolite extraction (Koek et al. 2011). When sampling is necessary within a marine environment, the methods established by Goulitquer et al. (2012) circumvent many of the problems associated with the extraction of metabolites from samples of a high salt concentration. As the transportation of frozen samples from a field to a laboratory can be problematic in terms of cost and logistics, some metabolite analysis can be carried out onsite. For example, the concentration of carotenoids, chlorophylls and anthocyanins can be obtained via a basic solvent extraction of cut leaf discs followed by spectrophotometry onsite (Sims and Gamon 2002).

After metabolism has been quenched and the sample has been collected, an appropriate method for collecting and concentrating all the metabolites must be determined. To obtain comprehensive and reproducible metabolomic profiles, metabolite extractions have to be nonselective, simple, and fast (Vuckovic 2012). Plant tissues and cells are inherently resistant to extraction because of the presence of cell wall and surface structures. Additionally, the macromolecules, such as proteins, polysaccharides and nucleic acids (DNA and RNA), should be separated from the small molecules (metabolites) during the extraction procedure. Metabolite extraction generally involves the addition of a mixture of organic solvents, lysis of the cells, a pelleting step to separate out dissolved metabolites from the contaminant debris and the subsequent evaporation of the solvent, leaving behind a dried sample in preparation for whatever analytical platform(s) will be used (Álvarez-Sánchez et al. 2010a,b). Since organic solvents were used, polar and non-polar molecules can be separated from one another, and then both fractions can be analyzed independently. Contrary to quenching, a mixture of water: methanol: chloroform has generally been accepted as a comprehensive extraction solution. Once extracted, the evaporated, concentrated samples can be frozen and stored until ready for analysis. The ensuing sample-preparation steps depend upon the analytical tool that will be used. For GC-MS analysis of the non-volatile components of the metabolome, the samples must first be derivatized into volatile analogs that will migrate through the GC column. This is done through the use of a deriviting agent that adds functional groups that allow for migration through the gas chromatography column (Vuckovic 2012). For ^{1}H-NMR, samples must first be dissolved in a deuterated solvent as any hydrogen-containing solvent produces a strong peak.

3.2. Analyzing Metabolites

Metabolite analysis requires a high-throughput tool capable of simultaneously identifying the structures of many chemically diverse substances. There are a wide suite of technologies that can be employed to analyze the metabolites in the plant solvent extracts. Of course, choosing which technology to use will depend upon the availability of equipment, but more importantly, it will depend upon the question or hypothesis that is being tested. Typically, the choice is divided between two main approaches: metabolite fingerprinting and metabolite profiling. These approaches are highly distinctive from one another- metabolite fingerprinting is a semi-quantitative technique with largely putative metabolite identification, whereas metabolite profiling involves accurate chemical identification and quantification (Dunn and Ellis 2005; Zhang et al. 2012).

Metabolic fingerprinting has been largely used to identify metabolic signatures or patterns associated with a particular stress response, like metal toxicity, without an identification or precise quantification of all the different metabolites in a given sample. These fingerprinting techniques predominantly aim to analyze the metabolites present in a complex mixture by either directly injecting the crude extract into a MS (direct injection mass spectrometry; Dunn and Ellis 2005; Walker 2011) or by obtaining an NMR spectra of the entire mixture (Forseth and Schroeder 2011; Viant et al. 2003), but as to be expected, NMR and MS each have their own distinct advantages and disadvantages. For example, NMR spectroscopy provides a low sensitivity, therefore making it difficult to detect cellular metabolites present in low abundance (Shulaev et al. 2008). MS, on the other hand, is advantageous over NMR in terms of resolving power, its higher sensitivity and its lower detection limit (Forseth and Schroeder 2011; Shulaevet al. 2008). However, MS generates a more complex spectrum because of the formation of product ions and adducts, and its results come in the form of discriminant ions. Meanwhile, direct infusion has its shortcomings, primarily due to a phenomenon known as co-suppression where the signals of many analysts can be lost at the mass spectrometer interface. To minimize the co-suppression effect, samples can be separated using very rapid gradients with a short chromatographic column, and then the HPLC-MS data can be analyzed using multivariate analysis in order to identify the discriminant ions. To confirm the fingerprinting results, samples are then re-analyzed with a long HPLC gradient. This two-step fingerprinting/validating strategy has been used to characterize the wound response in *Arabidopsis* (Bedair and Sumner 2008; Grata et al. 2007).

The resulting metabolite fingerprints should always be verified through quantitative metabolic profiling techniques. These profiling techniques separate the metabolites prior to identification either by capillary electrophoresis, LC, GC or 2D GC, a GC × GC technique where multiple GC columns are combined to increase the separation, resolution, and data acquisition time per sample (Almstetter et al. 2012; Davey et al. 2008). Of particular importance is the protocol paper by Dunn et al. (2011) that describes the foremost assays used for sample preparation, derivatization, and analysis by HPLC and GC-MS. No matter the separation approach used, the metabolites within the extract will have to be identified either by their molecular mass, the fragmentation pattern using MS and FT-IR spectroscopy, or chemical shifts using NMR (Dunn et al. 2011). Viant and Sommer (2013), Forseth and Schroeder (2011), and Jaroszewski (2005) provide reviews on how these identification techniques can be used to assign function to the metabolites within an environmental studies context, and in addition, the advantages and disadvantages associated with each metabolite profiling technique have been previously discussed (Shulaev 2006; Sumner et al. 2003). To date, GC-MS is the most developed analytical platform for plant metabolite profiling, as its major advantage is the availability of both commercially and publicly available EI spectral libraries (Halket et al. 2005). It is possible to profile several hundred volatile compounds or compounds that can be volatilized following chemical derivatization, such as sugars, organic acids, amino acids, sugar alcohols, aromatic amines and fatty acids. For non-volatile compounds, LC-MS and CE-MS provide a better alternative. The use of LC-MS in metabolomics has been on a steady rise, especially after the recent adoption of the ultra-performance liquid chromatography (UPLC) technology that can both dramatically increase separation efficiency as well as decrease analysis time (Giri et al. 2007; Granger et al. 2007). CE-MS provides a viable alternative for metabolite profiling due to its high resolving power, the low sample volume requirements, and the ability to simultaneously separate cations, anions and uncharged molecules (Soga et al. 2003).

3.3. Data interpretation and Bioinformatics

Following their acquisition by a given analytical tool, the metabolic fingerprints are then compared using multivariate statistical analyses, with an overall aim of reducing the complexity of the data sets and highlighting the analytical information of biological relevance (Liland et al. 2011). Due to the inherent size and complexity of metabolomics data, similar to the datasets obtained from other omics technologies; computer-assisted statistical analysis is extremely useful for deriving biologically relevant information from an experiment (Lindon et al. 2011; Issaq et al. 2009). Multivariate statistical tools, divided into unsupervised and supervised analysis, are available and greatly aid in the simplification and visualization of the metabolomics data. Unsupervised techniques, such as the principal component analysis (PCA) and hierarchical clustering, seek to distinguish the inherent variation in the data and subsequently cluster similar samples together (Spratlin et al. 2009). PCA also reduces the long list of metabolite concentrations into components of variation, which allows for a direct comparison of samples in either a 2D or 3D space. In supervised analyses, such as the Orthogonal Partial Least Squares Discriminant Analysis (OPLS-DA), the sample classes (such as metal exposed *vs.* unexposed) are provided which allows for a directed clustering of samples. Techniques such as OPLS-DA also provide information as to which metabolites are causing the most variation between samples, thereby providing a starting point for biological interpretation (Renberg et al. 2010).

Similar to genomics analysis, metabolomics relies on an ever-increasing number of bioinformatic tools and data repositories in order to be better understood and interpreted (Patti et al. 2012). Currently, a number of free software packages are already available for metabolomic data processing and analysis, and additionally, there are a number of both web services and desktop applications that are readily available. Meanwhile, large datasets that have been derived from metabolomic studies are usually assessed, annotated, and visualized using curated online portals such as www.plantcyc.org (Zhang et al. 2010) and www.plantmetabolomics.org, where environmental and genetic information related to the experiments can also be considered as co-variables (Bais et al. 2010, 2012). These large datasets can also be analyzed by univariate and multivariate statistics, such as a principal component analysis using online servers such as Metaboanalyst (http://www. metaboanalyst.ca/; Xia and Wishart 2011). Bassel et al. (2012) and Mochida and Shinozaki (2011) reviewed these portals and detailed the incorporation of metabolomic data into other omics.

4. APPLICATIONS OF PLANT METABOLOMICS FOR STUDYING THE METAL TOXICITY MECHANISM

Heavy metals such as cadmium (Cd), cesium (Cs), lead (Pb), zinc (Zn) and chromium (Cr) are all major soil pollutants that cause plant stress. Even essential nutrients, including copper (Cu) and iron (Fe), can cause heavy metal stresses with present in an unsuitable concentration. Several studies have investigated the mechanism underlying metal toxicity in various plants, as summarized in table 1.

In the field of plant metal toxicity, cadmium is a popular metal to study as it is a frequent contaminant of farmland due to a variety of industrial agriculture practices; therefore, the analysis of plant response to Cd has been extensively explored through proteomic and metabolomics approaches, as has been recently reviewed (Villiers et al. 2011). In plants, cadmium toxicity is associated with morphological, physiological, and biochemical defects such as the alteration of photosynthetic processes or enzyme inhibitions leading to growth inhibition and chlorosis. Thus, metabolomics has demonstrated the importance of both antioxidant defenses and detoxification processes in the mechanisms behind a plant's resistance to cadmium stress (Ahsan et al. 2012; Sarry et al. 2006; Sun et al. 2010), as well as the perturbations in energy metabolism (Liu et al. 2011). In addition, the metabolic consequences resulting from plant metal toxicity have been studied in both crop plants (i.e. tomatoes and rice) and in model systems (*Arabidopsis thaliana* and *green alga*). The first case was a metabolic fingerprinting using NMR spectroscopy combined with multivariate statistics analysis that was used to discriminate between a control and cadmium-treated *Silene cucubalus* cell cultures (Bailey et al. 2003). Malic acid and acetate were shown to increase in the cadmium-treated cells, while in contrast, glutamate and branched chain amino acids decreased. In the most recent study on cadmium's effect on whole *A. thaliana* plants, GC-MS metabolomics was used to identify a number of interesting metabolite changes. Several compounds with compatible solute properties, such as alanine, proline, glycerol and trehalose, were shown to increase in level in addition to an observed increase in antioxidant molecules, such as campesterol and isoflavone, in order to respectively counteract the osmotic and oxidative stress induced by cadmium exposure (Sun et al. 2010). In an older *Arabidopsis* cell culture study, LC-MS was used for metabolite analysis. As such, metabolites were not identified until after the multivariate statistical analysis had picked out the spectral peaks that most contributed to the variation between the control and the cadmium-exposed samples (D'Alessandro et al. 2013; Sarry et al. 2006). Additionally, the effects of cadmium were recently assessed in the freshwater alga *Chlamydomonas reinhardtii* using metabonomics based upon ^{1}H NMR and GC-MS (Jamers et al. 2013). Their observed reduction in glycine and homocysteine levels, compounds necessary for glutathione synthesis, provided more insight into metal oxidative stress. For this study, this kind of analysis was very useful as it led to the identification of many phytochelatins that were being produced in the exposed samples (Kieffer et al. 2008; Gratao et al. 2012; Villiers et al. 2012; Zoghlami et al. 2013). As for crop plants, two studies have examined both the short and long-term effects of cadmium on tomato plants using 1H-NMR metabolomics (Hédiji et al. 2010). Their results show that metabolite responses depend upon several different factors: the tissue (i.e. leaves *vs.* roots) and the tissue age, the exposure concentration, and the existence of similarities and differences between acute and chronic exposure. Citrate levels increased in both the roots and leaves although it was postulated that this accumulation was due to the photosynthetic activity of the leaves and because of its role as a chelating agent in the roots; however, a decrease in carotenoid metabolites was only observed in the mature leaves in response to cadmium stress. Chronic exposure (90 days) induced an increase in sucrose but a decrease in fructose and glucose levels in leaves, which was hypothesized to be a result of invertase inhibition. These alterations were not observed after acute exposure (10 days), which is suggestive of a more long term metabolic change (Hédiji et al. 2010).

Metabolite profiling based upon GC-MS was also used in order to study the nickel-rich latex of the hyperaccumulating tree *Sebertia acuminata* (Callahan et al. 2008). More than 120 compounds were detected; 57 of them were subsequently identified. A methylated aldaric acid was identified for the first time in any biological extracts, and its structure was confirmed by 1D and 2D NMR spectroscopy. After only citric acid, it appears to be one of the most abundant small organic molecules present in the studied latex. Nickel(II) complexes of stoichiometry, Ni(II): acid = 1:2, were detected for these two acids as well as for malic, itaconic, erythronic, galacturonic, tartaric, aconitic and saccharic acids. These results provide further evidence that organic acids potentially play an important role in the transport and possibly in the storage of the metal ions in hyperaccumulating plants.

Likewise, Wu et al investigated the toxicological effects of mercury (20 μgL^{-1}) in *S. salsa* under environmentally relevant salinity (500 mM) (Wu et al. 2012a). The metabolic responses included increased amino acids and decreased succinate, fructose, glucose, fumarate and ferulate in the above-ground part of *S. salsa* that had been exposed to mercury (Liu et al. 2013; Wu et al. 2012a). Wu et al also investigated the toxicological effects of Pb and Zn in *S. salsa* using NMR-based metabolomics combined with antioxidant enzyme activities. The significant metabolic responses included the increase of isocaproate, glucose and fructose as well as a decrease of malate, citrate and sucrose in the *S. salsa* root tissues that had been exposed to Pb for one month (Wu et al. 2012b). An increase in phosphocholine and betaine and a decrease in choline were uniquely found in the Zn-exposed samples. Metabolic changes consisting of a decreased malate, citrate and sucrose were detected in both the Pb and Zn-exposed groups. These metabolic biomarkers revealed that both Pb and Zn exposures could induce osmotic stress and disturbances in the energy metabolism in *S. salsa* after a one month exposure (Wu et al. 2012b, 2013).

Table 1. The application of plant metabolomic to studying the mechanism involved under metal toxicity

Metals	Plant Species	Analytical techniques	Mechanism	Reference
Cd	*Silene cucubalus*	NMR	Malic acid and acetate (-); glutamate and branched chain amino acids (+)	Bailey et al. 2003.
	Arabidopsis thaliana	LC-MS	Homo-PC(Ala), iso-PC(Ser), and desGluPC (-) ; phytochelatin ((gGlu-Cys)n-Gly) (+)	Sarry et al. 2006.
	Tomato	^{1}H NMR, HPLC-PDA	Carotenoid metabolites was only observed in mature leaves	Hédiji et al. 2010.
	Arabidopsis thaliana	GC–MS	Ala, β-ala, Pro, Ser, putrescine, Suc and other metabolites with compatible solute-like properties, notably 4-aminobutyric acid, glycerol, raffinose and trehalose, antioxidants (alfa-tocopherol, campesterol, beta-sitosterol and isoflavone) (+)	Sun et al. 2010.
	Suaeda salsa	NMR	The levels of amino acids (valine, leucine, glutamate, tyrosine, etc.), carbohydrates (glucose, sucrose and fructose), intermediates of tricarboxylic acid cycle (succinate, citrate, etc.) and osmolyte (betaine) were altered	Liu et al. 2011.
	Chlamydomonas reinhardtii	^{1}H NMR, GC-MS	Fumarate and Glucitol (-); Succinate, Malate and Threonate (+)	Jamers et al. 2013.
	Brassica juncea	LC-MS	Alterations of energy-generating metabolic pathways, sulfur-compound metabolism (GSH and PCs), and Calvin cycle.	D'Alessandro et al. 2013.
Ni(VI)	*Sebertia acuminata*	GC-MS, LC-MS, NMR	A methylated aldaric acid, citric acid and other high abundance metabolites bind to Ni	Callahan et al. 2010.
Hg	*Suaeda salsa*	NMR	Amino acids (valine, leucine, isoleucine, threonine, glutamate, aspartate and glutamine), malonate, choline, and phosphocholine (-); Leucine, betaine, glycine, fructose, sucrose and glucose (+)	Wu et al. 2012a.
	Suaeda salsa	NMR	Ethanol, acetate, succinate, malonate and choline (-);chain amino acids (valine, leucine and isoleucine) and phosphocholine (+)	Liu et al. 2013.
Cr	Rice	^{1}H NMR, GC-MS	Higher accumulation of various fatty acids, Proline accumulated 3-fold.	Dubey et al. 2010.
As(V)	*Cucumis sativus* L	LC-MS	Isoleucine (-); four metabolite compounds (+)	Uroic et al. 2012.
Zn	*Suaeda salsa*	NMR	Choline (-); phosphocholine and betaine (+)	Wu et al. 2012b.
Pb	*Suaeda salsa*	NMR	Malate, citrate and sucrose (-); isocaproate, glucose and fructose (+)	Wu et al. 2012b.
Cs	*Arabidopsis t haliana*	NMR	Malate (-); sucrose, glucose and alanine (+)	Le et al. 2006.
Li	*Brassica carinata*	HPLC-MS, NMR	Phenolic acid derivatives (1-*O*-sinapoylglucose , 1,2-disinapoylgentiobiose , 1,2-di-*O*-sinapoylglucose , and the chloroplast lipid) and monogalactosyldiacylglycerol (-); phenolics, benzoic acid, methyl benzoate, resveratrol glucoside and resveratrol (+)	Li et al. 2006.
Cu	*Brassica rapa*	NMR	Amino acids, phenolics and glucosinolates (+)	Jahangir al. 2008.
Fe	*Brassica rapa*	NMR	Amino acids, phenolics and glucosinolates (+)	Jahangir al. 2008.
Zn/Pb	*Suaeda salsa*	NMR	Malate, citrate and sucrose (-)	Wu et al. 2012b.

Note: (-) means decrease or disappearance; (+) means increase or appearance.

Jahangir et al. (2008) analyzed the effects of Cu, Fe and Mn on the metabolite levels of *Brassica rapa*, which is a known metal accumulator. Glucosinolates and hydroxycinnamic acids conjugated with malates as well as primary metabolites such as carbohydrates and amino acids were found to be the discriminating metabolites. Using NMR, metabolite profiling of the *Arabidopsis* cells that had been exposed to cesium stress revealed that Cs stress-induced metabolite changes include primarily sugar metabolism and glycolytic fluxes and depend upon the potassium levels in the cell (Le Lay et al. 2006). Additionally, Li et al. 2009, exposed *Brassica carinata* seedlings to increasing concentrations of the non-physiological ion lithium and found there to be significant effects on the germination rate, root length, chlorophyll content and fresh weight in brown-seeded and yellow-seeded near-isogenic lines (Li et al. 2009). Metal content analysis and phytochemical profiling indicated that lithium was hyper-accumulated, and the lipid and phenolic composition dramatically changed in the brown-seeded seedlings. Here, sinapic acid esters and chloroplast lipids had been replaced by benzoate derivatives, resveratrol and oxylipins after lithium exposure. In contrast, the yellow seeded plants maintained the same phenolic and lipid composition before and after lithium exposure and were not capable of tolerating the high metal concentrations tolerated by the brown-seeded line.

Recently, rice root metabolome analysis was also conducted in order to relate differential transcriptome data to the biological processes that are affected by Cr (VI) stress in rice. The findings clearly suggest that a complex network of regulatory pathways modulates the chromium-response of rice. After suitable normalization and initial calculations, the integrated matrix of both the transcriptome and metabolome data provided a visual picture of the correlations existing between the different components. Predominance of different motifs in the subsets of genes suggest the involvement of motif-specific transcription modulating proteins in chromium stress (Dubey et al. 2010; Singh et al. 2013). Interestingly, corresponding changes to the transcriptome were not observed; however, no specific protein regulatory mechanism was proposed. Increased levels of linoleic acid were also detected, an expected result as chromium stress is known to increase the levels of unsaturated fatty acids in plants. The metabolomic data was also integrated with the microarray dataset and co-analyzed leading to the find that the sucrose degradation pathway was down regulated whereas conversely, the fermentative pathways were activated as a rescue mechanism (Dubey et al. 2010; Shanker et al. 2009; Singh et al. 2013).

CONCLUSION

Plant metabolomics remains a relatively new approach, however, it is rapidly becoming one of the prevailing tools used in revealing the characteristic features of cellular metal toxicity that otherwise would be difficult to elucidate with other approaches. As shown above, significant new discoveries have already been made in the field through using metabolomics as it is capable of revealing the real- time physiology of a cell, giving a true global picture of the metabolic process and providing target pathways for downstream analysis. As this field is developing, we envision that more studies in the future will include metabolomics combined with other 'omics' techniques, such as proteomics and transcriptomics, as an integral part of the systems biology approach to studying both plant response to a variety of metal stress conditions as well as the underlying toxicity mechanism.

ACKNOWLEDGMENTS

This work was supported by the National Natural Science Foundation of China (31270540, 31070455 and 40971184), the National Science & Technology Pillar Program (2012BAC17B04), Hi-tech research and development program of China (2012AA06A202), Natural Science Foundation of Liaoning Province, China (201102224), the Geping green action-environmental research and education "123 project" of Liaoning Province, China (CEPF2011-123-1-1), the State Scholarship Fund organized by China Scholarship Council (CSC2013).

REFERENCES

Aardema MJ, MacGregor JT (2002) Toxicology and genetic toxicology in the new era of "toxicogenomics": Impact of "-omics" technologies. *Mut Res/Fund Mol Mech Mutag* 499: 13–25.

Ahsan N, Nakamura T, Komatsu S (2012) Differential responses of microsomal proteins and metabolites in two contrasting cadmium (Cd)-accumulating soybean cultivars under Cd stress. *Amino Acids* 42: 317–327.

Almstetter MF, Oefner PJ, Dettmer K (2012) Comprehensive two-dimensional gas chromatography in metabolomics. *Analyt Bioanalyt Chem* 402: 1993–2013.

Álvarez-Sánchez B, Priego-Capote F, Castro MD (2010a) Metabolomics analysis II. Preparation of biological samples prior to detection. *TrAC Trends Analyt Chem* 29: 120–127.

Álvarez-Sánchez B, Priego-Capote F, Luque de Castro MD (2010b) Metabolomics analysis I. Selection of biological samples and practical aspects preceding sample preparation. *TrAC Trends Analyt Chem* 29: 111–119.

Bailey NJ, Oven M, Holmes E, Nicholson JK, Zenk M H (2003) Metabolomic analysis of the consequences of cadmium exposure in *Silene cucubalus* cell cultures via ^{1}H NMR spectroscopy and chemometrics. *Phytochemistry* 62: 851–858.

Bais P, Moon, He K, Leitao R, Dreher K, Walk T, Sucaet Y, Barkan L, Wohlgemuth G, Roth MR, Wurtele ES, Dixon P, Fiehn O, Lange BM, Shulaev V, Sumner LW, Welti R, Nikolau BJ, Rhee SY, Dickerson JA (2010) Plant Metabolomics.org: a web portal for plant metabolomics experiments. *Plant Physiol* 152: 1807–1816.

Bais P, Moon-Quanbeck SM, Nikolau B J, Dickerson JA (2012) Plant metabolomics.org: mass spectrometry-based *Arabidopsis* metabolomics—database and tools update. *Nucl Acids Res* 40: D1216–D1220.

Bassel GW, Gaudinier A, Brady SM, Hennig L, Rhee SY, De Smet I (2012) Systems analysis of plant functional, transcriptional, physical interaction, and metabolic networks. *Plant Cell Online* 24: 3859–3875.

Bedair M, Sumner LW (2008) Current and emerging mass-spectrometry technologies for metabolomics. *TrAC Trends Analyt Chem* 27: 238–250.

Bino RJ, Hall RD, Fiehn O, Kopka J, Saito K, Draper J, Nikolau BJ, Mendes P, Roessner-Tunali U, Beale MH, Trethewey RN, Lange BM, Wurtele ES, Sumner LW(2004) Potential of metabolomics as a functional genomics tool. *Trends Plant Sci* 9: 418–425.

Booth SC, Workentine ML, Weljie AM, Turner RJ (2011) Metabolomics and its application to studying metal toxicity. *Metallomics* 3: 1142–1152.

Broadhurst DI, Kell DB (2006) Statistical strategies for avoiding false discoveries in metabolomics and related experiments. Metabolomics 2: 171–196.

Brunetti C, George RM, Tattini M, Field K, Davey MP (2013) Metabolomics in plant environmental physiology. *J Exp Bot* 64: 4011–4020.

Callahan DL, Roessner U, Dumontet V, Perrier N, Wedd AG, O'Hair RA, Baker AJ, Kolev SD (2008) LC–MS and GC–MS metabolite profiling of nickel (II) complexes in the latex of the nickel-hyperaccumulating tree*Sebertiaacuminate* and identification of methylated aldaric acid as a new nickel (II) ligand. *Phytochemistry* 69: 240–251.

Clemens S (2006) Toxic metal accumulation, responses to exposure and mechanisms of tolerance in plants. *Biochimie* 88: 1707–1719.

D'Alessandro A, Taamalli M, Gevi F, Timperio AM, Zolla L, Ghnaya T (2013) Cadmium stress responses in *Brassica juncea*: Hints from proteomics and metabolomics. *J Proteom Res* 12: 4979–4997

Davey MP, Burrell MM, Woodward FI, Quick WP (2008) Population-specific metabolic phenotypes of *Arabidopsis lyrata* ssp. petraea. *New Phytol* 177: 380–388.

Debnath M, Prasad GB, Bisen PS (2010) *Molecular Diagnostics: Promises and Possibilities* Springer Verlag, The Netherlands.

Dubey S, Misra P, Dwivedi S, Chatterjee S, Bag SK, Mantri S, Asif MH, Rai A, Kumar S, Shri M, Tripathi P, Tripathi RD, Trivedi PK, Chakrabarty D, Tuli R (2010) Transcriptomic and metabolomic shifts in rice roots in response to Cr (VI) stress. *BMC Genom* 11: 648.

Dunn WB, Ellis D I (2005) Metabolomics: Current analytical platforms and methodologies. *TrAC Trends Analyt Chem* 24: 285–294.

Dunn WB, Broadhurst D, Begley P, Zelena E, Francis-McIntyre S, Anderson N, Brown M, Knowles JD, Halsall A, Haselden JN, Nicholls AW, Wilson ID, Kell DB, Goodacre R; Human Serum Metabolome (HUSERMET) Consortium (2011) Procedures for large-scale metabolic profiling of serum and plasma using gas chromatography and liquid chromatography coupled to mass spectrometry. *Nat Prot* 6: 1060–1083.

Forseth RR, Schroeder FC (2011) NMR-spectroscopic analysis of mixtures: from structure to function. *Curr Opi Chem Biol* 15: 38–47.

Fukushima A, Kusano M, Redestig H, Arita M, Saito K (2009) Integrated omics approaches in plant systems biology. *CurrOpiChemBiol* 13: 532–538.

Gehlenborg N, O'Donoghue SI, Baliga NS, Goesmann A, Hibbs MA, Kitano H, Kohlbacher O, Neuweger H, Schneider R, Tenenbaum D, Gavin AC (2010) Visualization of omics data for systems biology. *Nat Met* 7: S56–S68.

Giri S, Krausz KW, Idle JR, Gonzalez FJ (2007) The metabolomics of (±)-arecoline 1-oxide in the mouse and its formation by human flavin-containing mono oxygenases. *Biochem Pharmacol* 73: 561–573.

Goulitquer S, Potin P, Tonon T (2012) Mass spectrometry-based metabolomics to elucidate functions in marine organisms and ecosystems. *Mar Dru* 10: 849–880.

Granger JH, Williams R, Lenz EM, Plumb RS, Stumpf CL, Wilson ID (2007) A metabonomic study of strain-and age-related differences in the Zucker rat. *Rap Comm Mass Spectrom* 21: 2039–2045.

Grata E, Boccard J, Glauser G, Carrupt PA, Farmer EE, Wolfender JL, Rudaz S (2007) Development of a two-step screening ESI-TOF-MS method for rapid determination of significant stress-induced metabolome modifications in plant leaf extracts: The wound response in *Arabidopsis thaliana* as a case study. *J Sep Sci* 30: 2268–2278.

Gratao PL, Monteiro CC, Carvalho RF, Tezotto T, Piotto FA, Peres LE, Azevedo RA (2012) Biochemical dissection of *Diageo tropica* and *Never ripe* tomato mutants to Cd-stressful conditions. *Plant Physiol Biochem* 56: 79–96.

Hagel JM, Facchini PJ (2008) Plant metabolomics: Analytical platforms and integration with functional genomics. *Phytochem Rev* 7: 479–497.

Halket JM, Waterman D, Przyborowska AM, Patel RK, Fraser PD, Bramley PM (2005) Chemical derivatization and mass spectral libraries in metabolic profiling by GC/MS and LC/MS/MS. *J Exp Bot* 56: 219–243.

Hardy NW, Hall RD (2012) *Plant metabolomics: Methods and protocols*. Humana Press.

Hédiji H, Djebali W, Cabasson C, Maucourt M, Baldet P, Bertrand A, Boulila Zoghlami L, Deborde C, Moing A, Brouquisse R, Chaïbi W, Gallusci P(2010) Effects of long-term cadmium exposure on growth and metabolomic profile of tomato plants. *Ecotoxicol Environ Saf* 73: 1965–1974.

Hines A, Bignell J, Stentiford GD, Widdows J, Staff F, Viant MR (2008) Considerations for omics experiments in field-sampled organisms: Key recommendations from environmental metabolomics. *Mar Environ Res* 66: 199–200.

Hong-Bo S, Li-Ye C, Cheng-JiangR, Hua L, Dong-Gang G, Wei-Xiang L (2010) Understanding molecular mechanisms for improving phytoremediation of heavy metal-contaminated soils. *Crit Rev Biotechnol* 30: 23–30.

Hossain MA, Piyatida P, da Silva JAT, Fujita M (2012) Molecular mechanism of heavy metal toxicity and tolerance in plants: Central role of glutathione in detoxification of reactive oxygen species and methylglyoxal and in heavy metal chelation. *J Bot* ID 872875.

Issaq HJ, Van QN, Waybright TJ, Muschik GM, Veenstra TD (2009) Analytical and statistical approaches to metabolomics research. *J Sep Sci* 32: 2183–2199.

Jahangir M, Abdel-Farid IB, Choi YH, Verpoorte R (2008) Metal ion-inducing metabolite accumulation in *Brassica rapa*. *J Plant Physiol* 165: 1429–1437.

Jamers A, Blust R, De Coen W, Griffin JL, Jones OA (2013) An omics based assessment of cadmium toxicity in the green alga *Chlamydomonas reinhardtii*. *Aquat Toxicol* 126: 355–364.

Jaroszewski JW (2005) Hyphenated NMR methods in natural products research, part 2: HPLC-SPE-NMR and other new trends in NMR hyphenation. *Planta Med* 71: 795.

Kell DB (2004) Metabolomics and systems biology: Making sense of the soup. *Curr Opi Microbiol* 7: 296–307.

Kell DB, Brown M, Davey HM, Dunn WB, Spasic I, Oliver SG (2005) Metabolic footprinting and systems biology: The medium is the message. *Nat Rev Microbiol* 3: 557–565.

Kieffer P, Planchon S, Oufir M, Ziebel J, Dommes J, Hoffmann L, Haisman JF, Renaut J (2008) Combining proteomics and metabolite analyses to unravel cadmium stress-response in poplar leaves. *J Proteom Res* 8: 400–417.

Kim HK, Verpoorte R (2010) Sample preparation for plant metabolomics. *Phytochem Anal* 21: 4–13.

Koek MM, Jellema RH, van der Greef J, Tas AC, Hankemeier T (2011) Quantitative metabolomics based on gas chromatography mass spectrometry: Status and perspectives. *Metabolomics* 7: 307–328.

Kopka J, Schauer N, Krueger S, Birkemeyer C, Usadel B, Bergmüller E, Dörmann P, Weckwerth W, Gibon Y, Stitt M, Willmitzer L, Fernie AR, Steinhauser D (2005) GMD@ CSB. DB: The Golmmetabolome database. *Bioinformatics* 21: 1635–1638.

Le Lay P, Isaure MP, Sarry JE, Kuhn L, Fayard B, Le Bail JL, Bastien O, Garin J, Roby C, Bourguignon J (2006) Metabolomic, proteomic and biophysical analyses of *Arabidopsis thaliana* cells exposed to a cesium stress. Influence of potassium supply. *Biochimie* 88: 1533–1547.

Li X, Gao P, Gjetvaj B, Westcott N, Gruber MY (2009) Analysis of the metabolome and transcriptome of *Brassica carinata* seedlings after lithium chloride exposure. *Plant Sci* 177: 68–80.

Liland KH (2011) Multivariate methods in metabolomics–from pre-processing to dimension reduction and statistical analysis. *TrAC Trends Analyt Chem* 30: 827-841.

Lindon JC, Nicholson JK, Holmes E (2011) *The handbook of metabonomics and metabolomics*. Elsevier.

Liu X, Wu H, Ji C, Wei L, Zhao J, Yu J (2013). An integrated proteomic and metabolomic study on the chronic effects of mercury in *Suaeda salsa* under an environmentally relevant salinity. *PLoS One* 8: e64041.

Liu X, Yang C, Zhang L, Li L, Liu S, Yu J, You L, Zhou D, Xia C, Zhao J, Wu H (2011) Metabolic profiling of cadmium-induced effects in one pioneer intertidal halophyte *Suaeda salsa* by NMR-based metabolomics. *Ecotoxicology* 20: 1422–1431.

Mochida K, Shinozaki K (2011) Advances in omics and bioinformatics tools for systems analyses of plant functions. *Plant Cell Physiol* 52: 2017–2038.

Morrison N, Bearden D, Bundy JG, Collette T, Currie F, Davey MP, Haigh NS, Hancock D, Jones OAH, Rochfort S, Sansone SA, Stys D, Teng Q, Field D, Viant MR (2007) Standard reporting requirements for biological samples in metabolomics experiments: environmental context. *Metabolomics* 3: 203–210.

Nielsen J, Oliver S (2005) The next wave in metabolome analysis. *Trends Biotechnol* 23: 544–546.

Oksman-Caldentey KM, Saito K (2005) Integrating genomics and metabolomics for engineering plant metabolic pathways. *Curr Opi Biotechnol* 16: 174–179.

Patti GJ, Yanes O, Siuzdak G (2012) Innovation: Metabolomics: The apogee of the omics trilogy. *Nat Rev Mol Cell Biol* 13: 263–269.

Quanbeck SM, Brachova L, Campbell AA, Guan X, Perera A, He K, Rhee SY, Bais P, Dickerson JA, Dixon P, Wohlgemuth G, Fiehn O, Barkan L, Lange I, Lange BM, Lee I, Cortes D, Salazar C, Shuman J, Shulaev V, Huhman DV, Sumner LW, Roth MR, Welti R, Ilarslan H, Wurtele ES, Nikolau BJ (2012) Metabolomics as a hypothesis-generating functional genomics tool for the annotation of *Arabidopsis thaliana* genes of "unknown function". *Front Plant Sci* 3: 15.

Reaves ML, Rabinowitz JD (2011) Metabolomics in systems microbiology. *Curr Opi Biotechnol* 22: 17–25.

Renberg L, Johansson AI, Shutova T, Stenlund H, Aksmann A, Raven JA, Gardestrom P, Moritz T, Samuelsson G (2010) A metabolomic approach to study major metabolite changes during acclimation to limiting CO_2 in *Chlamydomonas reinhardtii*. *Plant Physiol* 154: 187–196.

Rochfort S (2005) Metabolomics reviewed: A new "omics" platform technology for systems biology and implications for natural products research. *J Nat Prod* 68: 1813-1820.

Saito K, Matsuda F (2010) Metabolomics for functional genomics, systems biology, and biotechnology. *Ann Rev Plant Biol* 61: 463–489.

Sarry JE, Kuhn L, Ducruix C, Lafaye A, Junot C, Hugouvieux V, Jourdain A, Bastien O, Fievet JB, Vailhen D, Amekraz B, Moulin C, Ezan E, Garin J, Bourguignon J (2006) The early responses of *Arabidopsis thaliana* cells to cadmium exposure explored by protein and metabolite profiling analyses. *Proteomics* 6: 2180–2198.

Schneider MV, Orchard S (2011) Omics technologies, data and bioinformatics principles. *Meth Mol Biol* 719: 3–30.

Schuster S, Fell DA, Dandekar T (2000) A general definition of metabolic pathways useful for systematic organization and analysis of complex metabolic networks. *Nat Biotechnol* 18: 326–332.

Shanker AK, Djanaguiraman M, Venkateswarlu B (2009) Chromium interactions in plants: Current status and future strategies. *Metallomics* 1: 375–383.

Shulaev V (2006) Metabolomics technology and bioinformatics.Brief Bioinfo 7: 128–139.

Shulaev V, Cortes D, Miller G, Mittler R (2008) Metabolomics for plant stress response. *Physiol Planta* 132: 199–208.

Sims DA, Gamon JA (2002) Relationships between leaf pigment content and spectral reflectance across a wide range of species, leaf structures and developmental stages. *Rem Sens Environ* 81: 337–354.

Singh HP, Mahajan P, Kaur S, Batish DR, Kohli RK (2013) Chromium toxicity and tolerance in plants. *Environ Chem Lett* 11: 229–254.

Soga T, Ohashi Y, Ueno Y, Naraoka H, Tomita M, Nishioka T (2003) Quantitative metabolome analysis using capillary electrophoresis mass spectrometry. *J Proteo Res* 2: 488–494.

Spratlin JL, Serkova NJ, Eckhardt SG (2009) Clinical applications of metabolomics in oncology: A review. *Clin Can Res* 15: 431–440.

Sumner L W, Mendes P, Dixon RA (2003) Plant metabolomics: Large-scale phytochemistry in the functional genomics era. *Phytochemistry* 62: 817–836.

Sun X, Zhang J, Zhang H, Ni Y, Zhang Q, Chen J, Guan Y (2010) The responses of *Arabidopsis thaliana* to cadmium exposure explored via metabolite profiling. *Chemosphere* 78: 840–845.

Sytar O, Kumar A, Latowski D, Kuczynska P, Strzałka K, Prasad MNV (2013) Heavy metal-induced oxidative damage, defense reactions, and detoxification mechanisms in plants. *Acta Physiol Planta* 35: 985–999.

terKuile BH, Westerhoff HV (2001) Transcriptome meets metabolome: Hierarchical and metabolic regulation of the glycolytic pathway. *FEBS Lett*500: 169–171.

Tohge T, Fernie AR (2009) Web-based resources for mass-spectrometry-based metabolomics: A user's guide. *Phytochemistry* 70: 450–456.

Urbanczyk-Wochniak E, Luedemann A, Kopka J, Selbig J, Roessner-Tunali U, Willmitzer L, Fernie AR (2003) Parallel analysis of transcript and metabolic profiles: A new approach in systems biology. *EMBO Rep* 4: 989–993.

Vaidyanathan S (2005) Profiling microbial metabolomes: What do we stand to gain? *Metabolomics* 1: 17–28.

Viant MR, Sommer U (2013) Mass spectrometry based environmental metabolomics: A primer and review. *Metabolomics* 9: 144–158.

Viant MR, Rosenblum ES, Tjeerdema RS (2003) NMR-based metabolomics: A powerful approach for characterizing the effects of environmental stressors on organism health. *Environ Sci Technol* 37: 4982–4989.

Villas-Boas SG, Nielsen J, Smedsgaard J, Hansen MA, Roessner-Tunali U (2007) *Metabolome Analysis: An Introduction* (Vol. 24). John Wiley & Sons.

Villiers F, Ducruix C, Hugouvieux V, Jarno N, Ezan E, Garin J, Junot C, Bourguignon J (2011) Investigating the plant response to cadmium exposure by proteomic and metabolomic approaches. *Proteomics* 11: 1650–1663.

Villiers F, Hugouvieux V, Leonhardt N, Vavasseur A, Junot C, Vandenbrouck Y, Bourguignon J (2012) Exploring the plant response to cadmium exposure by transcriptomic, proteomic and metabolomic approaches: Potentiality of high-throughput methods, promises of integrative biology. In: Gupta DK, Sandalio LM (eds) *Metal Toxicity in Plants: Perception, Signaling and Remediation*. Springer Berlin Heidelberg pp 119–142.

Vuckovic D (2012) Current trends and challenges in sample preparation for global metabolomics using liquid chromatography–mass spectrometry. *Analyt Bioanalyt Chem* 403: 1523–1548.

Weckwerth W (2010) Metabolomics: An integral technique in systems biology. *Bioanalysis* 2: 829–836.

Weckwerth W (2011) Green systems biology—from single genomes, proteomes and metabolomes to ecosystems research and biotechnology. *J Proteom* 75: 284–305.

Wu H, Liu X, Zhao J, Yu J (2012a) Toxicological responses in halophyte *Suaeda salsa* to mercury under environmentally relevant salinity. *Ecotoxicol Environ Saf* 85:64–71.

Wu, H, Liu, X, Zhao J,Yu J (2013) Regulation of metabolites, gene expression, and antioxidant enzymes to environmentally relevant lead and zinc in the halophyte *Suaeda salsa*. *J Plant Grow Regul* 32: 353–361.

Wu H, Liu X, Zhao J, Yu J, Pang Q, Feng J (2012b) Toxicological effects of environmentally relevant lead and zinc in halophyte *Suaeda salsa* by NMR-based metabolomics. *Ecotoxicology* 21: 2363–2371.

Xia J, Wishart DS (2011) Web-based inference of biological patterns, functions and pathways from metabolomic data using Metabo Analyst. *Nat Proto* 6: 743–760.

Yuan JS, Galbraith DW, Dai SY, Griffin P, Stewart Jr CN (2008) Plant systems biology comes of age. *Trends Plant Sci* 13: 165–171.

Zhang A, Sun H, Wang P, Han Y, Wang X (2012) Modern analytical techniques in metabolomics analysis. *Analyst* 137: 293–300.

Zhang P, Dreher K, Karthikeyan A, Chi A, Pujar A, Caspi R, Karp P, Kirkup V, Latendresse M, Lee C, Mueller LA, Muller R, Rhee SY (2010) Creation of a genome-wide metabolic pathway database for *Populus trichocarpa* using a new approach for reconstruction and curation of metabolic pathways for plants. *Plant Physiol* 153: 1479–1491.

Zoghlami LB, Djebali W, Abbes Z, Hediji H, Maucourt M, Moing A, Brouquisse R, Chaïbi W (2013) Metabolite modifications in *Solanum lycopersicum* roots and leaves under cadmium stress. *Afr J Biotechnol* 10: 567–579.

In: Heavy Metal Remediation   ISBN: 978-1-63321-568-9
Editors: Dharmendra Kumar Gupta and Soumya Chatterjee © 2014 Nova Science Publishers, Inc.

Chapter 6

A REVIEW ON PLANT MECHANISMS FOR UPTAKE, TRANSPORT AND BIO-CONCENTRATION OF TOXIC HEAVY METALS

*Monalisa Mohanty**

Laboratory of Environmental Physiology and Biochemistry,
Post Graduate Department of Botany, Utkal University,
Bhubaneswar, Odisha, India

ABSTRACT

Scientific, industrial and technological progress release huge quantity of toxic pollutants to the surrounding environment. This pollution stress leads to a number of challenges towards environmental sustainability. Protection of environment from various biotic and abiotic stress could be achieved through suitable technological interventions. Heavy metal stress is considered as an major abiotic stress. Evaluation of heavy metal induced toxic impacts on living organisms especially in plants is an alarming feature for sustainable development of environment. Plants which form an integral component of ecosystem are severely affected by heavy metal toxicity stress. Plants growing in metal-polluted sites exhibit altered metabolism, growth diminution, reduced biomass production and high metal accumulation. Various physiological and biochemical processes in plants are affected by toxic heavy metals. Modern investigations on phytotoxic impacts of heavy metals and their mechanism for tolerance in metal-stressed plants are prompted by the increasing metal pollution in the environment. Present review highlights different mechanisms in plants for uptake, transport and bio-concentration of various heavy metals.

Keywords: Heavy metal, Bio-concentration, Phytotoxicity, Uptake, Transport

---

* Corresponding author: Dr. Monalisa Mohanty, Laboratory of Environmental Physiology and Biochemistry, Post Graduate Department of Botany, Utkal University, Bhubaneswar-751004, Odisha, India; Phone: 0091-9861077321; E. Mail: 18.monalisa@gmail.com.

1. INTRODUCTION

Hazardous substances are released from various anthropogenic activities, such as industrial activities for energy production, mineral excavation and transportation. Environmental contamination due to these toxic pollutants is a major issue now-a-days. Heavy metals are one such hazardous pollutant which pose serious threats to environment and human health. Though a number of conventional techniques are employed for combating these heavy metal stresses, still it is in need of an effective and affordable technological solution. Rapid urbanization and industrialization release large quantities of toxic contaminants to the environment (Mohanty and Patra 2011a). Heavy metal-contaminated agricultural land is a widely recognized important environmental health issue in India, attributed to both industrial as well as mining activities. Studies on the harmful effects caused by heavy metals on crop plants are receiving more attention now-a-days. Mine wastes containing Zn, Hg, Al, and Cr, etc. are the major sources of heavy metal contamination (Salt and Rauser 1995; Mohanty et al. 2011; Mohanty and Patra 2011b). Heavy metals accumulate in ecological food chain through uptake at primary producer level and then through consumption at consumer levels.

The term ''heavy metals'' refers to any metallic element that has a relatively high atomic weight, high density (those having a specific weights higher than 5 g cm^{-3}) and is toxic or poisonous even at low concentration (Hawkes 1997; Lenntech Water Treatment and Air Purification 2004). Heavy metals are integrated components of the environment and occur naturally in soils and plants. Heavy metals are mostly found in aquatic ecosystems and to a relatively smaller proportion in atmosphere as particulate or vapors. Among those, 90 elements are present in earth`s crust of which 80 % are metals and 60 % are heavy metals (Sharma and Dietz 2006). An alternative classification of metals based on their coordination chemistry, categorizes heavy metals as class B metals which include highly toxic non-essential trace elements such as Hg, Ag, Pb, Ni (Nieboer and Richardson 1980). Heavy metals are significant environmental pollutants and their toxicity is a problem of increasing significance for ecological, evolutionary, nutritional and environmental reasons.

Heavy metal toxicity in plants varies with plant species, specific metal concentration, chemical form, soil composition and pH. Many heavy metals are considered to be essential for plant growth (Nagajyoti et al. 2010).

Plants roots are the primary contact site for heavy metal ions. In aquatic systems, all parts of the submerged plant species are exposed to these ions. Heavy metals are also absorbed directly by leaves due to particles deposited on the foliar surfaces.

2. TOXIC HEAVY METALS - THEIR PHYTOTOXICITY AND USEFULNESS IN PLANTS

Heavy metals include lead (Pb), cadmium (Cd), nickel (Ni), cobalt (Co), zinc (Zn), chromium (Cr), iron (Fe), arsenic (As), silver (Ag) and the platinum group elements (Nagajyoti et al. 2010). The major sources of heavy metal contamination and their toxic effects on human beings are listed in Table 1 and Figure 1.

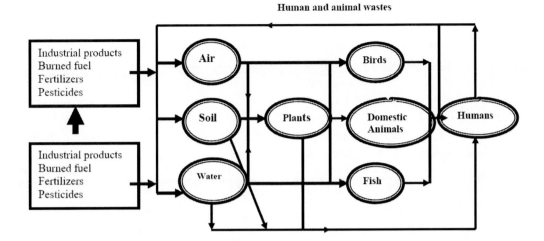

Figure 1. Heavy metal sources and their cycle through the soil-water-air-organism. Metals tends to build-up in the trophic levels (lower to higher; in this figure, from left to right) indicating the vulnerability of organisms residing at higher trophic level, like humans (Modified from Brady and Weil 1999).

Table 1. List of major heavy metals, their sources and uses
(Modified from Brady and Weil 1999)

Heavy metal	Sources of soil contamination	Major uses
Arsenic	Coal and petroleum, mine tailings and detergents	Pesticides, plant desiccants, animal feed additives
Cadmium	Plastic stabilizers, batteries, phosphate fertilizers	Electroplating, plastic and paints
Chromium	Refractory brick manufacture	Stainless steel, chrome plated metals, pigments,
Copper	Mine tailings, flyash, fertilizers	Windblown copper containing dust and water pipes
Lead	Combustion of oil, gasoline and coal,	Iron and steel production and solder on water pipe joints
Mercury	Metallurgy	Pesticide , catalysts for synthetic polymers
Nickel	Combustion of coal, gasoline and oil, mining	Alloy manufacture, electroplating, batteries
Selenium	High selenium geological formations irrigation water contaminated with Se	Nuclear power stations
Zinc	Mining	Galvanized iron and steel, alloys, batteries, brass, rubber manufacture

3. ESSENTIALITY OF HEAVY METALS

Some heavy metals such as Fe, Cu and Zn are essential for plants (detailed list are presented in Table 2) and animals. Metals such as Cu, Zn, Fe, Mn, Mo, Ni and Co are essential micronutrients as reported by several researchers (Reeves and Baker 2000; Wintz et al. 2002). Excess uptake of these heavy metals causes severe toxicity in plants (Monni et al. 2000; Blaylock and Huang 2000). Heavy metal composition of typical uncontaminated soils and agricultural crops were listed in Table 3. Heavy metals are also called as trace elements due to their presence in trace amounts (ppm level) or in ultra-trace quantities in the environmental matrices. Two major functions of essential heavy metals are (a) Participation in redox reaction, and (b) Direct participation in enzyme catalyzed reaction, being an integral part of several enzymes.

Table 2. Few important heavy metals and their average requirement in plants (Modified from Misra and Mani 1991)

Heavy metals/Elements	Land plants ($\mu g\ g^{-1}$ DW)
As	0.02–7
Cd	0.1–2.4
Hg	0.005–0.02
Pb	1–13
Sb	0.02–0.06
Co	0.05–0.5
Cr	0.2–1
Cu	4.15
Fe	140
Mn	15–100
Mo	1–10
Ni	1
Sr	0.30
Zn	8–100

Table 3. Heavy metal composition of typical uncontaminated soils and agricultural crops (Modified from Allaway 1968)

Heavy metals	Range in soil (ppm DW)	Range in agricultural Crops (ppm DW)
Cd	0.01–0.7	0.2–0.8
Co	1–40	0.05–0.5
Cr	5–3,000	0.2–1.0
Cu	2–100	4–15
Fe	7,000–55,000	–
Mn	100–4,000	15–100
Mo	0.2–5	1–100
Ni	10–100	1.0
Pb	2–200	0.1–10
Zn	10–300	15–200

Copper (Cu) is an essential heavy metal, particularly for photosynthesis in higher plants and algae (Mahmood and Islam 2006; Chatterjee et al. 2006). Cu is a constituent of primary electron donor in photosystem I of plants as it can readily gain and lose an electron. It is a cofactor of oxidase, mono- and di-oxygenase (e.g., amine oxidases, ammonia monoxidase, ceruloplasmin, lysyl oxidase) and of enzymes involved in the elimination of superoxide radicals (e.g., superoxide dismutase and ascorbate oxidase).

Zinc (Zn) is a requisite for maintaining ribosome integrity. It takes part in the formation of carbohydrates and catalyzes the oxidation processes in plants. Zinc also provides a structural role in many transcription factors and is a cofactor of RNA polymerase. Several enzymes like carbonic anhydrase, alcohol dehydrogenase, superoxide dismutase and RNA polymerase contain Zn.

Nickel (Ni) is recognized as another essential micronutrient for living organisms and is a component of the enzyme urease. Nickel is essential for its functional role leading to good health in animals. Manganese plays an important role in reactions of enzymes like mallic dehydrogenase, superoxide disumutase and oxalosuccinic decarboxylase. It is also needed for water splitting at photosystem II.

Iron (Fe) is an essential element in many metabolic processes and is indispensable for all organisms. It is a component of heme-containing protein such as hemoglobin, myoglobin and cytochrome. Innumerable non-heme iron-containing proteins plays vital functions in many metabolic processes. Iron and copper are found as components of protein and catalyze redox reactions (Nagajyoti et al. 2010).

4. HEAVY METAL PHYTOTOXICITY

Heavy metals severely impair central metabolic processes in plants. Heavy metals such as Cd, Hg and As at higher ionic concentrations are strongly poisonous to various metabolic activities. Research have been conducted throughout the globe on phytotoxic impacts of heavy metals in several plants (Fernandes and Henriques 1991; Reeves and Baker 2000; Zied 2001; Mohanty et al. 2005; Zou et al. 2009; Pattnaik et al. 2012; Mohanty and Patra 2012). Contamination of agricultural soil by heavy metals has become a critical environmental concern due to their adverse ecological effects. Such toxic elements are considered as soil pollutants due to their widespread occurrence and their acute and chronic toxic effect on plants grown on such contaminated soils. The list of various phytotoxic impacts of some selected heavy metals are given in Table 4.

5. FATE OF HEAVY METALS IN PLANTS

Plants can take up heavy metals by their roots or even via their stems and leaves. Plants accumulate these heavy metals in their organs and then selectively take up those. Accumulation and distribution of heavy metals in plant depends on type of plant species, element species, type of soil element and bioavailability, redox potential, pH, cation exchange capacity, dissolved oxygen, temperature and various secretions from plantroots.

Table 4. Heavy metals and their phytotoxic impacts

Heavy metal	Phytotoxicity	Plant species	References
Zn (Zinc)	Decrease in growth and development, metabolism and an induction of oxidative damage in various plant species; alternation in catalytic efficiency of enzymes; senescence; chlorosis; manganese (Mn) and copper (Cu) deficiencies in plant shoots; appearance of a purplish-red color in leaves, which is ascribed to phosphorus (P) deficiency	*Phaseolus vulgaris*, *Brassica juncea*, Pea plants etc.	Cakmak and Marshner 1993; Prasad et al. 1999; Van Assche et al. 1988; Somasekharaiah et al. 1992; Romero-Puertas et al. 2004; Lee et al. 1996.
Cd (Cadmium)	Visible symptoms of injury reflected in terms of chlorosis, growth inhibition, browning of root tips and finally death; The inhibition of root Fe(III) reductase induced by Cd led to Fe(II) deficiency, and it seriously affected photosynthesis; interfere with the uptake, transport and use of several elements (Ca, Mg, P and K) and water by plants; reduced the absorption of nitrate and its transport from roots to shoots, by inhibiting the nitrate reductase activity in the shoots; Nitrogen fixation and primary ammonia assimilation decreased in nodules of soybean plants; affect the plasma membrane permeability, causing a reduction in water content; in particular, Cd has been reported to interact with the water balance; reduce ATPase activity of the plasma membrane fraction of wheat and sunflower roots; disturbances in chloroplast metabolism by inhibiting chlorophyll biosynthesis and reducing the activity of enzymes involved in CO_2 fixation	*Silene Cucubalus* Soybean, Sunflower, and other plants.	Alcantara et al. 1994; Das et al. 1997; Hernandez et al. 1996; Mathys 1975; Balestrasse et al. 2003; Fodor et al. 1995; Costa and Morel 1994; De Filippis and Ziegler 1993.
Cu (Copper)	Cytotoxic role, induces stress and causes injury to plants; plant growth retardation and leaf chlorosis; generates oxidative stress and ROS	*Alyssum montanum* Cucumber *Brassica juncea* etc.	Lewis et al. 2001; Stadtman and Oliver 1991; Moreno-Caselles et al. 2000; Ouzoumidou 1994; Singh and Tewari 2003.
Mercury (Hg)	Hg^{+2} can bind to water channel proteins, thus inducing leaf stomata to close and physical obstruction of water flow in plants interfere the mitochondrial activity and induces oxidative stress by triggering the generation of ROS. This leads to the disruption of biomembrane lipids and cellular metabolism in plants	Cucumber, Wheat etc.	Zhang and Tyerman 1999; Messer et al. 2005; Cargnelutti et al. 2006.
Chromium (Cr)	Inhibition in seed germination, Decrease in root growth, affect photosynthesis in terms of CO2 fixation, electron transport, photophosphorylation and enzyme activities, disorganization of chloroplasts' ultrastructure, inhibition of electron transport and enzymes of the Calvin cycle.	*Medicago sativa*, Wheat, Rice, Green gram etc.	Peralta et al. 2001; Mohanty and Patra, 2012; Shanker et al. 2003.

Heavy metal	Phytotoxicity	Plant species	References
Lead (Pb)	Inhibit seed germination, inhibited protease and amylase by about 50% in rice endosperm, seedling growth was also inhibited by lead, induce oxidative stress with increased production of ROS in plants, affect photosynthesis by inhibiting activity of carboxylating enzymes, water imbalance, alterations in membrane permeability and disturbs mineral nutrition.	Rice, Soya bean, Barley, Tomato, Eggplant.	Nagajyoti et al. 2010; Reddy et al. 2005; Sharma and Dubey 2005.
Cobalt (Co)	Adverse effect on shoot growth and biomass, restricted the concentration of Fe, chlorophyll, protein and catalase activity in leaves of cauliflower, also affected the translocation of P, S, Mn, Zn and Cu from roots to tops.	*Hordeum vulgare* L., *Brassica napus* L. and *Lycopersicon esculentum* L. Cauliflower.	Kukier et al. 2004; Li et al. 2004; Bakkaus et al. 2005; Li et al. 2009; Nagajyoti et al. 2010.
Nickel (Ni)	Various physiological alterations and diverse toxicity symptoms such as chlorosis and necrosis in different plant species	Rice, wheat *Brassica* sps.	Zornoza et al. 1999; Pandey and Sharma 2002; Rahman et al. 2005; Pattnaik et al. 2012.

Plants are employed in decontamination of polluted water by removing heavy metals and have demonstrated high performances in treating mineral tailings, waste water and industrial effluents. Purification capacity of plants for heavy metals are affected by several factors such as concentration of the heavy metals, species of elements, plant species, duration of exposure, temperature and pH (Cheng 2003).

5.1. Metal Uptake and Transport Mechanism

To grow and complete the life cycle, plants must acquire not only macronutrients (N, P, K, S, Ca, and Mg), but also essential micronutrients such as Fe, Zn, Mn, Ni, Cu, and Mo. Plants have evolved highly specific mechanisms to take up, translocate and store these nutrients. For example, metal movement across biological membranes is mediated by proteins with transport functions. In addition, sensitive mechanisms maintain intracellular concentration of metal ions within the physiological range. In general, plants adopt selective uptake mechanism preferentially acquiring some ions over others. Structure and properties of membrane transporters determine the selective uptake of ions. These characteristics allow transporters to recognize, bind and mediate the trans-membrane transport of specific ions. For example, some transporters mediate the transport of divalent cations, but do not recognize mono- or trivalent ions. Because of their charge, metal ions cannot move freely across the cellular membranes. Therefore, ion transport into cells must be mediated by transporters. Transmembrane transporters possess an extracellular binding domain to which the ions attach just before the transport and a transmembrane structure which connects extracelluar and intracellular media. The binding domain is receptive only to specific ions and is responsible for transporter specificity. Transmembrane structure facilitates the transfer of bound ions from extracellular space through the hydrophobic environment of membrane into the cell.

Many metals such as Zn, Mn, Ni and Cu are essential micronutrients. Accumulation of these micronutrients does not exceed their metabolic needs (<10 ppm) in common non-accumulator plants,. In contrast, metal hyperaccumulator plant species can accumulate remarkably high amounts of metals (in thousands of ppm). Since metal accumulation is ultimately an energy consuming process, one would wonder what evolutionary advantage metal hyperaccumulation gives to these species. Metal accumulation in the foliage may allow hyperaccumulator species to evade predators including caterpillars, fungi and bacteria (Boyd and Martens 1994; Pollard and Baker 1997). Hyperaccumulator plants absorb significant amounts of nonessential metals, such as Cd along with the accumulation of high levels of essential micronutrients. Mechanism of Cd accumulation has not been elucidated. It is possible that the uptake of this metal in roots is via a system involved in the transport of another essential divalent micronutrient, possibly Zn^{2+}. Cadmium is a chemical analogue of the latter and plants may not be able to differentiate between these two ions (Chaney et al. 1994).

5.2. Factors Influencing Heavy Metal Uptake

Anthropogenic activities highly influence heavy metal uptake and phyto-availability in environment. Heavy metals interfere with physiological processes such as gaseous exchange,

CO_2 fixation, respiration and nutrient absorption. Heavy metal uptake is not linear in response to its increasing concentrations. Many factors influence the uptake of metals and include growing environment such as temperature, soil pH, soil aeration, Eh condition (particularly of aquatic environment), fertilization, competition between plant species, type of plant, its size, root system, availability of the elements in soil or foliar deposits, type of leaves, soil moisture and plant energy supply to roots and leaves.

As far as the growing environment is concerned increase in pH, (environment becoming more alkaline) and decrease in Eh (redox potential), (environment becoming more reducing) result in decreased phyto-availability of heavy metals (Nagajyoti et al. 2010). However, under a given environmental condition, uptake of a metal by plant can be estimated from the biological absorption coefficient (Nagajyoti et al. 2010).Levels of heavy metals in plants (both terrestrial and aquatic) vary widely due to influence of environmental factors and the type of plant itself. Metal accumulation and translocation through various plant parts involve several steps as shown in Figure 2 (modified from Clemens et al. 2002).

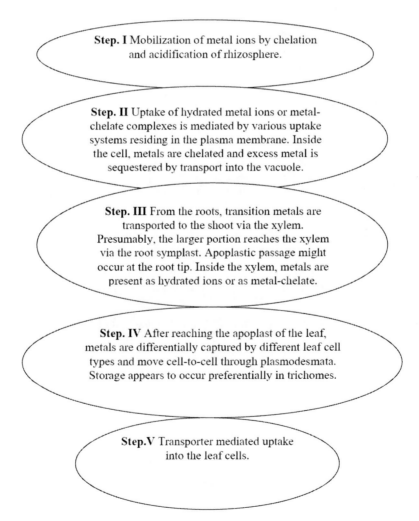

Step. I Mobilization of metal ions by chelation and acidification of rhizosphere.

Step. II Uptake of hydrated metal ions or metal-chelate complexes is mediated by various uptake systems residing in the plasma membrane. Inside the cell, metals are chelated and excess metal is sequestered by transport into the vacuole.

Step. III From the roots, transition metals are transported to the shoot via the xylem. Presumably, the larger portion reaches the xylem via the root symplast. Apoplastic passage might occur at the root tip. Inside the xylem, metals are present as hydrated ions or as metal-chelate.

Step. IV After reaching the apoplast of the leaf, metals are differentially captured by different leaf cell types and move cell-to-cell through plasmodesmata. Storage appears to occur preferentially in trichomes.

Step.V Transporter mediated uptake into the leaf cells.

Figure 2. Schematic diagram of molecular mechanisms proposed to be involved in transition metal accumulation by plants.

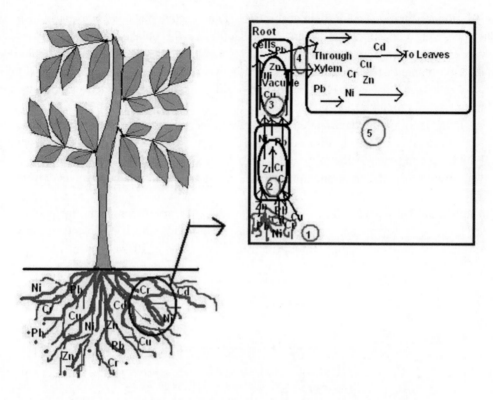

Figure 3. Metal uptake and accumulation in plants. 1. Sorbtion of metal fraction at root surface. 2. Movement of bioavailable metal across cellular membrane into root cells. 3. Immobilization of root absorbed metal fraction in the vacuole. 4. Entry of intracellular mobile metal across cellular membranes into root vascular tissue (xylem). 5. Translocation of metal from the root to aerial tissues (stems and leaves).

Intracellular distribution or trafficking of essential transition metals is mediated by specific metallochaperones and transporters localized in endomembranes. Mechanism responsible for metal immobilization into roots and subsequent inhibition of ion translocation to the shoot involves binding of metal to cell wall, metal complexation and sequestration in cellular structures (e.g., vacuole).

The process of metal absorption from soil and its subsequent metal accumulation was given in Figure 3. There are several factors which can affect the uptake mechanism of heavy metals, as shown in Figure 4. By having knowledge about these factors, metal uptake performance by plants can be greatly improved.

Plants are screened and those with superior remediation properties are selected. Uptake of a compound is affected by the characteristics of plant species. Success of phytoextraction technique depends upon identification of suitable plant species that hyperaccumulate heavy metals and produce large amounts of biomass using established crop production and management practices (Tangahu et al. 2011). Agronomical practices (pH adjustment, addition of chelators, fertilizers etc.) are developed to enhance remediation process. For example, the amount of lead absorbed by plants is affected by the pH, organic matter, and phosphorus content of soil. To reduce lead uptake by plants, the pH of soil is adjusted with lime to a level of 6.5 to 7.0 (Tangahu et al. 2011). The root zone is of special interest in phytoremediation of heavy metals. It can absorb contaminants and store or metabolize it inside the plant tissue.

Degradation of contaminants in soil by plant enzymes exuded from roots is another mechanism of phytoremediation technique.

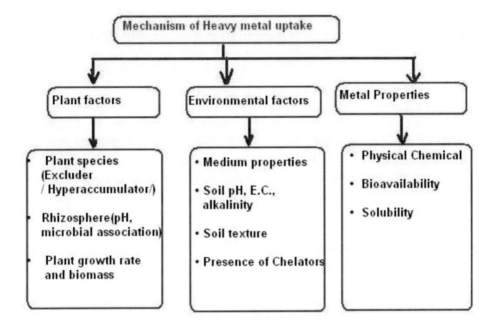

Figure 4. Factors which are affecting the uptake mechanisms of heavy metals.

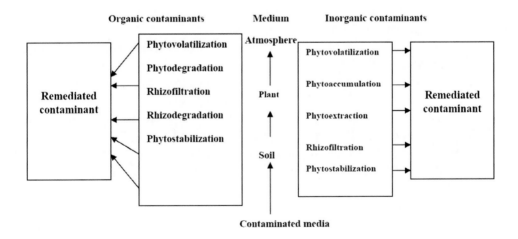

Figure 5. Uptake mechanisms on phytoremediation technology (Modified from Tangahu et al. 2010).

Vegetative uptake is affected by various environmental conditions. Success of phytoremediation, more specifically phytoextraction, depends on a contaminant specific hyperaccumulator. Understanding mass balance analyses and metabolic fate of pollutants in plants are the keys for the applicability of phytoremediation (Figure 5). Plants will affect the heavy metal content of soil through their ability to lower the pH and oxygenate the sediment. Increased bioavailability of heavy metals in plants are due to addition of biodegradable physicochemical factors, such as chelating agents and micronutrients (Tangahu et al. 2011) to the contaminated soil.

Increased uptake of heavy metals by energy crops can also be influenced by stimulating heavy-metal-uptake capacity of microbial community in and around the plant. This faster uptake of heavy metals will result in shorter and less expensive remediation periods. Use of a chelating agent is warranted and may be required in alkaline soils, since bioavailability of heavy metals in soils decreases above pH 5.5. Application of synthetic chelating agents (DTPA, EDTA, EDDHA etc.) favours hyperaccumulation of heavy metals (Mohanty and Patra 2011b). Plant roots exude organic acids such as citrate and oxalate, which affect the bioavailability of metals. In chelate-assisted phytoremediation, synthetic chelating agents such as NTA and EDTA are added to enhance the phytoextraction of soil-polluting heavy metals. Presence of a ligand affects biouptake of heavy metals through formation of metal-ligand complexes and changes the potential to leach metals below root zone (Tangahu et al. 2011).

5.3. Plant Responses to Heavy Metals

Plants have developed three basic strategies for growing on contaminated and metalliferous soils (Baker and Walker 1990; Tangahu et al. 2011). On the basis of these mechanisms plants can be categorized as following three types.

1. *Metal excluders:* These plants effectively prevent metal from entering their aerial parts over a broad range of metal concentrations in soil; however, they can still contain large amounts of metals in their roots.
2. *Metal indicators:* These plants accumulate metals in their above-ground tissues and the metal levels in the tissues of these plants generally reflect metal levels in soil.
3. *Accumulators:* These plant species (hyperaccumulators) can concentrate metals in their above-ground tissues to levels far exceeding those present in the soil or in the non-accumulating species growing nearby. It has been proposed that a plant containing more than 0.1% of Ni, Co, Cu, Cr or Pb or 1% of Zn in its leaves on a dry weight basis is called a hyperaccumulator, irrespective of the metal concentration in soil. Information related to accumulator plants is highly required in four areas: first - metal accumulating ability of various species as a function of soil metal concentrations, physical and chemical soil properties, physiological state of the plant, etc.; second - specificity of metal uptake, transport and accumulation; third - physiological, biochemical and molecular mechanisms of accumulation and hyperaccumulation; and fourth is the biological and evolutionary significance of metal accumulation.

6. MECHANISM OF METAL ACCUMULATION AND TOLERANCE

Plants distribute metals internally in different ways. They may localize selected metals mostly in roots and stems, or they may accumulate and store other metals in nontoxic form for latter distribution and use. A mechanism of tolerance or accumulation in some plants apparently involves binding potentiality of toxic metals at cell walls of roots and leaves, away from sensitive sites within the cell or storing them in a vacuolar compartment. Plant species which have no exclusion mechanism in roots can absorb and translocate large concentrations of metals and subsequently accumulate them in their growing parts, especially in their leaves without showing any toxicity symptoms via a sort of internal resistance or accumulation mechanism. Many types of heavy metal resistance and tolerance mechanisms have been suggested, especially for Cu, Zn, Ni and Cr in plants growing on metalliferous soils (Turner 1970; Turner and Marshall 1971; Mohanty and Patra 2012; Panda et al. 2005). Fe, Mn, Cu, Ni, Co, Cd, Zn, Pb and Se accumulator plants have been reported by Memon et al. (2001). Several other mechanisms may contribute to heavy metal tolerance depending on the type of metal and plant species among them:

6.1. Induction of Metal Chelating Proteins

Induction of metal chelating proteins related to phytochelatins (γ-glutmylcysteinyl isopeptides) (Zenk 1996; Clemens et al. 1999; Cobbett 2000) and/or metallothioneins (Robinson et al. 1997; Rauser 1999) by modifying cell metabolism increases the level of cell tolerance to excess metal ions. Chelators contribute to metal detoxification by buffering cytosolic metal concentrations whereas chaperones specifically deliver metal ions to organelles and metal requiring proteins. The principal classes of metal chelators in plants include phytochelatins, metallothioneins, organic acids and amino acids.

6.2. Induction of Heat Shock Proteins

Inductions of heat shock proteins in response to several transition metals (Zn, Cu, Cd, Hg) and sulfhydryl reagent of arsenite have recently been reported (Lewis et al., 2001). Heavy metal stress induced heat shock proteins protect membranes and its proteins in a similar way as under heat stress (Neumann et al. 1994). The induction of m-RNA for heat shock proteins or synthesis of heat shock proteins under heavy metal stress has been observed in different plants or plant cell cultures (Wollgiehn and Neumann 1995). However, the putative role of heat shock proteins in heavy metal tolerance is largely unknown.

6.3. Phytoremediation Technology

Phytoremediation defines the use of plants to extract, sequester and/or detoxify various kinds of environmental pollutant (Salt et al. 1998). It is a newly evolving field of biotechnology that uses plants to clean-up polluted soil, water and air. There are two types of phytoremediation process. One is elemental and the other one organic. Elemental pollutants include toxic heavy metals and radionucleotides, such as arsenic, cadmium, caesium, chromium, lead, mercury, strontium, technetium, tritium, and uranium. The use of metal—accumulating plants for removal of metals from contaminated soils and waters has a number of advantages such as lower cost, generation of a recyclable metal-rich plant residue, applicability over a range of toxic metals and radionuclides. These phytotechnological approaches have minimal environmental disturbance, elimination of secondary air or water-borne wastes and public acceptance.

6.4. Phytoremediation by Use of Metal-Accumulating Plants

Recently the importance of terrestrial metal hyperaccumulators for environmental remediation has given utmost priority. Phytoremediation of heavy metals is an emerging technology and four subsets of this technology are being developed (Salt et al. 1995; Pilon-Smits and Pilon 2000; Mohanty et al. 2010; Mohanty and Patra 2012) which are as follows.

1. *Phytoextraction*, in which metal-accumulating plants are used to transport and concentrate metals from soil into harvestable parts of roots and above-ground shoots.
2. *Rhizofiltration*, in which plant roots absorb, precipitates and concentrates the toxic metals from polluted effluents.
3. *Phytostabilization*, in which heavy metal tolerant plants are used to reduce the mobility of heavy metals thereby reducing the risk of further environmental degradation by leaching into ground water or by airborne spread.
4. *Plant assisted bioremediation*, in which plant roots in conjunction with their rhizospheric microorganisms are used to remediate soils contaminated with organics.

CONCLUSION

Careful investigation on mechanism of heavy metal uptake from soil, its transport and bioconcentration play a pivotal role in defending heavy metal induced abiotic stress in environment. Thus, it is evident from several research reports that presence of heavy metals has several toxic effects on plants, animals and other living organisms. Therefore, it is well needed to intensify the research programmes for better understanding of heavy metal toxicity on plants and allied areas to maintain the ecological harmony of the globe. Heavy metal accumulation in soils is of concern in agricultural production due to its adverse effects on food safety and marketability, reduced crop growth due to phytotoxicity and deteriorated environmental health of soil organisms. Influence of plants and their metabolic activities affects the geological and biological redistribution of heavy metals through pollution of air, water and soil. A better understanding of the biochemical processes involved in plant heavy metal uptake, transport, accumulation and resistance will help in systematic improvements in phytoremediation using molecular genetic approaches. Various studies of metal-ion homeostasis in plants suggest that there exists a complex regulated network for metal ion transport, chelation and sequestration. Present situation of metal pollution affects the whole ecosystem. Using genetic modifications, scientists have been able to expand the role of plants in environment. In order to restore environmental balance, bioremediation technique evidently indicate several benefits and is one of the most preferred methods to deal with this problem. Technologies with the use of new transgenic plants have also improved the capacity of biochemical processes such as metal uptake, transport, accumulation and detoxification of metal pollutants. Therefore, identification of a suitable candidate plant with essential mechanisms and subsequent transformation capacity of heavy metals to simpler and less toxic forms are necessary for future phytoremediation studies.

REFERENCES

Alcantara E, Romera FJ, Canete M, De La Guardia MD (1994) Effects of heavy metals on both induction and function of root Fe(III) reductase in Fe-deficient cucumber (*Cucumis sativus* L.) plants. *J Exp Bot* 45: 1893–1898.

Allaway WH (1968) Agronomic control over the environmental cycling of trace elements. *Adv Agron* 20: 235–274.

Baker AJM, Walker PL (1990) Ecophysiology of metal uptake by tolerant plants. In : AJ Shaw (ed) *Heavy Metal Tolerance in Plants: Evolutionary Aspects*, CRC Press, Boca Raton, FL. pp 155–177.

Bakkaus E, Gouget B, Gallien JP, Khodja H, Carrot H, Morel JL, Collins R (2005) Concentration and distribution of cobalt in higher plants: The use of micro-PIXE spectroscopy. *Nucl Instr Meth B* 231: 350–356.

Balestrasse KB, Benavides MP, Gallego SM, Tomaro ML (2003) Effect on cadmium stress on nitrogen metabolism in nodules and roots of soybean plants. *Func Plant Biol* 30: 57–64.

Blaylock MJ, Huang JW (2000) Phytoextraction of metals. In: Raskin I, Ensley BD (eds) *Phytoremediation of toxic metals-using plants to clean up the environment.* Wiley, New York. pp 53–70.

Boyd RS, Martens SN (1994) Nickel hyperaccumulated by *Thlaspi montanum* var. montanum is acutely toxic to an insect herbivore. *Oikos* 70: 21-25.

Brady NC, Weil RR (1999) *The nature and properties of soils.* 12th ed. Prentice Hall. Upper Saddle River, NJ.

Cakmak I, Marshner H (1993) Effect of zinc nutritional status on superoxide radical and hydrogen peroxide scavenging enzymes in bean leaves. In: Barrow NJ (ed) *Plant nutrition-from genetic engineering field practice.* Kluwer, The Netherlanads. pp 133–137.

Cargnelutti D, Tabaldi LA, Spanevello RM, Jucoski GO, Battisti V, Redin M, Linares CEB, Dressler VL, Flores MM, Nicoloso FT, Morsch VM, Schetinger MRC (2006) Mercury toxicity induces oxidative stress in growing cucumber seedlings. *Chemosphere* 65: 999–1106.

Chaney RL, Green CE, Filcheva E, Brown SL (1994) Effect of iron, manganese, and zinc enriched biosolids compost on uptake of cadmium by lettuce from cadmium-contaminated soils. In: Clapp CE, Larson WE DowdyRH (eds) *Sewage Sludge: Land Utilization and the Environment.* American Society of Agronomy Madison, WI. pp 205-207.

Chatterjee C, Gopal R, Dube BK (2006) Physiological and biochemical responses of French bean to excess cobalt. *J Plant Nutri* 29: 127–136.

Cheng S (2003) Heavy metals in plants and phytoremediation. *Environ Sci Pollut Res* 10: 335–340.

Clemens S, Palmgren MG, and Krämer U (2002) A long way ahead: Understanding and engineering plant metal accumulation. *Trends Plant Sci* 7: 309–315.

Clemens S, Kim EJ, Neumann D, Schroeder JI (1999) Tolerance to toxic metals by a gene family of phytochelatin synthases from plants and yeast. *EMBO J* 15: 3325–3333.

Cobbett CS (2000) Phytochelatins and their roles in heavy metal detoxification. *Plant Physiol* 123: 825–832.

Costa G, Morel JL (1994) Water relations, gas exchange and amino acid content in Cd-treated lettuce. *Plant Physiol Biochem* 32: 561–570.

Das P, Samantaray S, Rout GR (1997) Studies on cadmium toxicity in plants: A review. *Environ Pollut* 98: 29–36.

De Filippis LF, Ziegler H (1993) Effect of sub lethal concentrations of zinc, cadmium and mercury on the photosynthetic carbon reduction cycle of Euglena. *J Plant Physiol* 142: 167–172.

Fernandes JC, Henriques FS (1991) Biochemical, physiological and structural effects of excess copper in plants. *Bot Rev* 57: 247–273.

Fodor A, Szabo-Nagy A, Erdei L (1995) The effects of cadmium on the fluidity and H?-ATPase activity of plasma membrane from sunflower and wheat roots. *J Plant Physiol* 14:787–792.

Hawkes JS (1997) Heavy metals. *J Chem Edu* 74: 1369–1374.

Hernandez LE, Carpena-Ruiz R, Garate A (1996) Alterations in the mineral nutrition of pea seedlings exposed to cadmium. *J Plant Nutr* 19: 1581–1598.

Kukier U, Peters CA, Chaney RL, Angle JS, Roseberg RJ (2004) The effect of pH on metal accumulation in two Alyssum species. *J Environ Qual* 33: 2090–2102.

Lasat MM (2000) "Phytoextraction of metals from contaminated soil: A review of plant/soil/metal interaction and assessment of pertinent agronomic issues. *J Hazard Sub Res* 2: 1–25.

Lee CW, Choi JM, Pak CH (1996) Micronutrient toxicity in seed geranium (Pelargonium 9 hortorum Baley). *J Am Soc Horti Sci* 121: 77–82.

Lenntech Water Treatment and Air Purification. Water Treatment. Published by Lenntech, Rotterdamseweg, Netherlands. http://www.excelwater.com/thp/filters/Water-Purification.htm

Lewis S, Donkin ME, Depledge MH (2001) Hsp 70 expression in *Enteromorpha intestinalis* (Chlorophyta) exposed to environmental stressors. *Aqua Toxicol* 51: 277–291.

Li Z, McLaren RG, Metherell AK (2004) The availability of native and applied soil cobalt to ryegrass in relation to soil cobalt and manganese status and other soil properties. *New Zea J Agri Res* 47: 33–43.

Li HF, Gray C, Mico C, Zhao FJ, McGrath SP (2009) Phytotoxicity and bioavailability of cobalt to plants in a range of soils. *Chemosphere* 75: 979–986.

Mahmood T, Islam KR (2006) Response of rice seedlings to copper toxicity and acidity. *J Plant Nutri* 29: 943–957.

Mathys W (1975) Enzymes of heavy metal-resistant and non-resistant populations of *Silene cucubalus* and their interactions with some heavy metals in vitro and in vivo. *Physiol Plant* 33: 161–165.

Memon AR, Aktoprakligil D, Ozdemir A, Vertii A (2001). Heavy metal accumulation and detoxification mechanisms in plants. *Turk J Bot* 25: 111–121.

Messer RL, Lockwood PE, Tseng WY, Edwards K, Shaw M, Caughman GB, Lewis JB, Wataha JC (2005) Mercury (II) alters mitochondrial activity of monocytes at sub lethal doses via oxidative stress mechanisms. *J Biomed Mat Res* B 75: 257–263.

Misra SG, Mani D (1991) Soil pollution. Ashish Publishing House, Punjabi Bagh, N. Delhi.

Mohanty M, Patra HK (2011a) Attenuation of chromium toxicity by bioremediation technology. *Rev Env Contam Toxicol* 210: 1–34.

Mohanty M, Patra HK (2011b) Effect of Cr^{+6} and chelating agents on growth, pigment status, proline content and chromium bioavailability in rice seedlings. *Int J Biotech Appl* 3: 91–96.

Mohanty M, Patra HK (2012) Effect of chelate-assisted hexavalent chromium on physiological changes, biochemical alterations, and chromium bioavailability in crop plants—An in vitro phytoremediation approach. *Bioremed J* 16: 147–155.

Mohanty M, Dhal NK, Patra P, Das B, Reddy PSR (2010) Phytoremediation: A novel approach for utilization of iron-ore wastes. *Rev Env Contam Toxicol* 206: 29–44.

Mohanty M, Jena AK, Patra HK (2005) Effect of chelated chromium compounds on chlorophyll content and activities of catalase and peroxidase in wheat seedlings. *Ind J Agr Biochem* 18: 25–29.

Mohanty M , Pattnaik MM, Mishra AK, Patra HK (2011) Chromium bioaccumulation in rice grown in contaminated soil and irrigated mine wastewater—A case study at south Kaliapani Chromite Mine Area, Orissa, India. *Int J Phytorem* 13: 397–409.

Monni S, Salemma M, Millar N (2000) The tolerance of *Empetrum nigru*m to copper and nickel. *Environ Pollut* 109: 221–229.

Moreno-Caselles J, Moral R, Pera-Espinosa A, Marcia MD (2000) Cadmium accumulation and distribution in cucumber plants. *J Plant Nut* 23: 243–250.

Nagajyoti PC, Lee KD, Sreekanth T VM (2010) Heavy metals, occurrence and toxicity for plants: A review. *Environ Chem Lett* 8: 199–216.

Nieboer E, Richardson DHS (1980) The replacement of the nondescript term heavy metals by a biologically and chemistry significant classification of metal ions. *Environ Pollut Ser B* 1: 3–26.

Ouzounidou G (1994) Change in chlorophyll fluorescence as a result of copper treatment: Dose response relations in *Silene* and *Thlaspi*. *Photosynthetica* 29: 455–462.

Panda SK, Choudhury S, Matsumoto H (2005) Molecular physiology of heavy metal stress in plants. *Advances in Plant Physiology (9th Vol.)-International Treatese Series.* pp 169–192.

Pandey N, Sharma CP (2002) Effect of heavy metals Co^{+2},Ni^{+2}, and Cd^{+2} on growth and metabolism of cabbage. *Plant Sci* 163: 753–758.

Patnaik N, Mohanty M, Satpathy B, Patra HK (2012) Effect of chelating agents and metal ions on nickel bioavailability and chlorophyll fluorescence response in wheat- An approach for attenuation of Ni stress. *J Stress Physiol Biochem* 8: 99–112.

Peralta JR, Gardea Torresdey JL, Tiemann KJ, Gomez E, Arteaga S, Rascon E (2001) Uptake and effects of five heavy metals on seed germination and plant growth in alfalfa (*Medicago sativa*)L. *Bull Environ Contam Toxicol* 66: 727–734.

Pilon-Smits EAH, Pilon M (2000) Breeding mercury-breathing plants for environmental cleanup. *Trends Plant Sci* 6: 235–236.

Pollard JA, Baker AJM (1997) Deterrence of herbivory by zinc hyperaccumulation in *Thlaspi caerulescens* (Brassicacea). *New Phytol* 135: 655–658.

Prasad MNV, Hagmeyer J (1999) Heavy metal stress in plants. Springer, Berlin pp 16–20.

Rahman H, Sabreen S, Alam S, Kawai S (2005) Effects of nickel on growth and composition of metal micronutrients in barley plants grown in nutrient solution. *J Plant Nutri* 28: 393–404.

Rauser WE (1999) Structure and function of metal chelators produced by plants. The case for organic acids, amino acids, phytin and metallothioneins. *Cell Biochem Biophys* 31: 19–48.

Reddy AM, Kumar SG, Jyotsnakumari G, Thimmanayak S, Sudhakar C (2005) Lead induced changes in antioxidant metabolism of horsegram (*Macrotyloma uniflorum* (Lam.) Verdc.) and bengal-gram (*Cicer arietinum* L.). *Chemosphe* 60: 97–104.

Reeves RD, Baker AJM (2000) Metal-accumulating plants. In: Raskin I, Ensley BD (eds) *Phytoremediation of toxic metals: Using plants to clean up the environment.* Wiley, New York pp 193–229.

Robinson NJ, Wilson JR, Turner JS, Fordham-Skelton AP, Groom QJ (1997) Metal-gene-interactions in roots: Metallothionein-like genes and iron reductases. In: Anderson HM, Barlow PW, Clarkson DT, Jackson MB, Shewry PR (eds) *Plant Roots-from cells to systems,* Kluwer Academic Publishers, The Netherlands pp 117–130.

Romero-Puertas MC, Rodriquez-Serrano M, Corpas FJ, Gomez M, Del Rio LA, Sandalio LM (2004) Cadmium-induced subcellular accumulation of $O_2^{\cdot-}$ and H_2O_2 in pea leaves. *Plant Cell Env* 27: 1122–1134.

Salt DE, Blaylock M, Kumar NPBA, Dushenkov V, Ensley D, Chet I, Raskin I (1995) Phytoremediation: A novel strategy for the removal of toxic metals from the environment using plants. *Biotechnology* 13: 468–474.

Salt DE, Rauser WE (1995) Mg-ATP dependent transport of phytochelatins across the tonoplast of oat roots. *Plant Physiol* 107: 1293–1301.

Shah K, Nongkynrih JM (2007) Metal hyperaccumulation and bioremediation. *Biolog Plant* 51: 618–634.

Shanker AK, Djanaguiraman M, Pathmanabhan G, Sudhagar R, Avudainayagam S (2003b) Uptake and phytoaccumulation of chromium by selected tree species. In: *Proceedings of the international conference on water and environment held in Bhopal*, India.

Sharma SS, Dietz KJ (2006) The significance of amino acids and amino acid-derived molecules in plant responses and adaptation to heavy metal stress. *J Exp Bot* 57: 711–726.

Sharma P, Dubey RS (2005) Lead toxicity in plants. *Braz J Plant Physiol* 17: 35–52.

Singh PK, Tewari SK (2003) Cadmium toxicity induced changes in plant water relations and oxidative metabolism of *Brassica juncea* L. plants. *J Environ Biol* 24: 107–117.

Somasekharaiah BV, Padmaja K, Prasad ARK (1992) Phytotoxicity of cadmium ions on germinating seedlings of mung bean (*Phaseolus vulgaris*): Involvement of lipid peroxidase in chlorophyll degradation. *Physiol Plant* 85: 85–89.

Stadtman ER, Oliver CN (1991) Metal-catalyzed oxidation of proteins: Physiological consequences. *J Biol Chem* 266: 2005–2008.

Tangahu BV, Abdullah SRS, Basri H, Idris M, Anuar N, Mukhlisin M (2011) A Review on heavy metals (As, Pb, and Hg) uptake by plants through phytoremediation. *Int J Chem Eng* 1: 1–31.

Thomine S, Wang R, Ward JM, Crawford NM, Schroeder JI (2000) Cadmium and iron transport by members of a plant metal transporters family in *Arabidopsis* with homology to Nramp genes. *PNAS USA* 97: 4991–4996.

Turner RG, Marshall C (1971) The accumulation of 65Zn by root homogenates of zinc-tolerant clones of *Agrostis tenuis* Sibth. *New Phytol* 70: 539–545.

Turner RG (1970) The sub-cellular distribution of zinc and copper within roots of metal tolerant clones of *Agrostis tenuis* Sibth. *New Phytol* 69: 725–731.

Van Assche F, Cardinaels C, Clijsters H (1988) Induction of enzyme capacity on plants as a result of heavy metal toxicity, dose response relations in *Phaseolus vulgaris* L. treated with cadmium. *Environ Pollut* 6: 103–115.

Wintz H, Fox T, Vulpe C (2002) Responses of plants to iron, zinc and copper deficiencies. *Biochem Soc Trans* 30: 766–768.

Zeid IM (2001) Responses of *Phaseolus vulgaris* to chromium and cobalt treatments. *Biolog Planta* 44: 111–115.

Zenk MH (1996) Heavy metal detoxification in higher plants - A review. *Gene* 179: 21–30.

Zhang WH, Tyerman SD (1999) Inhibition of water channels by $HgCl_2$ in intact wheat root cells. *Plant Physiol* 120: 849–857.

Zornoza P, Robles S, Martin N (1999) Alleviation of nickel toxicity by ammonium supply to sunflower plants. *Plant Soil* 208: 221–226.

Zou J, Yu K, Zhang Z, Jiang W, Liu D (2009) Antioxidant response system and chlorophyll fluorescence in chromium (VI) treated *Zea mays* L. seedlings. *Acta Biol Cracov Ser Bot* 51: 23–33.

In: Heavy Metal Remediation   ISBN: 978-1-63321-568-9
Editors: Dharmendra Kumar Gupta and Soumya Chatterjee © 2014 Nova Science Publishers, Inc.

Chapter 7

HEAVY METAL UPTAKE AND THE EFFECT ON PLANT GROWTH

Paulo Ademar Avelar Ferreira[1], Gustavo Brunetto[1], Admir José Giachini[2] and Cláudio Roberto Fonsêca Sousa Soares[2]*

[1]Department of Soil Science, Federal University of Santa Maria,
Rio Grande do Sul, Brazil
[2]Center for Biological Sciences, Department of Microbiology, Immunology and
Parasitology, Federal University of Santa Catarina, Florianopolis, SC, Brazil

ABSTRACT

Heavy metal is the term used to classify metals and semimetals (metalloids), generally associated to environmental contamination and toxicity. In the ecosystems, the sources of these elements are both natural and anthropogenic, such as agricultural and industrial activities. In the soil, heavy metals can go through several precipitation /dissolution, adsorption/desorption, and oxidoreduction reactions, which are responsible for the partitioning of the metal in the solid phase or in solution, determining, therefore, its bioavailability to living beings. When these metals are absorbed and translocated and/or accumulated to a plant tissue, they may be involved in physiological changes, associated to plant toxicity. In plants, metabolic injuries caused by excessive heavy metals are dependent on the concentration and the extent of contact. Nevertheless, plants present several mechanisms to avoid absorption or to tolerate excessive metal concentration. In addition, plants that symbiotically associate with soil microorganisms, such as arbuscular mycorrhizal fungi (AMF) and nitrogen fixing bacteria have a clear advantage withstanding the toxic effects of high heavy metal concentrations in the soil. Hence, the aim of the present chapter is to present an overview of the dynamics of heavy metals in soil, the interaction these metals have with plants and soil microorganisms, the main pathways for absorption and transport through the plant, and the mechanisms of

---

* Corresponding author: Dr. Paulo Ademar Avelar Ferreira. Department of Soil Science, Federal University of Santa Maria, CEP 97105-900, Rio Grande do Sul, Brazil. Phone: 0055- 5599733656; Fax: 0055- 5532208256; E. Mail: ferreira.aap@gmail.com.

tolerance displayed by the tripartite combination soil-plant-microorganism to alleviate heavy metal toxicity in contaminated soils.

Keywords: Heavy metals, Environmental pollution, Phytochelatins, Phytoremediation, Heavy metal detoxification/sequestration

1. INTRODUCTION

Most of the metals present in the Earth crust help in nutrition and growth of living organism in particular concentration. However, since the industrial revolution, metal pollution has increased substantially, mainly due to intensifications in mining activities, disposal of industrial discards, use of pesticides and fertilizers, burning of fossil fuels, among others (Alleoni et al. 2005).

Some heavy metals are essential micronutrients, since small amounts are necessary for proper metabolic functioning of certain biological cells. On the other hand, metals like Cd, As, Pb and Hg seem to have no essential biological functions. Aside from the impacts over the functioning and biodiversity of most ecosystems, soils contaminated with heavy metals are also threatening to human health. Different from organic pollutants, heavy metals are not biodegradable. Furthermore, they tend to accumulate in the tissues of living species through the food chain, causing environmental pollution. These compounds may function as inhibitory agents, imperiling the activity of functional groups, modifying the active conformation of biological molecules, which can cause severe or chronic toxicity, as well as contributing to several mutagenic and carcinogenic events (Hassen et al. 1998).

In the soil, heavy metals can go through several precipitation/dissolution, adsorption/ desorption, and oxidoreduction reactions, which are responsible for the partitioning of the metals in the solid phase or in solution, determining, therefore, their bioavailability to living species. Soil pH, organic matter content, concentration of metals and anions, texture, level of amenders and fertilizers, humidity, redox potential, and plant-microorganism symbiotic associations, are factors directly related to the bioavailability of the metals in the soil (Alloway 1993; Alleoni et al. 2005). Specialized transporters, attached to transporting proteins located in the root cell membrane of plants, mediate the absorption of heavy metals from the soil solution. Once translocated and accumulated, heavy metals can cause physiological modifications in the plant, ultimately related to plant toxicity. Nevertheless, plants present several mechanisms to avoid absorption or to tolerate excessive metal concentration. These involve structural, physiological and biochemical changes that depend on the type, concentration and the extent of contact with the metal. The array of factors involved, when considering the physiological aspect, include uptake mechanisms, transport and tissue accumulation, primary mechanisms of molecular, cellular and sub-cellular toxicity, secondary mechanisms of interference with the plant´s functional processes, and homeostatic response mechanisms (Ali et al. 2013). Furthermore, some symbiotic soil microorganisms, such as arbuscular mycorrhizal fungi and nitrogen fixing bacteria, also contribute to plant tolerance and survivability in heavily contaminated soils (Heggo et al. 1990; Diaz et al. 1996; Siqueira et al. 1999; Trannin et al. 2001).

In the present chapter, we present an overview of the dynamics of heavy metals in the soil, the interaction these metals have with plants and soil microorganisms, the main pathways for absorption and transport through the plant, and the mechanisms of tolerance displayed by the tripartite combination soil-plant-microorganism. The knowledge and understanding of these complex mechanisms is essential for the planning and application of bioremediation strategies to alleviate the toxic effects of heavy metals in contaminated ecosystem.

2. SOURCES OF HEAVY METALS IN THE SOIL

Heavy metals is a term frequently used to characterize a group of elements that include metals and semimetals (metalloids) and have been associated to the contamination and potential toxicity or eco-toxicity of different environments (Duffus 2002). Aside from heavy metal, "trace element" is an alternative expression accepted for this group of elements (Pierzynski et al. 2005). Cobalt (Co), cadmium (Cd), cupper (Cu), lead (Pb), mercury (Hg), nickel (Ni) and zinc (Zn), are among the most frequently cited heavy metals in the literature, associated to environmental contamination and hazardous to live organisms, such as plants and soil microorganisms (Nagajyoti et al. 2010).

Natural sources, as well as volcanic, mining and anthropogenic activities (industry and agriculture) are the sources of heavy metals. Natural sources of these elements include rocks that experience physical and chemical modifications during intemperism, caused by the interaction of rock-atmosphere-biosphere. The resulting material, exposed to pedogenetic processes, creates a soil. Therefore, during the formation of soils, the dissolved primary elements of rocks release the once chemically bounded heavy metals (Toledo et al. 2000; Alleoni et al. 2005). However, the type and the concentration of the heavy metal in the soil are very dependent on the constitution of the rock and the environmental conditions involved during pedogenesis. For example, in igneous rocks, the mineral olivine adds significant amounts of Mn, Co, Ni, Cu and Zn to the soil. On the other hand, minerals from sedimentary rocks release Cr, Mn, Co, Ni, Cu, Zn, Cd, Pb and Hg into the soil (Nagajyoti et al. 2010).

Volcanic activities are natural sources of gases and particles that contain Al, Zn, Mn, Pb, Ni, Cu and Hg, contributing with the addition of metals to nearby or distantly located areas. The amounts of metals added are dependent on the travelling trajectories of these gases and particles (Nagajyoti et al. 2010; Pacyna 1986). Particles carried by winds, in deserts such as the Sahara, for example, have high levels of Fe and traces of Mn, Zn, Cr, Ni and Pb (Ross 1994). Emissions of heavy metals to the atmosphere, such as the volatilization of Pb, occur also during forest fires. Furthermore, ocean aerosols can carry Cu and Mn, for example, for several miles on land, causing land depositions by rain (Vermette and Bingham 1986; Nagajyoti et al. 2010).

Current intensifications on the industrial and agrarian activities have increased heavy metal soil pollution. The application of pesticides, industrialized fertilizers, soil conditioners and correctives, manure and sewage derivatives, are examples of practices/products that increase the levels of heavy metals in agricultural soils. In addition, the recurrent use of certain pesticides, such as cupric fungicides to control plant diseases, adds to the levels of certain heavy metals in the soil, as is the case for Cu.

In grapevine fields, the control of mildew (*Plasmopara viticola*; class: Oomycota) may add up to 30 kg of Cu ha^{-1} year^{-1} due to the application of cupric fungicides (Casali et al.

2008). The form of application, one direction towards the plant, leaf run-off during rain and leaf droppings via senescence, are mechanisms that can easily add to the levels of Cu in the soil (Komarek et al. 2010; Miotto et al. 2013; Brunetto et al. 2014). The literature reports an ample variation in the levels of Cu in grape yard soils, mainly resulting from cupric fungicide application. Values range from 20 to 500 mg kg^{-1} in France (Flores-Velez et al. 1996; Brun et al. 1998), 35 to 600 mg kg^{-1} in Spain (Arias et al. 2004; Novoa-Munoz et al. 2007), 50 to 300 mg kg^{-1} in Italy (Viti et al. 2008; Toselli et al. 2009), 100 to 210 mg kg^{-1} in Greece (Vavoulidou et al. 2005), and 40 to 250 mg kg^{-1} in Australia (Pietrzak et al. 2004; Wightwick et al. 2008). These values are generally much higher than those observed for non-anthropogenic forested soils. It is important to mention that the application of other types of fungicides, in other crops and production systems, can increment the levels of other heavy metals in the soil, as is the case for apple orchards receiving constant applications of fungicides rich in Zn (Ramalho et al. 1999; Park and Cho 2011).

The levels of impurity of soil fertilizers, such as phosphate-based ones, allied to the successive and generally high application dosages, can increase the levels of certain heavy metals in the soil, such as Cd, Hg and Pb (Ramalho et al. 1999; Nagajyoti et al. 2010). However, more problematic than industrialized fertilizers is the addition of farmyard manure and animal residues, as source of nutrients for plant growth. A good example is the application of swine farm slurry, which has triggered the accumulation and modification of heavy metal fractions in the soil, such as Cu, Zn and Mn, in typical hog farming regions of Brazil (Girotto et al. 2010; Mattias et al. 2010; Tiecher et al. 2013). The problematic is more severe for animals fed with a diet rich in heavy metals (L'Herroux et al. 1997; Graber et al. 2005). The frequent use of domestic sludge (Chang and Diaz 1994; Amarol Sobrinho et al. 2009), either as a source of nutrients for plant growth (Revoredo and Melo 2006; Andrade et al. 2008; Backes et al. 2009) or to improve soil physical attributes, may also increment the levels of certain heavy metals in the soil. These include Cd, Cr, Pb, Ni and Zn (Krebs et al. 1998; Ippolito and Barbarick 2006; Merlino et al. 2010).

In the industrial sector, mining activities stand out when it comes to heavy metal production and deposition, especially due to the generation of large amounts of residues rich in those pollutants. These activities generally remove the soil vegetation and, therefore, corroborate to extend soil disaggregation and degradation. This in turn promotes hydric and eolic erosion, with consequent lixiviation of contaminants into the ground water. Once in the ground water, the metals can travel reaching and causing contamination in adjacent areas. Coal extraction activities are generally associated with high levels of certain heavy metals, such as Zn, Cu, Pb and Cd, originated from the residues or coal dust (Vangronsveld et al. 1996). Other mining operations, such as those involved with gold extraction, are associated with an increase in the levels of Hg. In the metallurgic field, the high temperature used for iron forging emits particles and gases that are rich in As, Cd, Cu, Pb and Zn, among others. These, in contact with atmosphere water, may produce aerosols, which are dispersed by winds or deposited by rain in adjacent ecosystems (Nagajyoti et al. 2010). Aside from these human related activities responsible for the production and emission of heavy metals, others, such as non-treated residual waters and emission of ashes from coal burning, can increment the levels of heavy metals in the ecosystems (Nagajyoti et al. 2010).

3. DYNAMICS AND AVAILABILITY OF HEAVY METALS IN THE SOIL

Reactions such as precipitation/dissolution, adsorption/desorption and oxidoreduction, determine the partition of a particular heavy metal between the soil solid phase and the soil solution. In solution, heavy metals can be free or adsorbed. During the formation of a chemical complex, one unit, for example an ion acting as a central group, can attract and therefore create a close association with other atoms or molecules. Consequently, a combination between the metal and an inorganic ligand (such as anions) can take place, where oxygen is the electron donor with a preference for hard metals. Another sphere complex maybe formed between the metal and an organic ligand. These complexes are defined as organic matter hard and soft sites (normally carboxylic and phenolic sites), such as those containing S and N in their composition (Alleoni et al. 2005). Even though the metal sorption to the soil solid phase is generally facilitated, the formation of stable chemical compounds in the soil solution can delay the reaction response for the metal adsorption to functional groups from reactive particles. The organic acids in the soil solution, generally labeled dissolved organic carbon, are formed by a diverse group of substances with different dissociation constants, and are responsible for several interactions that can delay or impair the heavy metal sorption in the soil (Harter and Naidu 2001; Sparks 2003; Alleoni et al. 2005).

The concentration of heavy metals in the soil is subjected to constant fluxes and is dependent on the ionic forces, concentration of other ions, pH, humidity, oxidoreduction reactions, metal-rich residues, addition of ligands, plant and microbial uptake, surface run-off, lixiviation, etc. However, the concentration of heavy metals in the soil solution is generally low, mainly because most of the metals are chemically attached to the soil mineral solid fraction, or to the soil organic matter. Ionic adsorption are characterized as complex forming reactions between ions from the soil solution (adsorbate), and particle surface functional groups (adsorbent), creating a bidentate complex in the soil solid-liquid interface (Sposito 1989). Thus, since adsorption is responsible for the concentration and creation of chemical complexes in the soil solution, it also determines the availability of the element to plants and to the environment. Distinct mechanisms are involved in the adsorption of heavy metals, such as ionic exchanges, also known as non-specific adsorption, specific adsorption, and soil organic material sphere complexes (Alloway 1993; Alleoni et al. 2005).

The non-specific adsorption (electrostatic interactions) is generally weak and highly unstable. The electrons are not shared and the hydration water or solvation remains. Inasmuch, the formed complexes, described as outer-sphere complexes are, in theory, reactive. For this reason, this type of adsorption has little effect on the availability of heavy metals in the soil (Alleoni et al. 2005). However, some authors have reported that certain ions, such as Cu and Mn, among others, retain their inner-sphere hydration at a high rotational mobility in the exchangeable sites for smectite, demonstrating that electrostatic forces maybe involved in the adsorption of heavy metals (McBride et al. 1975; Mcbride 1979; Alleoni et al. 2005).

For inorganic particles, during the specific adsorption in functional groups, the heavy metal loses part or all of its hydration water. This produces an inner-sphere complex with the surface of particles, such as Fe, Mn and Al oxides, non-crystalized aluminosilicates, and mineral clay edges that present an OH^- or a molecule of H_2O attached to a metallic ion from the crystalline matrix (Camargo et al. 2001; Bradl 2004). Since for specific adsorption the chemical charge of the molecule is important to attract the metal to the solid phase, soil pH is a central factor. For instance, Fe oxides have an elevated point of zero charge (PZC) and, therefore, at the pH values commonly found for agricultural soils, are positively charged, retarding metal adsorption. On the other hand, Mn oxides have a reduced PZC (1.5 to 4.6) and elevated surface area, strongly adsorbing heavy metal molecules from the soil at low pH values (Alloway 1993). Consequently, Fe, together with Al and Mn oxides seem to be the main soil elements involved in the specific adsorption reactions.

The attachment between a heavy metal and the organic material, derived from the decomposition of plant and animal residues, driven by soil microorganisms, can take place by an ionic exchange between H^+, from functional groups, and the metallic ion. The highly selective affinity between humic substances and certain metals can result in the direct coordination with functional groups, creating an inner-sphere complex (Alleoni et al. 2005). Normally, the organic composites that interact with heavy metals are low molecular weight organic acids, dissolved organic carbon (polyphenols and aliphatic, amino, citric, oxalic and malic acids), aside from fulvic and humic acids. The structure of these acids are not fully understood, but the functional groups are well characterized, especially those with a reactive affinity for heavy metals. These are the carboxyl, phenolic and alcoholic hydroxyls, and the quinone, ketone-, amino- and sulphydric- carbonyl groups (Alloway 1993; Alleoni et al. 2005).

Many heavy metals can co-occur in more than one oxidoreduction state. The oxidoreduction potential is expressed in terms of pe (-log of the electron activity), being dependent on the soil pH, aeration, and microbial activity. Reduction of metals happens in low potential redox environments (low pe or high electron concentration), while oxidation takes place in the opposite conditions (high pe or low electron concentration) (Sposito 1984; Guilherme et al. 2005). Hence, chemical elements such as Cr can be found in the forms of Cr (3) and Cr (6) (Alleoni et al. 2005).

In this context, several approaches have been proposed for the remediation of contaminated soils. These generally include processes that aim at reducing metal concentration and solubility, in order to reduce uptake and attenuate the toxic effects over biological systems (Figure 1) (Bergmann 1992). Mitigating elements to reduce metal contamination are very similar to those used in agricultural practices (e.g., limestone, organic residues, silicates and phosphates). However, the levels applied for soil metal inactivation are much higher than those for soil correction or fertilization. The application of limestone or humic substances is appropriate for the reduction of metal availability to the plants. Soil correction with $CaCO_3$ to pH levels above 6.5, will reduce availability because of metal insolubility under these conditions. The effects associated to each attenuating approach, vary according to the method of choice (pH adjustments, sorption, complexation, etc.), the physical-chemical composition of the soil, and the concentration of the toxic compound. These factors interfere with the metal reactivity in the soil and, therefore, can alleviate metal toxicity to plants and soil organisms. Since metal behavior is hard to determine and it varies according to other soil components, factors involved in metal toxicity must be fully and interactively investigated. In many cases, plant metal toxicity, originated from the competition between essential and non-essential elements, can be alleviated by improvements in the plant´s nutritional balance, for example, by the addition of fertilizers.

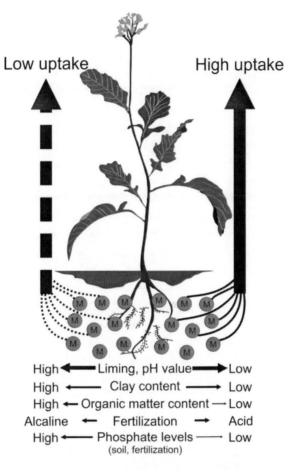

Figure 1. Factors involved in soil heavy metal availability. Arrow size and thickness indicate relative contribution of each factor in the absorption of metals by plants. Interrupted lines indicate limited uptake (from Bergmann 1992). Symbols: M = metal.

While in the soil, heavy metals can go through several precipitation/dissolution, adsorption/desorption, and oxidoreduction reactions, which are responsible for the partitioning of the metal in the solid phase or in solution, determining, therefore, its bioavailability to living beings. When these metals are absorbed and translocated and/or accumulated to a plant tissue, they may be involved in plant physiological changes, associated to toxicity. Metabolic injuries caused by excessive heavy metals are dependent on the concentration and the extent of contact. Nevertheless, plants present several mechanisms to avoid absorption or to tolerate excessive metal concentration, which is the subject of the upcoming topics.

4. PLANT UPTAKE AND TRANSPORT

Root exudates, organic acids, siderophores and different ions present in the soil can affect the availability of heavy metals in the rhizosphere (Figure 2a). Plants absorb these potentially toxic elements from the soil solution, preferentially in an ionic form. Heavy metals in the soil solution are mainly in the form of Zn^{2+}, Cu^{2+}, Cd^{2+}, Pb^{2+}, Ni^{2+}, Co^{2+}, Mn^{2+}, Cr^{3+} and Cr^{6+}, which are the forms preferentially absorbed by plants. An assorted array of molecules control and regulate the uptake and transport of heavy metals from the soil solution. Some molecules are involved in the trans-membrane transport, while others are involved with the metal complexation and subsequent sequestration (Figure 2b). Specialized transporters, coupled to transporting enzymes, present in the plasmatic membrane of the root cells, mediate the absorption of metallic ions from the soil solution (Clemens et al. 2002; Clemens 2006; Greipsson 2011). The transporters perform the active primary transport of ions, such as H^+ or Ca^{2+}, generating an electrochemical gradient against a concentration gradient, with the expenditure of energy-rich compounds, such as ATP. The main types of electrogenic pumps are type P H^+-ATPases, located in the plasmatic membrane (plasmalemma), type V H^+-ATPases, and type H^+-Pyrophosphatases (H^+-PPases), located in the membranes of the vacuoles (tonoplast) (Taiz and Zeiger 2002). Another mechanism participates in the orientation of the heavy metal active absorption, known as the secondary H^+ system. In this system, the membrane, in the direction of an electrochemical gradient, carries solutes by the combination of H^+ and an ion. The energy necessary for this co-transport system is derived from a proton-motive force, through the hydrolysis of ATP, with the aid of H^+-ATPases.

The negative potential inside the plasmatic membrane can exceed -200 mV in the root epidermic cells (Hirsch et al. 1998). This creates a strong motive force for the adsorption of cations via secondary transporters. In plants, transporter proteins for heavy metals fall within four distinct families: CPx-ATPases, Nramps, CDF (cationic diffusion facilitator) and ZIP, which are involved in the absorption of metals and general homeostasis, performing a key role in the tolerance of these elements (Seth 2012). Non-essential heavy metals can compete effectively with essential ones for the same trans-membrane transporters, since they have similar oxidation status and ionic radius (Thangavel and Subbhuraam 2004; Alford et al. 2010). The lack of selectivity in the trans-membrane transport may partially explain the reasons for the entrance of non-essential heavy metals in the cells of the root system, even against a concentration gradient (Seth 2012).

The ZIP transporters are proteins that are preferentially involved in the uptake and accumulation of Fe and Zn (Guerinot 2000). Nonetheless, they can also be involved in Cd and Ni (Nishida et al. 2011) tolerance reactions. The ZIP proteins have eight trans-membrane domains, aside from amino and carboxyl radicals located in the external surface of the plasmatic membrane. ZIP1 and ZIP3 are expressed in the roots in response to Zn deficiency, suggesting they are involved in the transportation of Zn from the soil solution to the plant. ZIP4, on the other hand, is expressed, both in the shoots, as well as in the roots, suggesting that this protein is involved in the intracellular movement of Zn, within the plant cells.

After metallic ions enter the root system, they can be stored in the roots or translocated to the shoots via the xylem (Prasad 2004; Jabeen et al. 2009). Once in the roots, the transport of metals assumes a radial patter, fundamentally apoplastic, encountering an initial diffusion and regulation filter formed by the cell endoderm (Figure 2c). Once in the stele, metals move essentially by the xylem, and due to interactions with surrounding cells, induce modifications in the differentiation of the vascular system (Barceló and Poschenrieder 1992). Adsorption and/or internal distribution can be distinct for different species or varieties of the same plant, even when exposed to similar heavy metal concentrations. This, in turn, potentially results in different capacities to retain the element adsorbed in the roots, or create variations in the capacity of the xylem (Shaw 1989).

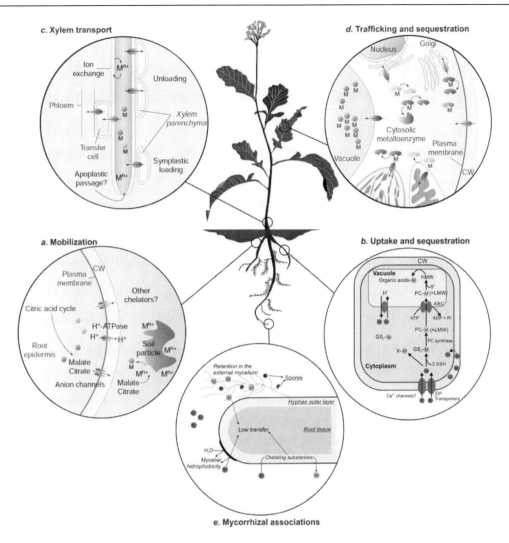

Figure 2. Mechanisms involved in the absorption and accumulation of heavy metals (M) by plants. (a) metal ions are mobilized by secretion of chelators and by acidification of the rhizosphere; (b) metallic ion root absorption and the production of cellular level chelating substances, with the contribution of antioxidant molecules (GSH – glutathione) and substances produced in the cytoplasm (PC – phytochelatins). Sulfur based (GS$_2$-M) chelating substances and other unknown molecules (X-M) participate in the complexation of heavy metals in the cytosol. Phytochelatin-metal complexes (PC-M) are hypothetically transferred to the vacuoles by ABC transporters; (c) from the roots, transitional metals are transported to the shoot via the xylem. Presumably, the larger portion reaches the xylem via the root symplast. Apoplastic passage might occur at the root tip. Inside the xylem, metals are present as hydrated ions or as metal-chelate complexes; (d) trafficking and sequestration of metallic elements in the leaves, mediated by several transporters located in the cellular membranes; (e) mechanisms mediated by mycorrhizal fungi, including adsoprtion, exclusion and bioaccumulation of heavy metals, with consequent plant transferring rate reductions (a, c and d from Clemens et al. 2002 and Clemens 2006, with permission). Abbreviations and symbols: CW = cell wall; HMW = high molecular weight; LMW – low molecular weight; M = metal; filled ovals = transporters.

After the absorption of the metallic ions via the root system symplast, three processes direct the movement of the metals from the roots to the shoots via the xylem: metal sequestration inside the root cells, symplastic transportation in the root stele, and liberation to the xylem. The transport of metallic ions in the xylem follows a pattern strictly controlled and mediated by proteins responsible for membrane transportation. Due to the metallic ions reactivity with -OH, -COO⁻, -SH, and -NH$_2$ functional groups, the carboxylic and amino acids represent potential ligands for the heavy metals. Some carboxylic acids (citric, malic and oxalic acids) are involved in several processes, including the transport through the xylem and vacuolar metal sequestration (Rauser 1999). Histidine is one of the amino acids produced by plants that are more responsive to metals. In *Alyssum lesbiacum*, it is involved in the translocation of Ni. High quantities of Ni chelating histidines increase in about 50 times the xylem transportation of that element (Kramer et al. 1996). Therefore, the chelation of metallic ions by histidine, nicotianamine (Pich et al. 1994) and citrate (Senden et al. 1995) seem to be the main route for the translocation of metals via the xylem. Once in the xylem, the transport of metallic ions depends on the pH homeostasis, formed between low molecular weight organic chelating agents, and the hydrated and free metallic ions. Moreover, the mobility of chelated metals depends on the evapotranspiration fluxes and on the concentration and essentiality of the metal form attached to the cell wall, around the xylem bundle (Senden and Wolterbeek 1990).

5. HEAVY METAL TOXICITY AND TOLERANCE OF PLANTS

Overall, the most visible symptoms of plant toxicity caused by heavy metals are reduction in growth, affecting especially the root system, foliar chlorosis and necrosis, followed by typical senescence and abscission symptoms (Figure 3) (Breckle and Kahle 1992; Punz and Sieghardt 1993). Chlorosis of young leaves is one of the most common heavy metal phytotoxic symptoms. It is frequently associated to low concentrations of Fe, generally caused by inhibition in mobilization, uptake, and/or translocation of this element through the plant (Smith and Specht 1952; Schmidt et al. 1997; Fontes and Cox 1998). Other symptoms associated to heavy metal toxicity are reduction in root hair numbers and premature hair collapsing, as a response to modifications in the plant hormonal balances (Punz and Sieghardt 1993). Another typical symptom is the browning of the roots, caused by an increase in root suberization that limits the absorption of water and, consequently, causes plant water deficits (Punz and Sieghardt 1993; Marchiol et al. 1996). Other factors, such as plant growth stage and development, the extent of contact, and the different chemical variations of the metal are involved in the uptake and metal movement through the different parts of the plant (Alloway 1993). This array of modes displays the plant response capabilities, adopting different defense, resistance, and tolerance strategies, associated to distinct mechanisms that will be opportunely discussed.

Response to stress and toxicity due to metal contamination varies greatly according to the metal. Successive concentrations of essential and non-essential elements result in phytotoxicity, creating dysfunctions such as: occupation and/or competition for metabolic sites; affinity to react with phosphate and ADP/ATP active groups; reaction with sulphydric (-SH) groups, modifying enzymes and polynucleotide active conformations; replacement of essential ions, mainly macronutrients and; alterations in the permeability of cellular membranes. The basis for the functioning of these five toxicity mechanisms, especially the former three, is the ability of metallic ions to covalently link to oxygen, nitrogen and sulfur atoms, which are abundant in biological systems (Alloway 1993; Foyer et al. 1997; Kabat-Pendias 2011).

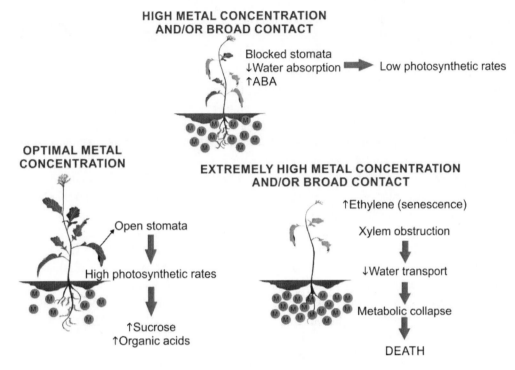

Figure 3. Plant physiologic responses to heavy metal toxicity: Influence of metallic ion concentration and extent of contact (Based on Barceló and Poschenrieder 1992). Abbreviations and symbols: ABA = abscisic acid; M = metal.

The membranes and the nucleus are definitely the primary locations to suffer the effects of heavy metal contamination. Even though, it is important to consider the interactions and structural properties of the plant cell wall. In the plasmalemma, interactions with H^+ translocating ATPases, and changes in the packing of phospholipids, are prominent (Barceló and Poschenrieder 1992). Other physiological modifications include: reduction in the activity of peroxidases (Foyer et al. 1997); reductions in the contents of chlorophyll a and b (Kastori et al. 1998); reduction in the integrity of membranes, causing ion effluxes, especially K^+ (Murphy and Taiz 1997); reduction in the synthesis and or extensibility of the cell wall material, and; effects over the cytosol and cell granules, mainly chloroplasts, mitochondria and the Golgi apparatus. As a result, the cell wall rigidity may increase, probably due to enzymatic modifications in the biosynthesis of the wall constituents, caused by alterations in the formation of the cell wall polymers. Changes in the disposition of microtubules, or increases in cellular adhesion to the middle lamella trigger this modification (Barceló and Poschenrieder 1992).

For plants, in general, the ranges considered critical for heavy metal toxicity, in mg kg^{-1} of dry weight are 5 to 30 for Cd, 100 to 400 for Zn, 20 to 100 for Cu, and 30 to 300 for Pb (Kabat-Pendias 2011). Nonetheless, these ranges can vary greatly according to the plant species and its behavior while in contact with the metal (Marques et al. 2000). Based on that, plant behavior is classified in: excluding (tissue concentration is maintained low and constant, up to the point that critical levels are reached in the soil), indicator (tissue concentration increases proportionally to the increase in metal soil concentration), or accumulator (tissue concentration is higher than soil concentration) (Acciolly and Siqueira 2000). For that reason, plants show distinct abilities to accumulate and tolerate heavy metals in their tissues. Hence, different species, varieties from the same species, and distinct developmental stages present substantial differences in these capabilities (Ali et al. 2013).

The plant responses to heavy metal toxicity involve structural, physiological and biochemical modifications, and are dependent on the metal type, the concentration, and the extent these plants have been exposed to the element (Figure 3). The array of factors involved, when considering the physiological aspect, include uptake mechanisms, transport and tissue accumulation, primary mechanisms of molecular, cellular and sub-cellular toxicity, secondary mechanisms of interference with the plant´s functional processes, and homeostatic response mechanisms. This display of conditions, in some cases, allows the plant to access the mechanisms of tolerance to a specific heavy metal (Barceló and Poschenrieder 1992). Cell protecting mechanisms act avoiding the accumulation of excess free ions in the cytosol, storing these ions in the vacuoles and, therefore, increasing the plant´s tolerance to the metal. The vacuoles are large cellular organelles with low metabolic activity (Denton 2007). The sequestration of heavy metals in the vacuole is one of the strategies to remove excess metallic ions from the cytosol favoring, in turn, cellular metabolism (Assunção et al. 2003; Sheoran et al. 2011). Hyper-accumulating plant species adopt a compartmentalization of complexed metallic ions in the vacuoles, as mechanism for metal tolerance (Tong et al. 2004).

Due to an adaptation capacity and in response to chemical conditions inherent to the soil, some plants species are able to accumulate heavy metals inside and outside their tissues, acting as passive receptors for these elements. Albeit, plants can also utilize a controlling mechanism for the absorption and translocation of toxic compounds, through different and specific physiological reactions. The mechanisms used by plants to express tolerance to excessive amounts of heavy metals include: i) metal selective exclusion; ii) changes in the absorption capacity, by altering the membrane´s permeability; iii) increase in the exudation of chelating agents that reduce metal availability to the plant; iv) restriction in the trafficking of metals, by cytosolic metalloenzymes; v) retention of the metal in the roots and/or transport tissues; vi) cell wall immobilization; vii) associations with mycorrhizae; viii) biochemical mechanisms (modifications in metal compartmentalization, vacuole immobilization, cellular metabolism and intercellular production of ligand compounds, resulting in sequestering constituents and toxic metal inactivators) and; ix) enzymatic metal tolerance (Shaw 1989). Independently of the mechanism, there are tolerant plants endemic to polluted soils, suggesting these may have gone through significant eco-physiological adaptations to inhabit these environments (Tong et al. 2004). Furthermore, multiple tolerance mechanisms, or co-tolerance mechanisms (induced by another chemical element), have been noticed for plants growing on multi-contaminated soils (Shaw 1989).

5.1. Mechanisms to Avoid the Absorption of Heavy Metals

Mechanisms that control the absorption of heavy metals include modifications in the cell´s membrane permeability, changes in the attaching affinity of the element to the cell wall, and increase of exuded substances involved in the formation of chelates. The latter is by far the main mechanism reported in the literature (Seth 2012).

The first barrier against excessive heavy metal absorption, expressed mainly in the root system, includes the immobilization of the metal in the cell wall. This is a task primarily performed by extracellular carbohydrates, including mucilage and callose. This immobilization promotes a reduction in the amounts of free ions in the root tissues, with consequential reduction of transported metals to the shoots (Wagner 1993; Sanita di Toppi and Gabbrielli 1999). In addition to these substances, pectines and histidines are also involved in cell wall immobilization, reducing plant toxicity (Leita et al. 1996). The retention to negatively charged chemical groups in the root cell walls reduces heavy metal contents in the shoots. A good example of this mechanism is seen for plants exposed to excessive concentrations of Pb. In this case, high affinity to cell wall attaching sites reduces the amounts of the element translocated to the shoots (Soares and Siqueira 2008).

Another strategy adopted by plants to avoid excessive uptake of toxic compounds involve mechanisms of exclusion, in which plants prevent the element to enter the cytosol by exuding low molecular weight organic compounds, such as malate, citrate and oxalate (Laheurte et al. 1990; Li et al. 1997). These substances protect the plant´s internal enzymatic activity from the deleterious effects of the metals. Besides these components, carbohydrates, amino acids, peptides and phenolic compounds can also reduce heavy metal uptake, and consequently plant toxicity (Vancura and Hovadik 1965; Rovira 1969). Soil exudation/addition of chelating substances with low availability of heavy metals increase the mobility and absorption of metals by the plants (Lasat 2002; Freitas et al. 2013). However, in contaminated soils, the mobility of dominant metals is the least important factor affecting absorption grades. In these soils, chelating elements exert an essential role reducing the absorption of these toxic compounds (Shaw 1989). The exudation of chelating materials by the plasmatic membrane is an important mechanism to prevent the entrance of extremely toxic compounds, such as Cd (Sanita di Toppi and Gabbrielli 1999). Citric acid has a high affinity for Cd^{2+} when this is present in low concentrations (Wagner 1993), forming complexes with Ni^{2+} in tolerant plants (Sagner et al. 1998) and, therefore, contributing to tolerance and accumulation of Zn^{2+}. Malic acid is another important agent responsible for the chelation of Zn in the cytosol of plants tolerant to this element (Mathys 1977). The study of organic acids present in the rhizosphere of several plant species, and the connection between these compounds and the absorption of heavy metals, is of great interest and may represent an important step towards understanding the mechanisms for heavy metal plant availability (Pires et al. 2007).

5.2. Metal Tolerance through Metabolism

Plants can have distinct mechanisms of tolerance responses to excess heavy metals, including the production of intracellular compounds that form ties with metals, such as the formation of thiolic-rich peptide groups (phytochelatins and metallothioneins), chelation via organic and amino acids, and heavy metal subcellular compartmentalization (Santos et al. 2006).

Chelating substances, produced inside the plant, contribute to metal detoxification through the reduction of free metal concentration in the cytosol, limiting the metal reactivity and solubility (Figure 2d). In plants, the main known classes of heavy metal chelating agents are phytochelatins (PC), metallothioneins, organic acids, and amino acids (Santos et al. 2006). Phytochelatins are believed to act as detoxifying agents for Cd, due to a Cd attaching ability. This complexation prevents the reaction of Cd with free sulfur groups from vital proteins and enzymes (Grant et al. 1998). Phytochelatins are formed by three amino acids: glutamate (Glu), cysteine (Cis), and glycine (Gli). The former two are linked through a γ-carboxyl amide bond (Santos et al. 2006). According to Inouhe (2005), the general structure of phytochelatins (γ-glutamyl-cysteine) contains n-glycine (n − 2-11), aside from variations of these units formed by repetitive copies of γ-glutamyl-cysteinyl, and are produced by plants and yeasts. Phytochelatins have an affinity to attach to several metals, including Cd, Cu, Zn, and As, as a result of sulfhydryl and carboxyl residues. Phytochelatins can form complexes with Cd, resulting in both high and low molecular weight structures (HMW and LMW, respectively). LMW complexes are believed to be formed in the cytosol. Afterwards, when transported to the vacuoles and by incorporating Cd^{2+} and S^{2-} atoms, they produce HMW complexes, resulting in the main storage strategy known for Cd (Santos et al. 2006). Due to the vacuolar acid pH, HMW complexes dissociate and the Cd can be complexed by vacuolar organic acids, such as citrate, oxalate, and malate (Krotz et al. 1989), and potentially also by amino acids. Phytochelatins can be degraded by vacuolar hydrolases and/or return to the cytosol to perform their original function (Figure 2b).

Plant species known to be hyper-accumulators of Cd, Zn and Ni have as common characteristic the capacity for massive transports of these elements to the shoots, and the production of phytochelatins, responsible for the storage of metals in the root system. According to Shaw (1989), phytochelatin heavy metal detoxification may represent an old evolutionary trait, originally established in microalgae and micro fungi. In vascular plants, the vacuolar transport system evolved later, independently of phytochelatins. Transporter compounds potentially related to this process have been identified both in fungi, such as *Saccharomyces cerevisae* and *Schizosaccharomyces pombe*, as well as in plants. In *S. pombe*, Ortiz et al. (1995) identified the gene hmt1, responsible for expressing the protein HMT1, which is capable of efficiently transporting the complex Cd-Phytochelatin to the vacuole. A similar mode of transport has been identified in the tonoplasts of barley root cells, indicating HMT1 as the operating transport mechanism in plant cells (Salt and Rauser 1995).

Plants exposed to high levels of toxic Cd for long periods tend to synthetize compounds rich in thiol groups that could complex and inactivate the metal. However, the activities of these complexes are quickly lost (Ding et al. 1994). Phytochelatin have an important tolerance role in plants, especially towards Cd. The results of several researchers have shown that the concentration of phytochelatins increase in response to the absorption of Cd. This is factual, both to tolerant as well and non-tolerant plants. The main difference lies in the fact that in Cd tolerant plants, the synthesis of phytochelatins seems to be faster and more bountiful (Barceló and Poschenrieder 1992; Salt and Rauser 1995; Jiang et al. 2001).

Another important mechanism associated to plant´s tolerance to heavy metals is the modification in the compartmentalization of metals, considering excessive metallic ions are removed from the cytosol. Some plants engage the vacuoles in the accumulation of heavy metals at the subcellular level (Barceló and Poschenrieder 1992; Santos et al. 2006). Additionally, vacuolar Cd compartmentalization plays an important detoxification role, since this mechanism prevents free circulation of Cd ions in the cytosol (Sanita di Toppi and Gabbrielli 1999).

Working with tobacco, Vögeli-Lange and Wagner (1990) isolated the protoplast mesophyll of plants exposed to Cd, and showed that a complex formed by Cd-PC was transported to the vacuole. These authors considered that the synthesis of PC occurs at the cytosol, with the trafficking of the complex to the vacuole. Once in the vacuoles, peptides and organic acids promote the chelation of Cd. Glutamate has been detected in foliar protoplasts, but not in the vacuoles. Based on this discovery, the authors suggest that the Cd-PC complexes are synthetized outside the vacuoles. Because the complex is generally found inside the vacuoles, this molecule must be involved in the transport of Cd to this tissue. Nonetheless, there are evidences showing that Cd^{+2} can go directly to the vacuoles by ionic trafficking (Rauser 1995). One important pathway for this movement is the $Cd^{+2}:2H^+$ antiport, detected in the tonoplast of barley root cells (Salt and Wagner 1993).

The compartmentalization of metals in the vacuoles is also part of a tolerance mechanism adopted by hyper-accumulating plants (Tong et al. 2004). The plant´s physiological, biochemical and genetic processes regulate the hyper-accumulation of metals (Baker 1987). However, the accumulation of metals in different plant organs does not follow a unique pattern. Generally, the root is the primary port of entrance and accumulation of these elements (Barceló and Poschenrieder 1992).

Several studies have demonstrated that certain plant species/genotypes have the capacity to grow in soils extremely contaminated with heavy metals, exhibiting tissue hyper-tolerant and hyper-accumulating capacities. This is the result of the physiological and biochemical mechanisms discussed previously (Brooks et al. 1977). Baker and Books (1989) define hyper-accumulating plants those capable of accumulating, in the dry biomass, more than 1 g kg^{-1} of Ni, Co or Pb, 10 g kg^{-1} of Zn, and 0.1 g kg^{-1} of Cd. About 400 species fall within this category (Baker et al. 2000; Ma et al. 2001). The identification of heavy metal hyper-accumulating plant species has demonstrated these plants have a genetic background to perform such tasks. The understanding of the mechanisms involved in this detoxification processes is important to unveil proper measures for soil phytoremediation. Furthermore, the identification and biochemical characterization of these mechanisms represent the initial steps towards isolating the plant´s gene(s), responsible for the expression of phytoremediation phenotypes. The identification and isolation of such genes create opportunities for biotechnological applications of genetically modified plants, aiming at environmental metal decontamination (Lasat 2000).

Hyper-accumulating plants are generally small and slow growing. Therefore, biotechnological approaches could transfer genes responsible for expressing metal hyper-accumulating features into non-accumulating, high biomass producing plants (Lasat 2002). According to Gonzaga et al. (2006), molecular techniques are the key to reach this goal. Therefore, the future of research must focus on technologies of molecular genetics, in order to create transgenic plants with high metal resistance and absorption capabilities. Thus, the unveiling of molecular mechanisms of tolerance and accumulation of heavy metals in hyper-accumulating plants, can facilitate the identification of essential and appropriate genes, capable of displaying these traits.

5.3. Mechanisms Involving Plant-Root Associations

Mycorrhizae are usually root associatied fungi. From the initial observations of Frank in the late XIX century, in his seminal work introducing and describing for the first time the term mycorrhyzae, up to the current days, where the knowledge about this association is very solid, several beneficial features have been associated to mycorrhizae (Smith and Read 2008). Mycorrhizae can be divided into a few types, depending on the fungi-plant association and the structures produced (Smith and Read 2008). Among the different types, arbuscular mycorrhizae (AM) are the most common. They are formed in a wide variety of host plants by obligatory symbiotic fungi, classified in the Phylum Glomeromycota (Schubler et al. 2001). Arbuscular mycorrhizal fungi (AMF) have a preponderant effect on soil nutrient uptake, especially phosphorous (P). Although to a lesser extent, AM act in the attenuation of plant biotic and abiotic stresses, such as those caused by excess heavy metal in the soil.

Albeit the evidences on the AM plant protection in soil with excessive heavy metals, results are often controversial, and the mechanisms induced by the fungi are not well known. Reduction of metal absorption, accumulation, and translocation to the plants, or even indirect effects that enhance the plant´s nutritional state, are among the main AM protection mechanisms used against heavy metal contamination (Heggo et al. 1990; Diaz et al. 1996; Siqueira et al. 1999). The outcomes from these mechanisms can oscillate according to the soil contamination levels, and, therefore, be insignificant or even contradictory (Guo et al. 1996; Killham and Firestone 1983). Despite the alleged controversies, there are known mechanisms associated to heavy metal attenuation. These include: i) dilution of trace elements in the plant's tissue, due to enhanced plant growth (Christie et al. 2004); ii) absorption impairment, due to rhizosphere element chelation (Karldorf et al.1999) and; iii) reduction in absorption rates, due to the retention of metals in the fungal structures (Khan et al. 2000; Gonzalez-Chavez et al. 2002). The latter reduces root to shoot metal translocation (Christie et al. 2004). The fact that AM fungi act as protecting agents, increasing the plant´s tolerance to heavy metal contamination, makes this association an extremely significant tool for soil heavy metal remediation, especially if considered that most of the knowing plants form the symbiotic association, even in soils highly contaminated by those elements (Klauberg-Filho et al. 2005; Lins et al. 2006).

Arbuscular mycorrhizal fungi present mechanisms capable of altering heavy metal bioavailability in the mycorrhyzospheric environment, with subsequent effects of the root´s absorption potential, aside from the typical protection mechanism described earlier. In a comprehensive, all-inclusive review on the topic, Meharg (2003) states that, both plants and AMF, can activate the mechanisms of plant tolerance to toxic metals as partners or individually. In general, mycorrhizae display two different protection strategies: absorption regulatory actions, and compartmentalization of toxic metals in specific tissues (Figure 2e).

There are evidences that mycorrhizae can function as physical barriers, interrupting the translocation of heavy metals from the roots to the shoots (Andrade et al. 2003; 2005; Soares and Siqueira 2008). This is the result of a complexation of metals to hydroxyl, carboxyl, amine and sulphydric functional groups attached to the AMF cell wall, reducing metal transferring from the fungi to the associated plants (Galli et al. 1994; Gomes et al. 1998). Surface complexation involving ligand, cysteine-rich proteins produced by the fungi are responsible for metal retention in the root system, and represent an important mechanism of plant resistance to heavy metals (Christie et al. 2004). In addition to complexation, metal retention can also take place in an insoluble glycoprotein called "glomalin", produced in large quantities by the hyphae of certain AMF. These substances are responsible for the sequestration of considerable amounts of heavy metals, reducing plant toxicity (Gonzalez-Chavez et al. 2004). In a relatively recent study involving different isolates, Cabral et al. (2010) observed that *in vitro* mycelia of AMF had high capacity for Cu retention, ranging from 900 to 3, 259 µg Cu g^{-1} of mycelium. For Cd and Pb, however, this capacity was lower than 70 µg g^{-1}. In another work, Andrade et al. (2008) found 728 mg kg^{-1} of Cd in the external hyphae of *Glomus intraradices*, suggesting that these hyphae act as physical barriers to excessive heavy metal absorption. Mycorrhizae increase in more than 1,000% the levels of Cu in the roots of *Brachiaria decumbens*. Nevertheless, this metal stays complexed, and therefore inactive in the root system, with little translocation to the plant´s shoots. The levels of other elements, for instance Zn, Cd, and Pb, are not as highly sequestered as it is Cu (Silva et al. 2006). Based on these effects, it is important to determine the placement and compartmentalization patters of these elements in the roots of the mycorrhizal plants and fungal hyphae, by employing comprehensive analytical techniques.

According to Meharg (2003), AMF can adopt compartmentalization strategies to translocate toxic metals into subcellular compartments, such as the vacuoles, and therefore withdraw these elements from the cytoplasm. Due to transportation or accumulation strategies, compounds that enter the cells can experience modifications to other chemical species, as is known, for example, for the production of metal chelating agents, such as dicarboxylic and amino acids, phytochelatins and metallothioneins, which are metal sequestration, high-affinity molecules (Figure 2e). Evidences suggest that these protecting events may involve a modulation of the induced expression by response proteins, while in the presence of heavy metals (Repetto et al. 2003).

There are indications that increases in the uptake of P by mycorrhizal fungi results in the reduction of heavy metal translocation from the plants roots to the shoots (Christie et al. 2004). Soares and Siqueira (2008) have shown this effect on *Brachiaria decumbens* inoculated with AMF, and grown in Zn, Cd, Cu, and Pb contaminated soils. The addition of P resulted in even higher heavy metal accumulation rates in the roots compared to the non-added P treatment. This unquestionably confirms the positive effects of P on the establishment and growth of mycorrhizal species on heavily contaminated soils. Mycorrhizae may help absorb the toxic metals, attenuating, therefore, the effects of these elements in highly contaminated soils.

Aside from P, nitrogen is another nutrient abundant in the living matter, and directly related to plant development. Nitrogen is generally limited in most soils, including highly contaminated ones, which results in reduction of plant growth. Plant´s nitrogen sources include nitrogen fertilizers, soil organic matter, and that fixed by free living or symbiotic bacteria.

Some symbiotic soil microorganisms, called rhizobia, are capable of enzymatically converting nitrogen from the atmosphere into ammonium, in a process known as the biological nitrogen fixation. The symbiotic biological nitrogen fixation, which generally involves soil bacteria and legume plants, can be highly affected by heavy metal contamination. The metals affect the bacteria infecting capacity, reducing plant nodulation, the activity of nitrogenase (enzyme responsible for the nitrogen fixation), and the production of leghemoglobin (Trannin et al. 2001).

High concentrations of heavy metals affect the process of effective nodule formation in contaminated soils (Smith and Giller 1992). The evaluation of rhizobia survival for long periods have been assessed for over 10 years, in soils treated with urban solid wastes presenting concentrations of Zn ranging from 90 to 250 mg kg^{-1}. These levels resulted in deleterious reductions in the bacteria survivability, reaching extremely low numbers, generally below 100 cells g^{-1} of soil (Chaudri et al. 1993, 2000).

Plants of white clover inoculated with 107 cells g^{-1} of soil of *Rhizobium leguminosarum* bv. *trifolii* had effective nodules in their root system. The same soil inoculated and incubated for two months before white clover sowing, had the formation of only ineffective nodules (Giller et al. 1989). However, high dosages of inoculum (1010 cells g^{-1} of soil) resulted in the formation of effective nodules after a two-month incubation of the same bacterial strain (*Rhizobium leguminosarum* bv. *trifolii*).

Soils from distinct regions of Europe, receiving the application of urban solid wastes for more than 10 years were inoculated with *Rhizobium leguminosarum* bv. *trifolii* (108 cells g^{-1} of soil), and incubated for six months, to determine bacterial survivability rates. The most probable number technique showed that numbers of viable cells in the contaminated and non-contaminated soil vary greatly over the six-month incubation period. While the non-contaminated soil had a decrease of 1 to 2 logarithmic units in the number of viable cells, the treated soil, rich in Zn and Cd, showed a drastic drop in these numbers, ranging from 5.8 to 7.4 logarithmic units (Broos et al. 2005).

While studying the effects of increasing levels of Cd on the development of soybean, Chen et al. (2003a) verified a drastic reduction in the number of nodules and in the activity of nitrogenase. The non-existent biological nitrogen fixation caused reduction in leaf area and yellowing of the plants. The presence of Cd caused a delay in the biosynthesis of chlorophyll, resulting in plant chlorosis (Singh and Tiwari 2003).

Silva et al. (2006) evaluated the effects of different concentrations of Cd (0, 50, 100, 150 μmol L^{-1}) in plants of chickpea inoculated with a *Rhizobium* strain. The authors verified that increases in the concentration of Cd reduced the plants´ dry weight, the number of nodules, the levels of leghemoblobin and chlorophyll, as wells as the activity of nitrate reductase.

Even though metals may have a deleterious effect on the nitrogen fixation symbiosis, some species of tolerant bacteria, associated to legumes, are still promising alternatives for the revegetation of contaminated areas (Vazquez et al. 2006). These metal tolerant bacteria, not only fix substantial amounts of nitrogen, but also stimulate plant growth in these contaminated soils. In that respect, several studies have determined the rhizobia tolerance levels to heavy metals in the soil, with the main objective of employing these high-tolerant microorganisms in soil bioremediation programs (Sriprang et al. 2002, 2003; Wu et al. 2006).

Recently, a bacterium species capable of fixing nitrogen in association with legumes, named *Cupriavidus taiwanensis* (syn. *Ralstonia taiwanensis*), not only had an efficient nodulation with *Mimosa pudica* (Chen et al. 2001, 2003a,b; 2008), but also an elevated capacity to accumulate Pb, Cd, and Cu (Chen et al. 2008). Recent studies reported that species of *Cupriavidus* (e.g, *Cupriavidus necator*) are able to form effective nodules with legumes from the subfamilies Papilionoideae and Mimosoideae (Florentino et al. 2009; Ferreira et al. 2012). Strains of *Cupriavidus necator* associated and formed effective nodules with *Leucaena leucocephala*, *Macroptilium atropurpureum*, *Mimosa caesalpiniaefolia*, *Phaseolus vulgaris*, *Sesbania virgate* and *Vigna unguiculata*, showing high capacity to grow in culture media rich in Zn, Cd, Cu, and Pb (Ferreira et al. 2012). Hence, it is important to develop studies that employ highly tolerant species of rhizobia, in association with plants capable of tolerating high levels of heavy metals, when developing bioremediation strategies for contaminated soils.

CONCLUSION

The absorption of heavy metals and the deleterious effects to plant growth are dependent on several aspects involving the soil-plant system. Therefore, to understand the processes behind these mechanisms, a deep knowledge about soil chemistry, plant nutrition and physiology, and soil microbiology is fundamental. The knowledge about soil chemistry is essential to give light into understanding the chemical transformations these metals are subject to in different soil compartments, determining, for example, if these chemical variants have distinct bioavailability patterns in different contaminated soils. The knowledge about plant nutrition can explain which, and how nutrients may cooperate in antagonistic and synergistic interactions that determine plant heavy metal absorption and translocation. Acquaintances about plant physiology can help to understand the mechanisms of cellular and molecular level toxicity, as well as the mechanisms of tolerance. In this chapter, we discussed about the tolerance mechanisms related to plant capacity to restrict the absorption of excessive metallic ions, and the metabolic mechanisms involved in the sequestration of heavy metals into cellular compartments. The knowledge about the soil microbiology helps understand how soil microorganisms participate in the transformations of metallic ions in the rhizosphere. Furthermore, the chapter also addresses the beneficial effects of some symbiotic soil microorganisms, such as AMF and nitrogen fixing bacteria, which contribute to plant tolerance and survivability in heavily contaminated soils. Consequently, the several mechanisms of tolerance displayed by plants, as a response to excessive heavy metals content, are directly related to an intrinsic, physiological and biochemical response of the plant species, the metal chemical form, how easily it translocates through the plant, the extent and level of the nutritional stress, and the interactions between plants and microorganisms.

Studies on the biosynthesis, expression and regulation of genes involved in heavy metal tolerance in hyper-accumulating plants, and the roles of the main mechanisms of tolerance have been significatively prompted in the last few years. The identification of biochemical and physiological pathways is essential, but even more essential is the connection of this knowledge with the plant´s genetic responses, in order to achieve a better understanding of the full scenario involving the complex metal-plant-soil, with the objective of formulating approaches for heavy metal bioremediation.

ACKNOWLEDGMENTS

The authors gratefully thank Lucia Helena Teles for figure drawings.

REFERENCES

Alleoni LRF, Borba RP, Camargo OA (2005) Metais pesados: Da cosmogênese aos solos brasileiros. In: Torrado-Vidal P, Alleoni LRF, Cooper M, Silva AP (eds) *Tópicos em Ciência do Solo*. Viçosa MG: Sociedade Brasileira de Ciência do Solo 4: 1–42.

Arias M, López E, Fernández D, Soto B (2004) Copper distribution and dynamics in acid vineyard soils treated with copper-based fungicides. *Soil Sci* 169: 796–805.

Amaral Sobrinho NMB, Lã OR, Barra CM (2009) Química dos metais pesados no solo. In: Alleoni LRF, Melo VF (eds) *Química e Mineralogia do Solo*. Viçosa MG: Sociedade Brasileira de Ciência do Solo 2: 249–312.

Andrade SAL, Silveira APD, Jorge RA, Abreu MF (2008) Cadmium accumulation in sunflower plants influenced by arbuscular mycorrhiza. *Int J Phytorem* 10: 1–13.

Alloway BJ (1993) *Heavy metals in soils*. Blackie Academic & Professional. Glasgow.

Alford ER, Pilon-Smits EAH, Paschke MW (2010) Metallophytes - A view from the rhizosphere. *Plant Soil* 337: 33–50.

Acciolly AMA, Siqueira JO (2000) Contaminação química e biorremediação do solo. In: Novais RF, Alvarez-V VH, Shcaefer CEGR (eds) *Tópicos em Ciência do Solo. Viçosa MG: Sociedade Brasileira de Ciência do Solo* 1: 299–352.

Ali H, Khan E, Sajad MA (2013) Phytoremediation of heavy metals - Concepts and applications. *Chemosphere* 91: 869–881.

Assunção AGL, Schat H, Aarts MGM (2003) *Thlaspi caerulescens*, an attractive model species to study heavy metal hyperaccumulation in plants. *New Phytol* 159: 351–360.

Andrade SAL, Abreu CA, De Abreu MF, Silveira APD (2003) Interação de chumbo, da saturação por bases do solo e de micorriza arbuscular no crescimento e nutrição mineral da soja. *Revista Brasileira de Ciência do Solo* 27: 945–954.

Andrade SAL, Jorge RA, Silveira APD (2005) Cadmium effect on the association of jackbean (*Canavalia ensiformis*) and arbuscular mycorrhizal fungi. *Sci Agri* 62: 389–394.

Andrade AFM, Amaral Sobrinho NMB, Magalhães MOL, Nascimento VS, Mazur N (2008) Zinco, chumbo e cádmio em plantas de arroz (*Oryza Sativa* L.) cultivadas em solo após adição de resíduo siderúrgico. *Ciência Rur* 38: 1877–1885.

Backes C, Lima CP, Fernandes DM, Godoy LJG, Kiihl TAM, Villas Bôas RL (2009) Efeito do lodo de esgoto e nitrogênio na nutrição e desenvolvimento inicial da mamoneira. *Biosci J* 25: 90–98.

Barceló J, Poschenrieder C (1992) Respuestas de las plantas a la contaminación por metales pesados. *Suelo Planta* 2: 345–361.

Baker AJM (1987) Metal tolerance. *New Phytol* 106: 93–111.

Baker AMJ, Books RR (1989) Terrestrial higher plants with hyperaccumulate metallic elements- A review of their distribution, ecology and phytochemistry. *Biorecovery* 1: 81–126.

Baker AJM, McGrath SP, Reeves RD, Smith JAC (2000) Metal hyperaccumulator plants: A review of the ecology and physiology of a biochemical resource for phytoremediation of metal polluted soils. In: Terry N, Bañuelos G (eds) *Phytoremediation of contaminated soil and water*. Lewis Publishers, Boca Raton pp 85–107.

Bergmann W (1992) *Nutritional disorders of plants – Development, visual and analytical diagnosis*. New York.

Bradl H (2004) Adsorption of heavy metal ions on soils and soils constituents. *J Coll Inter Sci* 277: 1–18.

Breckle SW, Kahle H (1992) Effects of toxic heavy metals (Cd, Pb) on growth and mineral nutrition of beech (*Fagus sylvatica* L.). *Vegetatio* 101: 43–53.

Brooks RR, Lee J, Reeves RD, Jafreé T (1977) Detection of nickeliferous rocks by analysis of herbarium specimens of indicator plants. *J Geochem Explor* 7: 49–57.

Broos K, Beyens H, Smolders E (2005) Survival of rhizobia in soil is sensitive to elevated zinc in the absence of the host plant. *Soil Biol Biochem* 37: 573–579.

Brun LA, Maillet J, Richarte J, Herrmann P, Remy JC (1998) Relationships between extractable copper, soil properties sand copper uptake by wild plants in vineyard soils. *Environ Pollut* 10: 151–161.

Brunetto G, Miotto A, Ceretta CA, Schmitt DE, Heinzen J, Moraes MP, Canton L, Tiecher TL, Comin JJ, Girotto E (2014) Mobility of copper and zinc fractions in fungicide-amended vineyard sandy soils. *Arch Agron Soil Sci* 60: 609–624.

Cabral L, Siqueira JO, Soares CRFS, Pinto JEBP (2010) Retenção de metais pesados em micélio de fungos micorrízicos arbusculares. *Química Nova* 33: 25–29.

Camargo OA, Alleoni LFF, Casagrande JC (2001) Reações dos micronutrientes e elementos tóxicos no solo. In: Ferreira ME, Cruz MCP, van Raij B, Abreu CA (eds) *Micronutrientes e elementos tóxicos na agricultura Jaboticabal, SP*: CNPq/FAPESP/POTAFOS pp 89–124.

Casali CA, Mortele DF, Rheinheimer DS, Brunetto G, Corsini ALM, Kaminski J (2008) Formas e dessorção de cobre em solos cultivados com videira na Serra Gaúcha do Rio Grande do Sul. *Revista Brasileira de Ciência do Solo* 32: 1479–1487.

Chang AC, Diaz JL (1994) Foreword symposium ID20: Rational use of sewage sludge and other waste material in agriculture. In: *World Congress of Soil Science Proceedings* pp 427–429.

Chaudri AM, McGrath SP, Giller KE, Rietz E, Sauerbeck DR (1993) Enumeration of indigenous *Rhizobium leguminosarum* biovar *trifolii* in soils previously treated with meal-contaminated sewage sludge. *Soil Biol Biochem* 25: 301–309.

Chaudri AM, Allain CMG, Barbosa-Jefferson VL, Nicholson FA, Chambers BJ, McGrath SP (2000) Study of the impacts of Zn and Cu on two rhizobial species in soils of a long-term field experiment. *Plant Soil* 22: 167–179.

Chen WM, Laevens S, Lee TM, Coenye T, De Vos P, Mergeay M, Vandamme P (2001) *Ralstonia taiwanensis* sp. nov., isolated from root nodules of Mimosa species and sputum of a cystic fibrosis patient. *Int J Sys Evolut Microbiol* 51: 1729–1735.

Chen WM, Moulin L, Bontemps C, Vandamme P, Béna G, Boivin-Masson C (2003a) Legume symbiotic nitrogen fixation by beta-proteo bacteria is widespread in nature. *J Bacteriol* 185: 7266–7272.

Chen WM, James EK, Prescott AR, Kierans M, Sprent JI (2003b) Nodulation of *Mimosa* spp. by the beta-proteobacterium *Ralstonia taiwanensis*. *Mol Plant Microb Inter* 16: 1051–1061.

Chen WM, Wu CH, James EK, Chang JS (2008) Metal biosorption capability of *Cupriavidus taiwanensis* and its effects on heavy metal removal by nodulated *Mimosa pudica*. *J Hazard Mater* 151: 364–371.

Christie P, Xiaolin L, Baodong C (2004) Arbuscular mycorrhiza can depress translocation of zinc to shoots of host plants in soil moderately polluted with zinc. *Plant Soil* 261: 209–217.

Clemens S, Palmgren MG, Krämer U (2002) A long way ahead: Understanding and engineering plant metal accumulation. *Trends Plant Sci* 7: 309–315.

Clemens S (2006) Toxic metal accumulation, responses to exposure and mechanisms of tolerance in plants. *Biochimie* 88: 1707–1719.

Denton B (2007) Advances in phytoremediation of heavy metals using plant growth promoting bacteria and fungi. *Basic Biotechnol* 3: 1–5.

Díaz G, Azcón-Aguilar C, Honrubia M (1996) Influence of arbuscular mycorrhizae on heavy metal (Zn and Pb) uptake and growth of *Lygeum spartum* and *Anthyllis cytisoides*. *Plant Soil* 180: 241–249.

Ding X, Jiang J, Wang Y, Wang W, Ru B (1994) Bioconcentration of cadmium in water hyacinth (*Eichhornia crassipes*) in relation to thiol group content. *Environ Pollut* 84: 93–96.

Duffus JH (2002) Heavy metal - a meaningless term? *Pure App Chem* 74: 793–807.

Ferreira PAA, Bomfeti CA, Júnior RS, Soares BL, Soares CRFS, Moreira FMS (2012) Symbiotic efficiency of *Cupriavidus necator* strains tolerant to zinc, cadmium, copper and lead. *Pesq Agropecu Brasil* 47: 85–95.

Florentino LA, Guimarães AP, Rufini M, Silva K, Moreira FMS (2009) *Sesbania virgata* stimulates the occurrence of its microsymbiont in soils but does not inhibit microsymbionts of other species. *Sci Agri* 66: 667–676.

Flores-Vélez J, Ducaroir A M, Jaunet MR (1996) Study of the distribution of Cu in an acid sandy vineyard soil by three different methods. *Europ J Soil Sci* 47: 523–532.

Fontes RLF, Cox R (1998) Iron deficiency and zinc toxicity in soybean grown in nutrient solution with different levels of sulfur. *J Plant Nut* 21: 1715–1722.

Foyer CH, Lopez-Delgado H, Dat JF, Scott IM (1997) Hydrogen peroxide- and glutathione-associated mechanisms of acclamatory stress tolerance and signalling. *Physiol Planta* 100: 241–254.

Freitas EV, Nascimento CW, Souza A, Silva FB (2013) Citric acid-assisted phytoextraction of lead: A field experiment. *Chemosphere* 92: 213–217.

Giller KE, McGrath SP, Hirsch PH (1989) Absence of nitrogenfixation in clover grown on soil subject to long-term contamination with heavy metal is due to survival of only ineffective *Rhizobium*. *Soil Biol Biochem* 21: 841–848.

Galli U, Schüepp H, Brunold C (1994) Heavy metal binding by mycorrhizal fungi. *Physiol Planta* 92: 364–368.

Girotto E, Ceretta CA, Brunetto G, Santos DR, Silva LS, Lourenzi CR, Lorensini F, Renan Vieira CB, Schmatz R (2010) Acúmulo e formas de cobre e zinco no solo após aplicações sucessivas de dejeto líquido de suínos. *Revista Brasileira de Ciência do Solo* 34: 955–965.

Gomes NCM, Mendonça-Hagler LCS, Savvaidis I (1998) Metal bioremediation by microorganisms. *Braz J Microbiol* 29: 85–92.

Gonzaga MIS, Santos JAG, Ma LQ (2006) Arsenic phytoextraction and hyperaccumulation by fern species. *Sci Agri* 63: 90–101.

González-Chávez C, D'Haen J, Vangronsveld J, Dodd JC (2002) Copper sorption and accumulation by the extra radical mycelium of different *Glomus* spp. (arbuscular mycorrhizal fungi) isolated from the same polluted soil. *Plant Soil* 240: 287–297.

González-Chávez MC, Carrillo-González R, Wrigth SF, Nichols KA (2004) The role of glomalin, a protein produced by arbuscular mycorrhizal fungi, in sequestering potentially toxic elements. *Environ Pollut* 130: 317–323.

Graber I, Hansen JF, Olesen SE, Petersen J, Østergaard HS, Krogh L (2005) Accumulation of copper and zinc in Danish agricultural soils in intensive pig production areas. *Dan J Geograp* 105: 15–22.

Grant CA, Buckley WT, Bailey LD, Selles F (1998) Cadmium accumulation in crops. *Can J Plant Sci* 78: 1–17.

Greipsson S (2011) *Phytoremediation.* Nat Educ Know 3: 7.

Guerinot ML (2000) The ZIP, family of metaltransporters. *Biochim Biophy Acta* 1465: 190–198.

Guilherme LRG, Marques JJ, Pierangeli MAP, Zuliani DQ, Campos ML, Marchi G (2005) Elementos-traço em solos e sistemas aquáticos. In: Torrado-Vidal P, Alleoni LRF, Cooper M, Silva AP (eds) Tópicos em Ciência do Solo. Viçosa MG: *Sociedade Brasileira de Ciência do Solo* 4: 345–390.

Guo Y, George E, Marschner H (1996) Contribution of an arbuscular mycorrhizal fungus to the uptake of cadmium and nickel in bean and maize plants. *Plant Soil* 184: 195–205.

Hassen A, Saidi N, Cherif M, Boudabous A (1998) Resistance of environmental bacteria to heavy metals. *Biores Technol* 64: 7–15.

Harter RD, Naidu R (2001) An assessment of environmental and solution parameter impact on trace-metal sorption by soils. *Soil Sci Soc Amer* J 65: 597–612.

Heggo A, Angle JS, Chaney RL (1990) Effects of vesicular-arbuscular mycorrhizal fungi on heavy metal uptake by soybeans. *Soil Biol Biochem* 22: 865–869.

Hirsch RE, Lewis BD, Spalding EP, Sussman MR (1998) A role for the AKT1 potassium channel in plant nutrition. *Science* 280: 918–921.

Inouhe M (2005) Phytochelatins. Braz J Plant Physiol 17: 65–78.

Ippolito JA, Barbarick KA (2006) Biosolids affect soil barium in a dry land went agro ecosystem. *J Environ Qual* 35: 2333–2341.

Jabeen R, Ahmad A, Iqbal M (2009) Phytoremediation of heavy metals: Physiological and molecular mechanisms. *Bot Rev* 75: 339–364.

Jiang W, Liu D, Hou W (2001). Hyperaccumulation of cadmium by roots, bulbs and shoots of garlic (*Allium sativum* L.) *Biores Technol* 76: 9–13.

Kabata-Pendias A (2011) *Trace Elements in Soils and Plants.* Taylor and Francis, Boca Raton, FL.

Karldorf M, Kuhn AJ, Schroder WH, Hildebrandt U, Bothe H (1999) Selective element deposits in maize colonized by a heavy metal tolerance conferring arbuscular mycorrhizal fungus. *J Plant Physiol* 154: 718–728.

Kastori R, Plesnicar M, Sazac Z, Pancovic D, Arsenijevic-Maksimovic I (1998) Effect of excess lead on sunflower growth and photosynthesis. *J Plant Nut* 21: 75–85.

Khan AG, Kuek C, Chaudhry TM, Khoo CS, Hayes WJ (2000) Role of plants, mycorrhizae and phytochelators in heavy metal contaminated land remediation. *Chemosphere* 41: 197–207.

Killham K, Firestone MK (1983) Vesicular arbuscular mycorrhizal mediation of grass response to acidic and heavy metal depositions. *Plant Soil* 72: 39–48.

Klauberg-Filho O, Siqueira JO, Moreira FMS, Soares CRFS, Silva S (2005) Ecologia, função e potencial de aplicação de fungos micorrízicos arbusculares em condições de excesso de metais pesados. In: Vidal-Torrado P, Alleoni LRF, Cooper M, Silva AP, CARDOSO EJBN (eds) *Tópicos em Ciência do Solo.* Viçosa MG: Sociedade Brasileira de Ciência do Solo 4: 85–144.

Komárek M, Cadkova E, Chrastny V, Bordas F, Bollinger JC (2010) Contamination of vineyard soils with fungicides: A review of environmental and toxicological aspects. *Environ Int* 36: 138–151.

Krämer U, Cotter-Howells JD, Charnock JM, Baker AJM, Smith AC (1996) Free histidine as a metal chelator in plants that accumulate nickel. *Nature* 379: 635–638.

Krebs R, Gupta SK, Furrer G, Schulin R (1998) Solubility and plant uptake of metals with and without liming of sludge-amended soils. *J Environ Qual* 27: 18–23.

Krotz RM, Evangelou BP, Wagner GJ (1989) Relationships between cadmium, zinc, Cd-binding peptide, and organic acid in tobacco suspension cells. *Plant Physiol* 91: 780–787.

Laheurte F, Leyval C, Berthelin J (1990) Root exudates of maize, pine and beech seedlings influenced by mycorrhizal and bacterial inoculation. *Symbiosis* 9: 111–116.

Lasat MM (2000) Phytoextracion of metals from contaminated soil: A review of plant/soil/metal interaction and assessment of pertinent agrononomic issues. *J Hazard Sub Res* 2: 1–25.

Lasat MM (2002) Phytoextraction of toxic metals: A review of biological mechanisms. *J Environ Qual* 31: 109–120.

Leita L, De Nobili M, Cesco S, Mondini C (1996) Analysis of intercellular cadmium forms in roots and leaves of bush bean. *J Plant Nut* 19: 527–533.

L'Herroux L, Le Roux S, Appriou P, Martinez J (1997) Behavior of metals following intensive pig slurry applications to a natural field treatment process in Brittany (France). *Environ Pollut* 97: 119–130.

Li MG, Shinano T, Tadano T (1997) Distribution of exudates of lupin roots in the rhizosphere under phosphorus deficient conditions. *Soil Sci Plant Nut* 43: 237–245.

Lins CEL, Cavalcante UMT, Sampaio EVSB, Messias AS, Maia LC (2006) Growth of mycorrhized seedlings of *Leucaena leucocephala* (Lam.) de Wit. in a copper contaminated soil. *App Soil Ecol* 31: 181–185.

Ma LQ, Komar KM, Tu C, Zhang WH, Cai Y, Kennelley ED (2001) A fern that hyperaccumulates arsenic – A hardy, versatile, fast-growing plant helps to remove arsenic from contaminated soils. *Nature* 409: 579–579.

Marchiol L, Leita L, Martin M, Peressotti A, Zerbi G (1996) Physiological responses of two soybean cultivars to cadmium. *J Environ Qual* 25: 562–566.

Marques TCLLSM, Moreira FMS, Siqueira JO (2000) Crescimento e absorção de metais em mudas de espécies arbóreas em solo contaminado com metais pesados. *Pes Agro Brasil* 35: 121–132.

Mathys W (1977) The role of malate, oxalate, and mustard oil glucosides in the evolution of zinc-resistance in herbage plants. *Physiol Planta* 40: 130–136.

Mattias JL, Ceretta CA, Nesi CN, Girotto E, Trentin EE, Lorenzi CR, Vieira RCB (2010) Copper, zinc and manganese in soils of two watersheds in Santa Catarina with intensive use of pig slurry. *Revista Brasileira de Ciência do Solo* 34: 1445–1454.

Meharg AA (2003) The mechanistic basis of interactions between mycorrhizal associations and toxic metal cations. *Mycol Res* 107: 1253–1265.

McBride MB, Pinnavaia TJ, Mortland MM (1975) Electron spin relaxation and the mobility of manganese (II) exchange ions in smectites. *Amer Mineral* 60: 66–72.

McBride MB (1979) Mobility and reactions of VO^{2+} on hydrated smectite surfaces. *Clays Clay Miner* 27: 91–96.

Merlino LCS, Melo WJ, Macedo FG, Guedes ACTP, Ribeiro MH, Melo VP, Melo GMP (2010) Bário, cádmio, cromo e chumbo em plantas de milho e em Latossolo após onze aplicações anuais de lodo de esgoto. *Revista Brasileira de Ciência do Solo* 34: 2031–2039.

Miotto A, Ceretta CA, Brunetto G, Nicoloso F, Girotto E, Farias J, Tiecher T, De Conti L, Trentin G (2013) Copper uptake, accumulation and physiological changes in adult grapevines in response to excess copper in soil. *Plant Soil* 374: 593–610.

Murphy A, Taiz L (1997) Correlation between potassium efflux and copper sensitivity in 10 *Arabidopsis ecotypes*. *New Phytol* 136: 211–222.

Nagajyoti PC, Lee KD, Sreekanth TVM (2010) Heavy metals, occurrence and toxicity for plants: A review. *Environ Chem Lett* 8: 199–216.

Neilsen D, Hoyt PB, Mackenzie AF (1986) Distribution of soil Zn fractions in Bristish Columbia interior orchard soils. *Can J Soil Sci* 662: 445–454.

Nishida S, Tsuzuki C, Kato A, Aisu A, Yoshida J, Mizuno T (2011) AtIRT1, the primary iron uptake transporter in the root, mediates excess nickel accumulation in *Arabidopsis thaliana*. *Plant Cell Physiol* 52: 1433–1442.

Nóvoa-Munõz JC, Queijeiro JMG, Blanco-Ward D, Álvarez-Olleros C, Martínez-Cortizas A, Garciarodeja E (2007) Total copper content and its distribution in acid vineyards soils developed from granitic rocks. *Sci Total Environ* 378: 23–27.

Ortiz DF, Ruscitti T, McCue K, Ow DW (1995) Transport of metal-binding peptides by HMT1, a fission yeast ABC-Type vacuolar membrane protein. *J Biol Chem* 270: 4721–4728.

Pacyna JM (1986) Atmospheric trace elements from natural and anthropogenic sources. In: Nriagu JO, Davidson CI (eds) *Toxic Metals in the Atmosphere*. Wiley, New York.

Park BJ, Cho JH (2011) Assessment of copper and zinc in soils and fruit with the age of an apple orchard. *J Kor Soc App Biol Chem* 54: 910–914.

Pich A, Scholz G, Stephan UW (1994) Iron-dependent changes of heavy metals, nicotianamine, and citrate in different plant organs and in the xylem exudate of two tomato genotypes: Nicotianamine as possible copper translocator. *Plant Soil* 165: 189–196.

Pierzynski GM, Sims JT, Vance GF (2005) *Soils and Environmental Quality*. Taylor and Francis, Boca Raton, FL.

Pietrzak U, McPhail DC (2004) Copper accumulation, distribution and fractionation in vineyard soils of Victoria, Australia. *Geoderma* 122: 151–166.

Pires AMM, Marchi G, Mattiazzo ME, Guilherme LRG (2007) Organic acids in the rhizosphere and phytoavailability of sewage sludge-borne trace elements. *Pes Agro Brasil* 42: 917–924.

Prasad MNV (2004) Phytoremediation of metals in the environment for sustainable development. *Pro Ind Acad Sci Sec* B 70: 71–98.

Punz WF, Sieghardt H (1993) The response of roots of herbaceous plant species to heavy metals. *Environ Exp Bot* 44: 85–98.

Ramalho JFGP, Amaral Sobrinho NMB, Velloso ACX (1999) Acúmulo de metais pesados em solos cultivados com cana de açúcar pelo uso contínuo de adubação fosfatada e água de irrigação. *Revista Brasileira de Ciência do Solo* 2: 971–979.

Rauser WE (1995) Phytochelatins and related peptides: Structure, biosynthesis, and function. *Plant Physiol* 109: 1141–1149.

Rauser WE (1999) Structure and function of metal chelators produced by plants. *Cell Biochem Biophy* 31: 19–48.

Repetto O, Bestel-Corre G, Dumas-Gaudot E, Berta G, Gianinazzi-Pearson V, Gianinazzi S (2003) Targeted proteomics to identify cadmium-induced protein modifications in *Glomus mosseae* -inoculated pea roots. *New Phytol* 157: 555–567.

Revoredo MD, Melo WJ (2006) Disponibilidade de níquel em solo tratado com lodo de esgoto e cultivado com sorgo. *Bragantia* 65: 679–685.

Ross SM (1994) Toxic metals in soil-plant systems. Wiley, Chichester.

Rovira AD (1969) Plant root exudates. *Bot Rev* 35: 35–57.

Sagner S, Kneer R, Wanner G, Cosson JP, Deus-Neumann B, Zenk MH (1998) Hyperaccumulation, complexation and distribution of nickel in *Sebertia acuminata*. *Phytochemistry* 47: 339–347.

Salt DE, Wagner GJ (1993) Cadmium transport across tonoplast of vesicles from oat roots. *J Biol Chem* 268: 12297-12302.

Salt DE, Rauser WE (1995) MgATP-dependent transport of phytochelatins across the tonoplast of oat roots. *Plant Physiol* 107: 1293–1301.

Sanità di Toppi L, Gabbrielli R (1999) Response to cadmium in higher plants. *Environ Exp Bot* 41: 105–130.

Santos FS, Amaral Sobrinho NMB, Mazur N (2006) Mecanismos de tolerância de plantas a metais pesados. In: Fernandes MS (eds) *Nutrição Mineral de Plantas.* Viçosa MG: Sociedade Brasileira de Ciência do Solo 1: 419–432.

Schmidt W, Bartels M, Tittel J, Fuhner C (1997) Physiological effects of copper on iron acquisition processes in Plantago. *New Phytol* 135: 659–666.

Schübler A, Schwarzott D, Walker C (2001) A new fungal phylum, the Glomeromycota: Phylogeny and evolution. *Mycol Res* 102: 1413–1421.

Seth CS (2012) A review on mechanisms of plant tolerance and role of transgenic plants in environmental clean-up. *Bot Rev* 78: 32–62.

Senden MHM, Wolterbeek HAT (1990) Effect of citric acid on the transport of cadmium through xylem vessels of excised tomato stem-leaf systems. *Acta Bot Nederlan* 39: 297–303.

Senden MHM, van der Meer AJGM, Verburg TG, Wolterbeek HAT (1995) Citric acid in tomato plant roots and its effect on cadmium uptake and distribution. *Plant Soil* 171: 333–339.

Shaw AJ (1989) *Heavy Metal Tolerance inPlants: Evolutionary Aspects.* CRC Press, New York.

Sheoran V, Sheoran A, Poonia P (2011) Role of hyperaccumulators in phytoextraction of metals from contaminated mining sites: A review. *Crit Rev Environ Sci Technol* 41: 168–214.

Silva S, Siqueira JO, Soares CRFS (2006) Fungos micorrízicos no crescimento e na extração de metais pesados pela braquiária em solo contaminado. *Pes Agro Brasil* 12: 1749–1757.

Siqueira JO, Pouyú-Rojas E, Moreira FMS (1999) Micorrizas arbusculares no crescimento pós-transplantio de mudas de árvores em solo com excesso de metais pesados. *Revista Brasileira de Ciência do Solo* 23: 569–580.

Singh PK, Tewari RK (2003) Cadmium toxicity induced changes in plant water relations and oxidative metabolism of *Brassica juncea* L. plants. *J Environ Biol* 24: 107–112.

Smith PF, Specht AW (1952) Heavy-metal nutrition and iron chlorosis of citrus seedlings. *Plant Physiol* 1: 371–382.

Smith SE, Read DJ (2008) *Mycorrhizal Symbiosis.* Academic Press, NY.

Smith SR, Giller KE (1992) Effective *Rhizobium leguminosarum* bv. *trifolii* present five soil contaminated with heavy metal from long-term applications of sewage sludge or metal mine spoil. *Soil Biol Biochem* 24: 781–788.

Soares CRFS, Siqueira JO (2008) Mycorrhiza and phosphate protection of tropical grass species against heavy metal toxicity in multi-contaminated soil. *Biol Fert Soils* 44: 833–841.

Sparks DL (2003) *Environmental Soil Chemistry.* Academic Press, San Diego, CA.

Sposito G (1984) *The Surface Chemistry of Soils.* Oxford University Press, New York.

Sposito G (1989) *The Chemistry of Soils.* Oxford University Press, New York.

Sriprang R, Hayashi M, Yamashita M, Ono H, Saeki K, Murooka Y (2002) Novel bioremediation system for heavy metals using the symbiosis between leguminous plant and genetically engineered rhizobia. *J Biotechnol* 99: 279–293.

Sriprang R, Hayashi M, Ono H, Takagi M, Hirata K, Murooka Y (2003) Enhanced accumulation of Cd^{2+} by a *Mesorhizobium sp.* transformed with a gene from *Arabidopsis thaliana* coding for phytochelatin synthase. *App Environ Microbiol* 69: 1791–1796.

Taiz L, Zeiger E (2002) *Plant Physiology.* Sinauer Associates, Sunderland, MA.

Thangavel P, Subbhuraam C (2004) Phytoextraction: role of hyperaccumulators in metal contaminated soils. *Pro Ind Acad Sci Section* B 70: 109–130.

Tiecher T, Brunetto G, Ceretta CA, Comin JJ, Girotto E, Miotto A, Moraes MP, Benedett L, Ferreira PA, Lourenzi CR, Couto R (2013) Forms and accumulation of copper and zinc in a sandy typical hapludalf soil after long-term application of pig slurry and deep litter. *Revista Brasileira de Ciência do* Solo 37: 812–824.

Toledo MCM, Oliveira SMB, Melfi AJ (2000) *Intemperismo e formação do solo.* In: Teixeira W, Toledo MCM, Fairchild TR, Taioli F (eds) Decifrando a terra São Paulo, SP: *Oficinas de* Textos 1: 139–166.

Tong YP, Kneer R, Zhu YG (2004) Vacuolar compartmentalization: a second generation approach to engineering plants for phytoremediation. *Trends Plant Sci* 9: 7–9.

Toselli M, Schiatti P, Ara D, Bertacchini A, Quartieri M (2009) The accumulation of copper in soils of the Italian region Emilia-Romagna. *Plant Soil Environ* 55: 74–79.

Trannin ICB, Moreira FMS, Siqueira JO, Lima A (2001) Tolerância de estirpes e isolados de *Bradyrhizobium* e *Azorhizobium* a zinco, cádmio e cobre in vitro. *Revista Brasileira de Ciência do Solo* 25: 305–316.

Vancura V, Hovadik A (1965) Root exudates of plants. II. Composition of root exudates of some vegetables. *Plant Soil* 22: 21–32.

Vangronsveld J, Colpaert JV, Van Tichelen KK (1996) Reclamation of a bare industrial area contaminated by non-ferrous metals: Physico-chemical and biological evaluation of the durability of soil treatment and revegetation. *Environ Pollut 94*: 131–140.

Vavoulidou E, Avramides EJ, Papadopoulos P, Dimirkou A, Charoulis A, Konstantinidou-Doltsinis S (2005) Copper content in agricultural soils related to cropping systems in different regions of Greece. *Comm Soil Sci Plant Anal* 36: 759–773.

Vázquez S, Agha R, Granado A, Sarro MJ, Esteban E, Peñalosa JM, Carpena RO (2006) Use of white lupin plant for phytostabilization of Cd and As polluted acid soil. *Water Air Soil Pollut* 177: 349–365.

Vermette SJ, Bingham VG (1986) Trace elements in Frobisher Bay rain water. *Arctic* 39: 177–179.

Viti DC, Quaranta R, Dephilippis G, Corti A, Agnelli R, Cuniglio L, Giovannetti L (2008) Characterizing cultivable soil microbial communities from copper fungicide amended olive orchard and vineyard soils. *World J Microbiol Biotechnol* 24: 309–318.

Vögeli-Lange R, Wagner GJ (1990) Subcellular localization of cadmium and cadmium-binding peptides in tobacco leaves. *Plant Physiol* 92: 1086–1093.

Wagner GJ (1993) Accumulation of cadmium in crop plants and its consequences to human health. *Adv Agron* 51: 173–212.

Wightwick AM, Mollah MR, Partington DL, Allinson G (2008) Copper fungicide residues in Australian vineyard soils. *J Agricult Food Chem* 56: 2457–2464.

Wu CH, Wood TK, Mulchandani A, Chen W (2006) Engineering plant-microbe symbiosis for rhizoremediation of heavy metals. *App Veg Sci 72*: 1129–1134.

In: Heavy Metal Remediation   ISBN: 978-1-63321-568-9
Editors: Dharmendra Kumar Gupta and Soumya Chatterjee © 2014 Nova Science Publishers, Inc.

Chapter 8

IN VITRO SELECTION OF PLANTS FOR THE REMOVAL OF TOXIC METALS FROM CONTAMINATED SOIL: ROLE OF GENETIC VARIATION IN PHYTOREMEDIATION

Sonika Sharma[1], Soumya Chatterjee[1,], Sibnarayan Datta[1], Anindita Mitra[2], Mohan G. Vairale[1], Vijay Veer[1], Ankita Chourasia[3] and Dharmendra K. Gupta[4]*

[1]Defence Research Laboratory, DRDO, Tezpur-784001, Assam, India
[2]Department of Zoology, Bankura Christian College, Bankura, West Bengal, India
[3]Department of Medicine, Institute of Medical Sciences,
Banaras Hindu University, Varanasi, India
[4]Gottfried Wilhelm Leibniz Universität Hannover,
Institut für Radioökologie und Strahlenschutz (IRS), Hannover, Germany

ABSTRACT

Phytoremediation is a promising, cost effective, green substitute to traditional soil remediation technologies, which can treat different environmental pollutants including heavy metals. However, selection of an ideal plant for cleaning the environment being polluted with specific pollutant(s) is a major task leading to potential possibilities of implementation. High biomass production, tolerance to high metal contamination, accumulation, and/or degradation is the keys to choose the technology. Genetic manipulation helps to manipulate the capacity of a plant to tolerate, accumulate, and/or metabolize pollutant(s), for crafting the ideal plant for pollution amelioration and subsequent clean-up of the environment. It is necessary to know the intricate molecular pathways related to the development of mechanisms for metal tolerance or accumulation in plants. In this chapter, an overview of plant metal tolerance and accumulation

---

* Corresponding Author: Dr. Soumya Chatterjee, Defence Research Laboratory, DRDO, Tezpur 784001, Assam, India, Phone:0091-3712 258 836, Fax:0091-3712 258 534, Email: drlsoumya@gmail.com.

mechanisms, possible strategies for genetic engineering of plants for metal phytoremediation has been envisaged.

Keywords: Phytoremediation, Metal transporters, Overexpression, Genetic engineering, Metal chelators

1. INTRODUCTION

Exponential increase in the release of varied organic and inorganic hazardous pollutants by anthropogenic activities like industrial discharges, mining, sewage effluents, agriculture and urban run-offs has become a serious issue of concern. According to the nature and fate of these pollutants, they may either contaminate the environment and/or its components like air, soil and water (both surface and groundwater). Among these pollutants, metals play an important role in controlling quality of the environment, as varied metal compounds released from different sources are often more available to biological systems (Gupta et al. 2013). Further, contrasting to the degradation process of many other contaminant types, natural degradation of metals is an extremely slow process. While, organic pollutants like polychlorinated biphenyl (PCBs), dioxin, and polycyclic aromatic hydrocarbons (PAH), trichloroethylene can be degraded into less harmful forms within comparatively shorter time frame. Prolong residence of metals in the environment leads to increase in their accumulation at different trophic levels (Leahy and Colwell 1990; Rogers et al. 2002).

Constituting a diverse group of elements, metals vary widely in their chemical characteristics, biological functions and toxicity (Chatterjee et al. 2007). All metals are toxic to organisms depending upon their requirement within the system. Metals impart their toxicity to organisms through oxidative stress by generation of high amount of free radicals and disruption of function of essential cellular enzymes (especially in case of metalloenzymes) (Prasad and Freitas 2003). According to the list of metals published by Toxic Substances and Disease Registry,Centers for Disease Control and Prevention, USA (http://www.atsdr.cdc.gov) on potential toxicity (2007 CERCLA Priority List of Hazardous Substances), arsenic (ranked first), lead (ranked second), mercury (ranked third) and cadmium (ranked seventh) are among the top 10 toxic substances (CERCLA 2007). Further, metals like cadmium (Cd), arsenic (As), lead (Pb), and mercury (Hg) do not have any known biological functions (Chetia et al. 2011).

Plants do have unique potentiality to deal a diverse and fluctuating ambience of different conditions like climate, temperature, moisture, soil conditions etc. (Norman 1962). Along with water, nutrients and minerals essential for their growth, plants take up a diversity of non-essential compounds and heavy metals from soil and ground water through their roots and survive by developing diverse detoxification mechanisms within their system (Singer 2006). Plant root rhizosphere is an important site for the process, where, microorganisms present in the region have the ability to get rid of several contaminants from the surroundings by a range of enzymatic processes. Environment specific diversity of microorganisms along with plants acts as the excellent system to remediate diverse group of environmental contaminants (Lovley 2003). These attributes of plants help them to signify fundamentally as a "natural, solar powered pump and treat system" (Pilon-Smits 2005) for cleaning of contaminated sites leading to the concept of phytoremediation, a natural, aesthetically pleasing and low cost technology.

2. HEAVY METALS AND THEIR TOXICITY

Elements with metallic properties like ductility, conductivity, stability (as cations), ligand specificity, etc. with an atomic number >20 and having specific weight > 5g cm^{-3} constitute heavy metals having an exceptionally diverse assembly of metals with varied chemical characteristics and biological functions. Heavy metals are major environmental pollutants imparting toxic effects to living organisms due to bioaccumulation or biotransformation (Prasad and Freitas 2003). Heavy metals enter into the environment either naturally or due to anthropogenic activities like metal mining operations, dumping of untreated industrial wastes (Hutton and Symon 1986; Nriagu 1989). Contamination and subsequent accumulation of metals occur either in soil/sediments or in water which may seep into the underground water resources. Extensive heavy metal pollution due to industrial activities has been reported from different regions of the planet. Many countries like Indonesia, China (with Cd, Zn and Cu), Japan, Australia (Ni, Cu, Zn, Pb and Cd), Greece (Pb and Cu) are contaminated with heavy metals (Zantopoulos et al. 1999; Herawati et al. 2000). In EU, an estimated 52 million hectares (approximately 16% of the total land area) are affected by some level of degradation of soil quality (Peuke and Rennenberg 2005). Likewise in India, several locations in the states like Gujarat, Maharashtra and Andhra Pradesh are heavily contaminated with metals due to industrial activities causing a major environmental problem (INSA, A Position Paper 2011; Chatterjee et al. 2013).

Toxicity through metal contamination may be manifested through several symptoms or diseases in living beings (Nath et al. 2005). Reports suggest that metals like lead (Pb), arsenic (As), cadmium (Cd) and mercury (Hg) may not have any important biological functions (Duruibe 2007; Chetia et al. 2011) as they are known to be toxic to plants, animals and microorganisms. Pb affects child's nervous system by slowing down nerve responses, affecting learning abilities and behaviour. While Hg forms very toxic methylmercury compounds, that are likely to be accumulated within different organisms and affecting nervous system when released into the environment (Ke et al. 2001). Cd toxicity results in kidney dysfunction and increased proteinuria (excretion of proteins in urine). As is a potent poison that disrupts ATP production which leads to death from necrotic cell death and multi-system organ failure (http://en.wikipedia.org/wiki/Arsenic_toxicity). Although, Cr is essential in form of Cr(III) to humans and animals, but Cr(VI) compounds are generally considered to be toxic, and assumed to cause cancer (Shanker et al. 2005).

Elements like sodium (Na), potassium (K), calcium (Ca), magnesium (Mg), Iron (Fe), Copper (Cu), Zinc (Zn), Cobalt (Co), and Nickel (Ni) are essential micronutrients, and are required by most of the living organisms in varying quantities. Plants need these elements for varied physiological and biochemical processes, such as electron transfer mechanisms, redox reactions, structural functions, nucleic acid metabolism, functioning of proteins and enzymes etc. (Reeves and Baker 2000; Nagajyoti et al. 2010). However, being sessile in nature, plants may get exposure to a wide range of metal concentrations which can adversely affect their essential biochemical and physiological functions.

3. TOWARD RESTORATION
OF HEAVY METAL CONTAMINATED AREAS

Metals in environment typically are linked with different fractions like free metal ions or soluble complexes, adsorbed inorganic soil constituents, organic complexes, silicate minerals or precipitated as carbonates, oxides, and hydroxides (Lasat 2000). Anthropogenic activities like industrial, agricultural and mining activities increase the concentration of the metal(s), in turn, affecting the food chain (Kalay and Canli 2000). It is reported that, approximately, 9,300 km of streams and rivers, and 72,000 ha of lakes and wetlands have been contaminated with metals due to the mining activities worldwide (Schaller et al. 2011), where more than 180 million tonnes of perilous mine wastes are discarded by the mining companies every year (Earthworks and mining watch 2012; USEPA 2009a). This poses serious threats of heavy metal and different chemical contaminations of the environment. Conventional methods for reducing metal concentration in soils and water include isolation or creation of physical barrier (i.e. concrete, steel), chemical solidification or stabilization, processes like hydrocyclone, fluidized bed, flotation, electrokinetic processes, pump-and-treat systems or soil washing. However, these technology based methods for metal amelioration are not viable options for most of the developing countries as these technologies are extremely expensive (around 400 to 750 billion USD in the United States alone), non-eco-friendly, energy intensive and can reduce fertility and bioactivity of soils (Mulligan 2001). Additionally, incineration and land-filling is also not recommended for all the conditions as these may facilitate air/soil/groundwater pollution and translocation of contaminants among different sites. These limitations of technology based remediation are conceivably motivating factors in advancement of alternative remediation technologies (Korda et al. 1997; Brim et al. 2000).

Cleaning up of varied types of environmental contaminants including heavy metals may be practised using the natural biodegradation/ bioremediation processes. Organisms like bacteria and fungi or plants have the capability to degrade or detoxify hazardous environmental pollutants into less toxic forms. Biodegradation is a multifaceted process involving coordinated actions of a group of organisms where specific contaminants like metal(s) may be targeted for bioremediation (Cozzarelli et al. 2010; Chatterjee et al. 2013). A number of microorganisms along with plants (phytoremediation), as a result of their versatility, adaptability and diversity, are supposed to be the best option in remediating inorganic contaminants like heavy metals through natural biogeochemical cycle (Lovley 2003).

4. OVERVIEW OF THE PROCESS PHYTOREMEDIATION

Phytoremediation (Ancient Greek: phyto-"plant", and Latin remedium-"restoring balance") 'describes the treatment of environmental problems through the use of plants that mitigate environmental problem without the need to excavate the contaminant material and dispose of it elsewhere' (http://en.wikipedia.org/wiki/Phytoremediation). It is natural solar-powered, environment-friendly, low-cost, aesthetically pleasing technology that can treat different environmental pollutants including heavy metals. It also helps in maintaining ecosystem by preserving quality landscape and enhances diversity of soil microorganisms.

Basic mechanisms of phytoremediation technology involve phytoextraction, phytostabilisation, rhizofiltration, and phytovolatilization. The uptake/absorption and translocation of heavy metals by roots into the above ground parts (like shoots, leaves) of the plants is termed as phytoextraction. Harvested shoot part of the plant may be incinerated for energy and the ash may be recycled for metals. However, it is reported that, metal uptake and phytoextraction coefficients decrease in the order $Cr^{6+}> Cd^{2+}> Ni^{2+}> Zn^{2+}> Cu^{2+}> Pb^{2+}> Cr^{3+}$ (USEPA 2000). Phytostabilisation process involves, immobilization of contaminants using certain plant species either by adsorption of contaminants onto roots or precipitation within the root zone for avoiding their exodus in soil or movement by erosion. Rhizofiltration is the technology where, adsorption or precipitation onto plant roots or absorption and sequestration of contaminants take place in the roots. Transpiration of contaminant after its uptake by a plant is known as Phytovolatilization, that occurs along with the natural growth processes as it takes up water along with the pollutant (i.e. for Hg, Se, As) (Meagher 2000; Lasat 2000; Ghosh and Singh 2005; Tangahu et al. 2011; Chatterjee et al. 2013). It has been reported that some plants have the capacity to accumulate heavy metals at higher concentration within their body without disturbing their metabolic processes. This category of plants are termed as 'hyperaccumulator' as these plants can accumulate pollutants in a proportion which differs according to the pollutant concerned (for example: more than 1000 mgkg^{-1} of dry weight for Cr, Ni, Co, Cu, Pb; or more than 10,000 mgkg^{-1} for Zn, Mn). These plants have developed adaptive evolution towards hypertolerance or phytotolerance to metals leading to several relations towards, defence, mutualism (mycorrhizae, pollen and seed dispersal), interferences with neighbouring plant species, commensalism, and biofilm formation (Michel et al. 2007; Burken et al. 2011). Interestingly, hyperaccumulator plant species have the ability to transfer metals from root to shoot efficiently and show shoot-to-root metal concentration ratio of >1 and thus, more metal concentration is found especially in the aerial parts (McGrath et al. 2002). Major steps involved in hyperaccumulation include bioactivation of metals in the rhizospheric zone with help of root–microbe interaction, activity of metal transporters for enhanced uptake by plasma membranes, detoxification of metals by distributing to the apoplasts through chelation with various ligands, such as phytochelatins, metallothioneins, metal-binding proteins and sequestration of metals into the vacuole. Further, versatile enzymatic machineries like cytochrome P450 monoxygenases, glutathione *S*-transferases, glycosyltransferases and transporters that are contributing in decontamination process may further be explored for augmenting the potentiality of the hyperaccumulators (Tangahu et al. 2011).

5. RHIZOSPERE, RHIZOBACTERIA AND METAL TRANSPORTERS IN PHYTOREMEDIATION

Heavy metal absorption in higher plants is a critical issue. Rhizosphere (region of soil at the root-soil interface, which is subjected to root secretions and related soil microorganisms) region play an important role in this process. Plant roots primarily secrete exudates in its adjacent soil matrix that helps in the chelation of metals for controlling the transportation inside the cell. Plants root exudates support the growth and metabolic activities of diverse fungal and bacterial communities in the rhizosphere capable of degrading varied pollutants

(Anderson et al. 1994). In the rhizosphere, plants normally increase the abundance of soil microflora by 1-4 orders of magnitude compared to the surrounding bulk soil. This microflora show better range of metabolic capabilities than the microbes present in the surrounding loose soil (Salt et al. 1998). However, heavy metals are mostly co-transported in the form of cation across the plasma membrane (Manara 2012). Immobilization of toxic heavy metal ions is managed by the pectic sites, a number of extra cellular carbohydrate molecules present on the cell wall and molecules like histidine (His) and citrate (Manara 2012). Variety of root exudates are secreted by plants at rhizosphere level that includes diffusates (eg. amino or organic acids, water, inorganic ions, sugars etc.), excretions (eg. bicarbonates, protons, carbon dioxide etc.), secretions (eg. mucilage, siderophores, allelopathic compounds etc.) which form stable heavy metal-ligand complexes in the vicinity of the root to control the metal ion uptake (Hall 2002). For example, Ni uptake from the soil is prevented by the secretion of histidine (His) and citrate (Salt et al. 2000).

Plant-microorganisms interactions at the rhizosphere level play an important role in phytoremediation. Microbial community in the rhizosphere can catalyze redox reactions in soil that alter mobility of metals and tendency of plants in uptake process (Lasat 2002). In totality, plants and microbes in the rhizosphere is having a unique gene pool that capable them to deal with variety of heavy metals for detoxification (Danika and Norman 2005). These genes could be of interest for transferring to fast-growing plant species for enhanced phytoremediation. Similarly, large number of plant enzymes may also be explored that can efficiently detoxify organic chemicals (De Souza et al. 1998). Heavy metal toxicity restricts plant to grow, thereby limiting biomass where, plant growth-promoting rhizobacteria (PGPR) helps a lot to counter the stress of plant. PGPR group of bacteria usually gets attached to the plant root and perform rhizospheric colonization by inciting the production of plant growth regulators like indoleacetic acid, gibberellic acid, cytokinins and ethylene contributing to plant health and better response. Some rhizobateria secretion, such as antibiotics, phosphate solubilising substances, hydrocyanic acid, siderophores, 1-aminocyclopropane-1-carboxylic acid (ACC) increase bioavailability and facilitate root absorption of metals like Fe, Mn, Cd, P etc. (Salt et al. 1995; Meyer 2000; Davies et al. 2001). Augmentation up to 50%~100% in the plant size of Indian mustard (*Brassica juncea*) seeds that germinated in a nickel-contaminated soil, was reported after the addition of *Kluyvera ascorbata* SUD165/26, an associated plant growth- promoting rhizobacteria, to the soil in field trials (Burd et al. 1998). High efficiency of phytoremediation seems to be provided by the rhizobacteria in association with plants (Abou-Shanab et al. 2003; Whiting et al. 2001).

Metal transporter-proteins present on the plasma membrane of root cells play an important role in heavy metal homeostasis. Among various families of transporters, NRAMP (natural resistance-associated macrophage protein), ZIP families (ZRT, IRT-like Protein; [ZRT-Zincregulated transporter, IRT-ironregulated transporter]), CDF (cation diffusion facilitator) family, heavy metal ATPases (HMAs) family like P1B-ATPases are most well-known transporters (Guerinot 2000). The ZIP family transporters are well characterized for divalent metal uptake. Their histidine-rich domain is believed to engage in specific metal binding that gets activated in response to Fe or Zn loading. AtZIP4 (*Arabidopsis thaliana* ZIP4) proteins expressed in roots and shoots are involved in Zn transport and also help in Cd uptake from soil into the root cells and Cd transport from root to shoot (Krämer et al. 2007). IRT1 in *Arabidopsis thaliana*, is an important transporter for Fe in root cells; also transport other metals like Mn^{2+}, Zn^{2+}, and Cd^{2+} (Korshunova et al. 1999; Vert et al. 2002; Nishida et al. 2008). Plant cell walls act as a cation exchanger, sharing or excluding varied amount of metals, to maintain the homeostasis in cell (Rauser 1999). Again, HMAs family transporters (P1B-type ATPases) are essentially internal transporters to load Cd and Zn metals into the xylem from the surrounding tissues and act as an efflux pump (Krämer et al. 2007). In *Arabidopsis thaliana*, AtHMA3 transporter present in the tonoplast membrane helps in sequestration of a wider range of heavy metals and its over-expression increases the tolerance to heavy metals like Cd, Pb, Co, and Zn (Manara 2012; Gupta et al. 2013). As cytosol and cellular compartments are important sites where sensitive metabolic activities take place, Strategies for sequestration of the metals into vacuoles are activated as heavy metal enters the plant cell (Dalcorso et al. 2010; Hossain et al. 2012). Major vacuole in a plant cell is the suitable storage reservoir for heavy metal accumulation. Proton pumps in vacuole, especially, vacuolar proton-ATPase (V-ATPase) and vacuolar proton-pyrophosphatase (V-PPase) help in vacuolar uptake of most of the solutes. Again, heavy metal transporter proteins like ZRT, IRT, CDF family of proteins, P-type metal ATPases, NRAMP, copper transporter (COPT) family proteins, ATP-binding cassette (ABC) transporters, ABC transporters of the mitochondria (ATM), multidrug resistance-associated proteins (MRP), yellow-stripe-like (YSL) transporter, Ca^{2+}cation antiporter (CAX), pleiotropic drug resistance (PDR) transporters, etc. help in this sequestration process (Lee et al. 2005; Chiang et al. 2006; Krämer et al. 2007; Dubey 2011; Huang et al. 2012; Gupta et al. 2013).

6. COMMON METAL-BINDING LIGANDS AND THEIR ROLE

Metal-binding ligands play an important role in plants by maintaining concentrations of essential biometals at optimum levels and reducing the toxicity thresholds of nonessential metals. Hyperaccumulators have the ability to concentrate metal(s) greater than that of 1% of dry mass through a concerted effort of selective ligand(s). Common ligands include organic acids, amino acids, peptides and proteins, intracellular ion carriers (chaperones) for the specific delivery of the metal to a particular destination. As for example, Cu chaperones control intracellular Cu concentration to avoid any damage by 'free' ionic Cu by production of free radicals (Callahan et al. 2006). A number of different metal-binding ligands have now been recognized which help plants survive in hostile environments (Callahan et al. 2006). For example, organic acids like citrate and malate helps in extracellular chelation for aluminium (Al) and are reported to be correlated with tolerance of Al in plants (Delhaize and Ryan 1995), which are also evident in Al-resistant mutants of *Arabidopsis* (Larsen et al. 1998). Histidine (His), a nitrogen-donor ligand, has a number of known coordination modes that made the amino acid one of the most important ligands in metal hyperaccumulation. Reports suggest that, in hyperaccumulators, exposure to metals like Ni elicits a large and proportional increase in the level of free His that help to chelate metal ions within the cells (Callahan et al. 2006). Along with the amino acid ligands, peptide ligands are also common in plants. Phytochelatins (PCs) and metallothioneins (MTs) are well characterized peptide ligands. Thiol group is present in these cysteine-rich polypeptides that help to bind different kind of metals helping in cellular metal homeostasis and detoxification. However, detoxification mechanism through synthesis of PCs to lessen toxic effects of non-essential heavy metals such as As, or Cd is a highly complicated enzyme-catalyzed process, identified in plants, algae, fungi and in some invertebrates (Rea 2012; Gupta et al. 2013). Importance of PC peptides in toxic ion sequestration of borderline class of metals in plants, yeast and microorganisms is enormous. Heavy metal tolerance and its association with PCs were also observed using chemicals for inhibitor GSH biosynthesis like Buthionine sulfoximine (BSO) and augmented PC synthesis has been found in both non-tolerant, and non-accumulator, as well as in hypertolerant and hyperaccumulator plants (Grill et al. 2006; Gupta et al. 2002, 2008, 2010).

Another metal chelating ligand phytate found in cereals and grains have been accounted for the principal form of reserve phosphorous in plants (Hocking and Pate 1977). Phytate or hexaphosphoric acid of myo-inositol have six orthophosphate moieties that provide twelve co-ordinate ligands which allow the chelation of multiple cations, including Ca^{2+}, Mg^{2+}, and K^+ and also Fe^{2+}, Zn^{2+}, and Mn^{2+} (Mikus et al. 1992). The distribution of phytate within plant tissues and its chelating ability suggest that it might have a role in detoxification of heavy metals (Manara 2012). Zn inactivation within the vacuole of root cell in the form of Zn-phytate (van Steveninck et al. 1993) supports this view.

7. GENETIC MANIPULATION AND PHYTOREMEDIATION

The choice of plant for phytoremediation purpose is the most essential step, where ideal plant species that produces a high biomass, sufficiently hardy and viable in specific geo-climatic areas are selected.

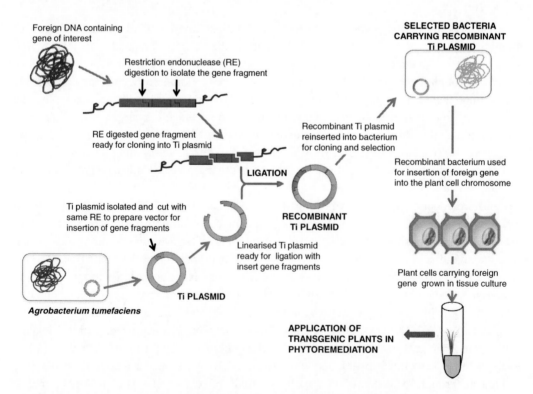

Figure 1. Typical genetic engineering approaches in phytoremediation practices.

Some examples of suitable species are Indian mustard (*Brassica juncea*), cordgrass (*Spartina* spp.), poplar (*Populus* spp.) and yellow poplar (*Liriodendron tulipifera*) (Pilon-Smits and Pilon 2002). The promising advances of phytoremediation is the production of transgenic plants targeted for secreting the enzymes or factors involved in the detoxification and/ or hyperaccumulation processes in plants (Spaczynski et al. 2012).Usually, quantity of bioremediation is directly proportional to the total biomass of a plant. Further efficient accumulation of metals without succumbing to stress along with maintaining the growth or biomass production of a plant is sometimes critical. Again, many wastelands are co-contaminated or subsequent contamination with more than one metal is common, which hinders the typical application of phytoremediation, thus making the process very slow. Usually hyperaccumulators are metal specific, genotypes with more strong metal accumulating capacity may be chosen for the accumulation of heavy metals. Steps of phytoremediation process includes, root uptake, root-shoot translocation, sequestration in specific tissues or cell compartments like vacuoles, biotransformation of the metal, plant-microbe interactions etc. (Pilon-Smits and Pilon 2002), where several genes are involved. It is very important to know the genes involved in the process for each of the above mentioned factors and identify the rate-limiting gene product(s).

Genetic engineering approaches have effectively modified primary and secondary metabolisms facilitating an alteration of biological functions (figure 1). Thus, novel phenotypic and genotypic characters through over expression of biosynthetic genes to manage the favored sub-cellular localization are being introduced in the plants, intended the improvement of remediation processes in varied conditions (Davison 2005). Tissue culture is another option to select genes having enhanced properties of biodegradation or bioaccumulation of heavy metals. In this process, new varieties of plant may be selected by analyzing them with desired characters through by studying molecular variance of the RAPD (random amplified polymorphic DNA) markers (Fulekar et al. 2009). A number of classical studies suggest that adaptive metal tolerance that help a plant species to hyper-accumulate a certain metal ion is governed by a limited number of major genes along with few minor modifier genes (McNair et al. 2000; Schat et al. 2002; Fulekar et al. 2009). The presence of major tolerance genes for Cu (in *Mimulus guttatus*) and Zn (in hyperaccumulator *Arabidopsis halleri* and the non-accumulator *Arabidopsis petrea*) is evident in different studies that led to advancements in our understanding of phytoremediation capabilities. Several factors like identification of transporter genes for transfer and/or over expression of particular gene candidate proteins, metal chelators are important to augment the transgenic plants for better performance (McNair et al. 2000).

Rapid advancements in recombinant DNA technology and computational informatics have enormously helped the scientists to choose the traits to be introduced into plant cell. The gene of interest for the trait may be obtained from any living sources or designed synthetically to encode a specific enzyme which can be inserted into plant cells after splicing with a vector molecule. The vector is introduced either by physical (using electroporation or via high-velocity micro-projectiles) or biological processes (e.g. using bacteria like *Agrobacterium* that can insert and help to incorporate DNA into plant cells), where upon integration, desired gene is "expressed" in the subset of cells and subsequently selected in tissue culture for its desired function. Reports suggest many successful attempts have been made with transgenic plants. Mammalian Cytochrome P450 gene inserted into the plants such as *Nicotiana tabacum*, *Solanum tuberosum*, *Oryza sativa*, *Arabidopsis thaliana* exhibit increased tolerance to herbicides like atrazine and simazine and show a marked increase in the capability of metabolism of various xenobiotics (Doty et al. 2000; Eapen et al. 2007). Transgenic Indian mustard (*Brassica juncea*) expressing glutathione transferase (GSTs), a phase II cellular detoxification gene, shows increased tolerance to atrazine, metachlor, phenanthrene and 1-chloro-2,4, dinitrobenzene (Flocco et al. 2004). Overexpression of GST genes enhances the potential for phytodegradation of herbicides (Kawahigashi 2009). Rhizodegradation of pollutant bisphenol A and polychlorinated biphenyls (PCBs) was efficiently carried out by transgenic tobacco plants inoculated with the gene coding laccase obtained from a fungus *Coriolus vericolar* (Sonoki et al. 2005). Transgenic plants are reported to remove even explosive residues successfully from soil contaminated by highly toxic and mutagenic nitroglycerin, TNT, RDX, aminodinitrotoluene (Hannink et al. 2001; Rylott et al. 2006). *Arabidopsis thaliana* transformed with an extradiol dioxygenase gene were shown to remove 2,3- dihydroxybiphenol with high efficiency (Uchida et al. 2005).

8. ROLE OF GENETIC VARIATION: ACQUISITIONS AND APPLICATIONS ON METAL ACCUMULATION

Several genes are involved in metal uptake, translocation, chemical modification, sequestration, and tolerance in plants. Strategies for genetic manipulation may be followed through the over-expression of any (or combination) of these genes which also depends upon the specific application of plants for phytoremediation. However, enhancement of plant metal tolerance is essential which can be achieved through efficient metals sequestration, storage, sufficient production of metal chelating agents/ molecules and also with increase in activity of (oxidative) stress resistance enzymes (Pilon-Smits and Pilon 2002). However, overexpression of gene(s) related to metal transporter may lead to several assorted functions either related to uptake, translocation, and/or sequestration. These functions depend upon the tissue location (root, shoot, vascular tissue, or all) and intracellular target regions (e.g. cell membrane, vacuolar membrane) where the gene is expressed or modulate the synthesis of metal chelators within the cell.

8.1. Natural Metal Chelators: Phytochelatins, Metallothioneins and others

Among different heavy metal-binding ligands in plants, phytochelatins (PCs) and metallothioneins (MTs) are the best characterized cysteine-rich, heavy metal-binding protein molecules. MTs are gene-encoded polypeptides, while PCs are enzymatically synthesized peptides. PCs are induced to varying levels by a wide range of metal ions like Ag, arsenate, Cd, Cu, Hg, and Pb. PCs were first discovered in the yeast *S. pombe,* and were found to be structurally related to glutathione (GSH; γ-GluCysGly). Numerous physiological, biochemical, and genetic studies have confirmed that GSH (or, in some cases, related compounds) is the substrate for PC biosynthesis; GSH-deficient mutants of *S. pombe* as well as *Arabidopsis* are PC deficient and hypersensitive to Cd and arsenate (Rauser 1995, 1999; Zenk 1996; Cobbett 2000). On the other hand, MTs are low molecular weight, cysteine-rich, metal-binding proteins that can bind a variety of metals by mercaptide bonds (Cobbett and Goldsbrough 2002). MTs play a crucial role in the chain of activities leading to sequestration of toxic metals, transportation of Zn and Cu, prevention of reactions of toxic metals with other biomolecules, thereby attenuating their toxicity (Choi et al. 1996).

8.1.1. PC Synthase Genes

The PC synthase gene was genetically identified in *Arabidopsis*. Cd-sensitive, *cad1*, mutants are PC deficient but have wild-type levels of GSH. Studies on the gene have been carried out using different approaches, either using the expression of *Arabidopsis* and wheat cDNA libraries in *S. cerevisiae* to identify genes (*AtPCS1* (Vatamaniuk et al. 1999) and *TaPCS1*(Clemens et al. 1999), respectively) conferring increased Cd resistance or through the identification of *AtPCS1* through the positional cloning of the *CAD1* gene of *Arabidopsis* (Vatamaniuk et al. 1999; Cobbett and Goldsbrough 2002). Similarly, overexpression of phytochelatin synthase AtPCS1in Indian mustard helped in enhanced tolerance to As and Cd; while, two ABCC-type transporters, AtABCC1 and AtABCC2 deficient mutants of *A. thaliana* is extremely sensitive to As and As-based herbicides (Tripathi et al. 2012). PC synthase enzymes range from 42 kD to 70 kD proteins with 40–50% identical N-terminal regions and multiple Cys residues in the C-terminal regions of different organisms. Kinetic studies using plant cell cultures demonstrated that PC biosynthesis occurs within minutes of exposure to Cd and is independent of *de novo* protein synthesis; further, a range of metal ions in *S. pombe* can induce the PC synthesis (Rauser 1995, Smith 2009). Overexpression of PCs via expression of enzymes involved in their biosynthesis (expressing either of two glutathione synthesizing enzymes, glutathione synthetase, GS or γ-glutamylcysteine synthetase, γECS) in transgenic mustard (*Brassica juncea*) demonstrated better Cd tolerance and accumulation (Zhu et al. 1999). Similarly, transgenic plants with knocked out γECS showed decreased GSH levels and reduced Cd tolerance, suggesting its important role in Cd accumulation and/or tolerance.

8.1.2. MT Gene Expression

Reports on RNA blot hybridization studies and reporter gene expression studies confirm the expressions of MT genes during development and in response to various environmental factors. MT genes may be expressed at high levels in plant tissues, in terms of transcript abundance (García-Hernández et al. 1998; Cobbett and Goldsbrough 2002). Cu-induced expression of Type-1 MT gene were apparent in diverse plants including *Arabidopsis*, tobacco, wheat, rice (Hsieh et al. 1995; Vatamaniuk et al. 1999; Smith 2009), *Fucus* (Morris et al. 1999) and *P. oceanica* (Giordani et al. 2000). Several fold higher Cu accumulation was reported after the overexpression of a pea MT in *A. thaliana* (Evans et al. 1992). Again, expression of human or mouse MT gene showed higher metal tolerance in plants, like expression of human MT2 gene in oil rape seed or human MT2 and mouse MT1 in tobacco helped better Cd tolerance (Smith 2009) (). Interestingly in a study by Hasegawa et al. (1997), sixteen-fold higher Cd tolerance was observed when yeast gene CUP1 was overexpressed in cauliflower (*Brassica oleracea*). As for example, in yeast, Cu activates the transcription factor Ace1 which in turn binds to the CUP1 promoter to stimulate transcription of the MT gene (Labbe and Thiele 1999). Range of other stresses, metal toxicity, nutrient deprivation, heat shock can induce MT genes expression in wheat and rice (Hsieh et al. 1995), suggesting that MTs may be a promising candidate countering stress responses in transgenic plants.

8.1.3. CYP: The Novel Enzyme

In the detoxification mechanism, the first enzymatic defence against foreign compounds is achieved essentially by the cytochrome P450 (abbreviated as CYP) supergene family of enzymes, usually attached to the inner mitochondrial membranes or endoplasmic reticulum in eukaryotes and prokaryotes. CYPs are soluble proteins found in the cytosol. Though P450 genes are found in the genomes of almost all organisms, but their quantity has exploded in plants. Although amino-acid sequences of this group of proteins is extremely diverse (levels of identity as low as 16%), but their structural features have remained almost identical throughout the evolution. The reactions carried out by P450s, can be extremely diverse contributing to vital processes such as chemical defence in plants, carbon source assimilation, biosynthesis of hormones, structural components of living organisms, degradation of xenobiotics and even protection against carcinogens (Cobbett and Goldsbrough 2002; Gillam 2008).

8.1.4. Overexpression of Organic Acids, Phytosiderophores

It has been demonstrated that overexpression of citrate synthase (CS transgenics) for over-production of the organic metal chelator citric acid results in improved Al tolerance (de la Fuente et al. 1997), better resistance to iron deficiency (Guerinot 2001), enhanced phosphorus and uranium uptake (Huang et al. 1998; Lopez-Bucio et al. 2000). Thus CS transgenics may be explored for many different purposes including uranium remediation. Iron phytosiderophores like deoxymugineic acid when expressed (by overexpressing the nicotianamine aminotransferase (NAAT) gene) in rice helps the plant to grow in Fe deficient soil (Takahashi et al. 2001).

8.2. Membrane Metal Transporters

Genetic manipulation of metal transporters is an important area to develop transgenic plants having altered metal tolerance and/or accumulation. Zn accumulation in roots is found to be enhanced by two-folds in *A. thaliana* after overexpression of Zn transporter ZAT (also known as AtMTP1). This is also a putative vacuolar transporter and of the same gene family as the TgMTP1 isolated from the hyperaccumulator *T. goesingense* (van der Zaal et al. 1999; Persans et al. 2001; Pilon-Smits and Pilon 2002). Similarly, calcium vacuolar transporter CAX2 of *A. thaliana*, when overexpressed in tobacco resulted in higher Mn tolerance and more accumulation of Ca, Cd, and Mn (Hirschi et al. 2000). Calmodulin-binding protein encoding metal transporter gene from tobacco (NtCBP4) when overexpressed, resulted in enhanced Ni tolerance and Pb accumulation and reduced Ni accumulation and Pb tolerance (Arazi et al. 1999). Overexpression of metal transporter AtNramp1 resulted in an increase in Fe tolerance, however, AtNramp3 overexpression led to reduced Cd tolerance (Thomine et al. 2000). Metal specificity can also be altered through the genetic manipulation of desired protein to tailor transgenic plants to accumulate specific metals. As for example, substitution of one amino acid in IRT1, the *Arabidopsis* Fe, Zn, Mn, and Cd transporter, resulted in loss of capacity of either Fe and Mn or Zn transport (Rogers et al. 2000; Pilon-Smits and Pilon 2002).

Yeast cadmium factor1(YCF1), a member of the ABC transporter family, when introduced to *Brassica juncea* was found to confer enhanced tolerance to Cd[III] and Pb[II] stress than the wild type plants and showed significantly increased accumulation of both Cd[III] and Pb[II] (Bhuiyan et al. 2011). BjYSL7 gene (*Brassica juncea* YSL7) overexpressed in transgenic tobacco plants exhibited greater concentration of Cd and Ni in shoot than wild type (Wang et al. 2013). Transgenic tomato plants expressing *Arabidopsis halleri* AhHMA4 gene showed Zn overload in the apoplast thus become Zn hypertolerant (Barabasz et al.2012). The metal transporter IREG1 of hyperaccumulator *Psychotria gabriellae* (Rubiaceae) confers Ni tolerance and hyperaccumulation when expresses in non-accumulator transgenic plants (Merlot et al. 2014).

8.3. Metabolism of Metals

Introduction of a completely novel pathway from a different organism is an alternative approach for the development of transgenic plant. In a classical work, two bacterial genes (MerA encoding mercuric reductase, that reduces ionic mercury to elemental mercury Hg(0) and MerB encoding organomercuriallyase, that converts methylmercury to ionic mercury or Hg(II) were introduced in the plants that together can convert methylmercury to volatile elemental mercury (Summers 1986). However, the MerA-MerB double-transgenics were found to be 50-fold more tolerant and capable to transfer organic mercury to volatile elemental mercury. The concept has already been tested in different plants (transgenic MerA and MerB yellow poplar and tobacco) that showed enhanced mercury tolerance (Bizily et al. 2000). Hairy root cultures of plants using *Agrobacterium rhizogenes* is another approach to metal metabolism to rhizo-filtration studies. It was found that *Thlaspi caerulescens* with hairy root culture showed more tolerance and accumulation (1.5- to 1.7-fold more) of Cd (Pilon-Smits and Pilon 2002).

8.4. Countering Oxidative Stress

Heavy metal toxicity within the plant tissues directly or indirectly generates variety of ROS and, which in turn leads to oxidative damage to different cell constituents. Development of transgenics to tolerate more oxidative stress is another approach. Studies have shown that enzymes like glutathione-S-transferase, peroxidase when overexpressed, resulted in better Al tolerance indicative of enhanced oxidative stress response (Ezaki et al. 2000). Further, more metal tolerance/ accumulation were found in several other studies when different anti-stress enzymes like aldose/ aldehyde reductase, 1-aminocyclopropane-1-carboxylic acid (ACC) deaminase were overexpressed in plants (Oberschall et al. 2000; Grichko et al. 2000).

CONCLUSION

Different studies have shown promise in genetic modification and development of transgenic plants for metal uptake, tolerance and accumulation. Compared to the wild types, accelerated, cost-effective phytoremediation process can be achieved if field level applications successfully show the same result in the open environment. Overexpresssion or introduction of genes or new pathway to detoxify several metals including mercury through the process of phytoremediation can open potential avenues of implementation. Discovery of more metal-related genes may generate new transgenics with favourable properties. Recent revolution on 'omics' based approaches like genotypic profiling, metagenomics, genome pyrosequencing, metatranscriptomics, metaproteomics, metabolomics and bioinformatics in research and development help to leaps in our understanding on variety of aspects including soil microbial communities and rhizosphere, plant metabolism and activity prediction etc. Deciphering physiological mechanisms involved in the stress response through monitoring molecular dynamics of proteins and metabolites is the excellent approach to get information about molecular changes involved during metal stress, in vitro development of transgenics, their efficacy determination and implementation (Desai et al. 2010; Bell et al. 2014). Restoring environmental balance through the phytoremediation technique obviously does point towards a number of benefits and is largely chosen methods to restore the environment.

REFERENCES

Abou-Shanab RA, Ghozlan H, Ghanem K, Moawad H (2005) Behaviour of bacterial populations isolated from rhizosphere of *Diplachne fusca* dominant in industrial sites. *World J Microbiol Biotechnol* 21: 1095–1101.

Anderson TA, Kruger EL, Coats JR (1994) Enhanced degradation of a mixture of three herbicides in the rhizosphere of a herbicide-tolerant plant. *Chemosphere* 28: 1551–1557.

Arazi T, Sunka R, Kaplan B, Fromm H (1999) A tobacco plasma membrane calmodulin-binding transporter confers Ni^{2+} tolerance and Pb^{2+} hypersensitivity in transgenic plants. *Plant J* 20: 171–182.

Barac T, Taghavi S, Borremans B, Provoost A, Oeyen L, Colpaert JV, Vangronsveld J, van der Lelie D (2004) Engineered endophytic bacteria improve phytoremediation of water-soluble, volatile, organic pollutants. *Nat Biotechnol* 22: 583–588.

Anna B, Anna W, Anna R, Bulska E, Hanikenne M, Czarny M, Krämer U, Antosiewicz DM, (2012) Metal response of transgenic tomato plants expressing P_{1B}-ATPase. *Physiol Planta* 145 : 315–331

Bell TH, Joly S, Pitre FE, Yergeau E (2014) Increasing phytoremediation efficiency and reliability using novel omics approaches. Trends Biotechnol (In press).doi: 10.1016/j.tibtech.2014.02.008.

Bell MJ, McLaughlin MJ, Wright GC, Cruickshank J (1997) Inter- and intra-specific variation in accumulation of cadmium by peanut, soybean, and navy bean. *Aust J Agric Res* 48: 1151–1160.

Bennett LE, Burkhead JL, Hale KL, Terry N, Pilon M, Pilon-Smits EA (2003) Analysis of transgenic Indian mustard plants for phytoremediation of metalcontaminated mine tailings. *J Environ Qual* 32: 432–440.

Bernard C, Roosens N, Czernic P, Lebrun M, Verbruggen N (2004) A novel CPx-ATPase from the cadmium hyperaccumulator *Thlaspi caerulescens*. *FEBS Lett* 569: 140– 148.

Bhuiyan MSU, Min SR, Jeong WJ, Sultana S, Choi KS, Song WY, Lee Y, LimYP, LiuJang R (2011) Overexpression of a yeast cadmium factor 1 *(YCF1)* enhances heavy metal tolerance and accumulation in *Brassica juncea. PCTOC* 105:85–91.

Bizily SP, Rugh CL, Meagher RB (2000) Phytodetoxification of hazardous organomercurials by genetically engineered plants. *Nat Biotechnol* 18: 213–217.

Brim H, McFarlan SC, Fredrickson JK, Minton KW, Zhai M, Wackett LP, Daly MJ (2000) Engineering *Deinococcus radiodurans* for metal remediation in radioactive mixed waste environments. *Nat Biotechnol* 18: 85–90.

Burd GI, Dixon DG, Glick BR (1998) A plant growth-promoting bacterium that decreases nickel toxicity in seedlings. *App Environ Microbiol* 64: 3663–3668.

Burken J, Vroblesky D, Balouet JC (2011) Phytoforensics, dendrochemistry, and phytoscreening: New green tools for delineating contaminants from past and present. *Environ Sci Technol* 45: 6218–6226.

Callahan DL, Baker AJ, Kolev SD, Wedd AG (2006) Metal ion ligands in hyperaccumulating plants. *J Biol Inorg Chem* 11: 2–12.

CERCLA (2007) Priority list of hazardous substances. http://www.atsdr.cdc.gov/spl /supportdocs appendix-d.pdf.Accessed 30 Jan 2013.

Chatterjee S, Chattopadhyay B, Mukhopadhyay SK (2007) Sequestration and localization of metals in two common wetland plants of contaminated East Calcutta Wetlands, A Ramsar site in India. *Land Cont Reclam* 15: 437–452.

Chatterjee S, Datta S, Mallick PH, Mitra A, Veer V, Mukhopadhyay SK (2013) Use of wetland plants in bioaccumulation of heavy metals. In: Gupta DK (ed) Plant-Based Remediation Processes, *Spriger,* Germany.

Chetia M, Chatterjee S, Banerjee S, Nath MJ, Singh L, Srivastava RB, Sarma HP (2011) Groundwater arsenic contamination in Brahmaputra river basin: Awater quality assessment in Golaghat (Assam), India. *Environ Monit Assess* 173: 371–385.

Chiang HC, Lo JC, Yeh KC (2006) Genes associated with heavy metal tolerance and accumulation in Zn/Cd hyperaccumulator *Arabidopsis halleri*: A genomic survey with cDNA microarray. *Environ Sci Technol* 40: 6792–6798

Choi D, Kim HM, Yun HK, Park JA, Kim WT, Bok SH (1996) Molecular cloning of a metallothionein-like gene from *Nicotiana glutinosa* L. and its induction by wounding and tobacco mosaic virus infection. *Plant Physiol* 112: 353–359.

Clemens S, Kim EJ, Neumann D, Schroeder JI (1999) Tolerance to toxic metals by a gene family of phytochelatin synthases from plants and yeast. EMBO J18: 3325–3333.

Cobbett C, Goldsbrough P (2002) Phytochelatins and metallothioneins: Roles in heavy metal detoxification and homeostasis. *Annu Rev Plant Biol* 53: 159–182.

Cobbett CS (2000) Phytochelatins and their role in heavy metal detoxification. *Plant Physio* l123: 825–833.

Cozzarelli IM, Bekins BA, Eganhouse RP, Warren E, Essaid HI (2010) In situ measurements of volatile aromatic hydrocarbon biodegradation rates in groundwater. *J Contam Hydrol* 111: 48–64.

Dalcorso G, Farinati S, Furini A (2010) Regulatory networks of cadmium stress in plants. *Plant Sig Behav* 5: 1–5.

Danika L, LeDuc Norman T (2005). Phytoremediation of toxic trace elements in soil and water. *J Ind Microbiol Biotechnol* 32: 514–520.

Davies FT Jr, Puryear JD, Newton RJ (2001) Mycorrhizal fungi enhance accumulation and tolerance of chromium in sunflower (*Helianthus annuus*). *J Plant Physiol* 158: 777–786.

Davison J (2005). Risk mitigation of genetically modified bacteria and plants designed for bioremediation. *J Ind Microbiol Biotechnol* 32: 639–650.

De la Fuente JM, Ramírez-Rodríguez V, Cabrera-Ponce JL, Herrera-Estrella L (1997) Aluminum tolerance in transgenic plants by alteration of citrate synthesis. *Science* 276: 1566–1568.

De Souza MP, Pilon-Smits EAH, Lytle CM, Hwang S, Tai J, Honma TSU, Yeh L, Terry N (1998) Rate-limiting steps in selenium assimilation and volatilization by Indian mustard. *Plant Physiol* 117: 1487–1494.

Delhaize EP, Ryan R (1995) Aluminum toxicity and tolerance in plants. *Plant Physiol* 107: 315–321.

Desai C, Pathak H, Madamwar D (2010) Advances in molecular and "-omics" technologies to gauge microbial communities and bioremediation at xenobiotic/anthropogen contaminated sites. *Biores Technol* 101: 1558–11569.

Doty S, Shang Q, Wilson A, Moore A, Newman L, Strand S, Gordon M (2000) Enhanced metabolism of halogenated hydrocarbons in transgenic plants contain mammalian P450 2E1. *PNAS USA,* 97: 6287–6291.

Dubey RS (2011) Metal toxicity, oxidative stress and antioxidative defense system in plants. In: Gupta SD (ed) Reactive Oxygen Species and Antioxidants in Higher Plants, CRC Press, Boca Raton, Florida, USA.

Dubois S, Cheptou PO, Petit C, Meerts P, Poncelet M, Vekemans X, Lefebvre C, Escarré J (2003) Genetic structure and mating systems ofmetallicolous and nonmetallicolous populations of Thlaspi caerulescens. *New Phytol* 157: 633–641.

Duruibe JO, Ogwuegbu MOC, Egwurugwu JN (2007) Heavy metal pollution and human biotoxic effects. *Int J Phys Sci* 2:112–118.

Eapen S, Singh S, D'Souza S (2007) Advances in development of transgenic plants for remediation of xenobiotic pollutants. *Biotechnol Adv* 25: 442–451.

Earthworks and mining watch Canada, February (2012) TROUBLED WATERS- HOW mine waste dumping is poisoning our oceans, rivers, and lakes http://www.earth worksaction.org/files/publications/Troubled-Waters_FINAL.pdfAccessed 30 August 2012.

Escarré J, Lefèbvre C, Gruber W, Leblanc M, Lepart J, Rivière Y, Delay B (2000) Zinc and cadmium hyperaccumulation by Thlaspi caerulescens from metalliferous and non-metalliferous sites in the mediterranean area: Implications for phytoremediation. *New Phytol 145*: 429–437.

Evans KM, Gatehouse JA, Lindsay WP, Shi J, Tommey AM, Robinson NJ (1992) Expressionof the pea metallothionein-like gene PsMTA in *Escherichia coli* and *Arabidopsis thaliana* and analysis of trace metal ion accumulation: Implications for gene PsMTA function. *Plant Mol Biol* 20: 1019–1028.

Ezaki B1, Gardner RC, Ezaki Y, Matsumoto H (2000) Expression of aluminum-induced genes in transgenic *Arabidopsis* plants can ameliorate aluminium stress and/or oxidative stress. *Plant Physiol* 122: 657–665.

Flocco CG, Lindblom SD, Smits EA (2004) Overexpression of enzymes involved in glutathione synthesis enhances tolerance to organic pollutants in *Brassica juncea*. *Int J Phytorem* 6: 289–304.

Foyer CH (1997) Oxygen metabolism and electron transport in photosynthesis.In:Scandalios J (ed)Molecular Biology of Free Radical Scavenging Systems. Cold Spring Harbor Laboratory Press, New York pp 587–621.

Foyer CH, Noctor G (2003) Redox sensing and signalling associated with reactive oxygen in chloroplasts, peroxisomes and mitochondria. *Physiol Plant* 119: 355–364.

Fulekar MH, Singh A, Bhaduri AM (2009) Genetic engineering strategies for enhancing phytoremediation of heavy metals. *Afr J Biotechnol* 8: 529–535.

García-Hernández M, Murphy A, Taiz L (1998) Metallothioneins 1 and 2 have distinct but overlapping expression patterns in Arabidopsis. *Plant Physiol* 118: 387–397.

Ghosh M, Singh SP (2005) A review on phytoremediation of heavy metals and utilization of its byproducts. *Appl Ecol Environ Res* 3:1–18.

Gillam EMJ (2008) Engineering Cytochrome P450 Enzymes. Chem Res Toxicol 21: 220–231.

Giordani T, Natali L, Maserti BE, Taddei S, Cavallini A (2000) Characterization and expression of DNA sequences encoding putative Type-II metallothioneins in the seagrass *Posidonia oceanica. Plant Physiol* 123: 571–581.

Grichko VP, Filby B, Glick BR (2000) Increased ability of transgenic plants expressing the bacterial enzyme ACC deaminase to accumulate Cd, Co, Cu, Ni, Pb, and Zn. *J Biotechno* 81: 45–53.

Grill E, Mishra S, Srivastava S, Tripathi RD (2006) Role of phytochelatins inphytoremediation ofheavy metals. In: Singh SN, Tripathi RD (eds) *Environmental Bioremediation Technologies. Springer,* Heidelberg.

Guerinot ML (2000) The ZIP family of metal transporters. *Biochim Biophys Acta* 1465: 190–198.

Guerinot ML (2001) Improving rice yields — ironing out the details. *Nat Biotechnol* 19: 417–418.

Gupta DK, Huang HG Corpas FJ (2013) Lead tolerance in plants: Strategies for phytoremediation. *Environ Sci Pollut Res* 20:2150–2161.

Gupta DK, Huang HG, Yang XE, Razafindrabe BHN, Inouhe M (2010) The detoxification of lead in *Sedum alfredii* H. is not related with phytochelatins but the glutathione. *J Hazard Mater* 177:437–444.

Gupta DK, Tripathi RD, Mishra S, Srivastava S, Dwivedi S, Rai UN, Yang XE, Huang H, Inouhe M (2008) Arsenic accumulation in roots and shoots vis-a-vis its effects on growth and level of phytochelatins in seedlings of *Cicer arietinum* L. . *Environ Biol* 29: 281–286.

Gupta DK, Tohoyama H, Joho M, Inouhe M (2002) Possible roles of phytochelatins and glutathione metabolism in cadmium tolerance in chickpea roots. *J Plant Res* 115:429–437.

Hall JL (2002) Cellular mechanism for heavy metal detoxification and tolerance. *J Exp Bot* 53: 1–11.

Hannink N, Rosser SJ, French CE, Basran A, Murray JA, Nicklin S, Bruce NC (2001) Phytodetoxification of TNT by transgenic plants expressing a bacterial nitroreductase. *Nat Biotechnol* 19: 1168–1172.

Hasegawa I, Terada E, Sunairi M, Wakita H, Shinmachi F, Noguchi A, Nakajima M, Yazaki J (1997) Genetic improvement of heavy metal tolerance in plants by transfer of the yeast metallothionein gene (CUP1). *Plant Soil* 196: 277–281.

Herawati N, Susuki S, Hayashi K, Rivai IF, Koyama H (2000).Cadmium, copper and zinc levels in rice and soil of Japan, Indonesia and China by soil type. *Bull Env Cont Toxi* 64: 33–39.

Hertel H, Paul M (2001) Field testing of model of Norway spruce (*Picea abies* L. Karst.) with different genetic structures reforestation in air polluted regions. In: Müller-Starck G, Schubert R (eds) Response of Forest Systems to Changing Environmental Conditions. Kluwer Academic Publishers, Dordrecht, Boston, London 70: 339–352.

Heyno E, Mary V, Schopfer P, Krieger-Liszkay A (2011) Oxygen activation at the plasma membrane: Relation between superoxide and hydroxyl radical production by isolated membranes. *Planta* 234: 35–45.

Hinesly TD, Alexander DE, Redborg KE, Ziegler EL (1982) Differential accumulations of cadmium and zinc by corn hybrids grown on soil amended with sewage sludge. *Agron J* 74: 469–474.

Hirschi KD, Korenkov VD, Wilganowski NL, Wagner GJ (2000) Expression of *Arabidopsis* CAX2 in tobacco. Altered metal accumulation and increased manganese tolerance. *Plant Physiol* 124: 125–133.

Hocking PJ, Pate JS (1977) Mobilization of minerals to developing seeds of legumes. *Ann Bot* 41:1259–1278.

Horst WJ (1983) Factors responsible for genotypic manganese tolerance in cowpea (*Vigna unguiculata*). Plant Soil 72: 213–218.

Hossain MA, Piyatida P, Teixeira da Silva JA, Fujita M (2012) Molecular mechanism of heavy metal toxicity and tolerance in plants: Central role of glutathione in detoxification of reactive oxygen species and Methylglyoxal and in heavy metal chelation. *J Bot ID* 872875.

Howden R, Goldsbrough PB, Andersen CR, Cobbett CS (1995) Cadmium-sensitive cad1 mutants of *Arabidopsis thaliana* are phytochelatin deficient. *Plant Physiol* 107:1059–1066.

Hsieh HM, Liu WK, Huang PC (1995) A novel stress-inducible metallothionein like gene from rice. *Plant Mol Biol* 28: 381–389.

Huang J, Zhang Y, Peng JS, Zhong C, Yi HY, Ow DW, Gong JM (2012) Fission yeast HMT1 lowers seed cadmium through phytochelatin-dependent vacuolar sequestration in Arabidopsis. *Plant Physiol* 158:1779–1788.

Huang JW, Blaylock MJ, Kapulnik Y, Ensley BD (1998) Phytoremediation of uranium-contaminated soils: Role of organic acids in triggering uranium hyperaccumulation in plants. *Environ Sci Technol* 32: 2004–2008.

Hutton M, Symon C (1986) Thequantities of cadmium, lead, mercury and arsenic entering the U.K. environment from human activities. *Sci Total Environ* 57: 129–150.

INSA, A Position Paper (2011) Hazardous metals and minerals pollution in Indiahttp://insaindia.org/pdf/Hazardous_Metals.pdf Accessed 30 August 2012.

Jarvis SC, Jones LHP Hopper MJ (1976) Cadmium uptake from solution by plants and its transport from roots to shoots. *Plant Soil* 44: 179–191.

Kalay M, Canli M (2000) Elimination of essential (Cu, Zn) and nonessential (Cd, Pb) metals from tissue of a freshwater fish *Tilapia zillii* following and uptake protocol. *Turk J Zool* 24: 429–436.

Kawahigashi H (2009) Transgenic plants for phytoremediation of herbicides. *Curr Opin Biotechnol* 20: 225–230.

Ke HY, Sun JG, Feng XZ, Czako M, Marton L (2001) Differential mercury volatilization by tobacco organs expressing a modified bacterial merA gene. *Cell Res* 11: 231–236.

Keck RW, Redlich L (1975) Cadmium tolerance in soybeans. *Plant Physiol Suppl* 56: 13 (Abstract 68).

Korda A, Santas P, Tenente A, Santas R (1997) Petroleum hydrocarbon bioremediation: Sampling and analytical techniques, in situ treatments and commercial microorganisms currently used. *Appl Microbial Biotechnol* 48: 677–689.

Korshikov II, Velikoridko TI, Butilskaya LA (2002) Genetic structure and variation in *Pinus sylvestris* L. populations degrading due to pollution-induced injury. *Silv Genet* 51: 45–49.

Korshunova YO, Eide D, Clark WG, Guerinot ML, Pakrasi HB (1999) The IRT1 protein from *Arabidopsis thaliana* is a metal transporter with a broad substrate range. *Plant Mol Biol* 40: 37–44.

Krämer U (2010) Metal hyperaccumulation in plants. *Annu Rev Plant Biol* 61: 517–534.

Krämer U, Talke IN, Hanikenne M (2007) Transition metal transport. *FEBS Lett* 581:2263–2272.

Kuboi T, Noguchi A, Yazaki J (1986) Family-dependent cadmium accumulation characteristics in higher plants. *Plant Soil* 92: 405–415.

Kumar PBA, Dushenkov V, Motto H, Raskin I (1995) Phytoextraction: The use of plants to remove heavy metals from soils. *Environ Sci Technol* 29: 1232–1238.

Labbe S, Thiele DJ (1999) Pipes and wiring: The regulation of copper uptake and distribution in yeast. *Trends Microbiol* 7: 500–505.

Larsen PB, Degenhardt J, Stenzler LM, Howell SH, Kochian LV (1998) Aluminium-resistant *Arabidopsis* mutant that exhibit altered patterns of aluminum accumulation and organic acid release from roots. *Plant Physiol* 117: 9–18.

Lasat MM (2000) Phytoextraction of metals from contaminated soil: A review of plant/soil/metal interaction and assessment of pertinent agronomic issues. *J Haz Subst Res* 2: 5.

Lasat MM (2002) Phytoextraction of toxic metals: A review of biological mechanisms. *J Environ Qual* 31:109–120.

Leahy JG, Colwell RR (1990) Microbial degradation of hydrocarbons in the environment. *Microbiol Rev* 54: 305–315.

Lee M, Lee K, Lee J, Noh EW, Lee Y (2005) AtPDR12 contributes to lead resistance in Arabidopsis. *Plant Physiol* 138: 827–836.

López-Bucio J, Martinez de la Vega O, Guevara-García A, Herrera-Estrella L (2000) Enhanced phosphorus uptake in transgenic tobacco plants that overproduce citrate. *Nat Biotechnol* .18: 450–453.

Lovley DR (2003) Cleaning up with genomics: Applying molecular biology to bioremediation. *Nature* 1: 35–44.

Lovley DR (2001) Anaerobes to the rescue. *Science* 293: 1444–1446.

Macnair MR (2002) Within and between population genetic variance for zinc accumulation in *Arabidopsis halleri*. *New Phytol* 155: 59–66.

Manara A (2012) Plant responses to heavy metal toxicity. In: Furini A (ed) Plants and Heavy Metals, Springer Briefs in Biometals.

McGrath SP, Zhao FJ (2003) Phytoextraction of metals and metalloids from contaminated soils. *Curr Opin Biotechnol* 14: 277–282.

McNair MR, Tilstone GH, Smith SS (2000) The genetics of metal tolerance and accumulation in higher plants. In: Terry N, Bañuelos G (eds) Phytoremediation of Contaminated Soil and Water. Lewis Publishers, Boca Raton pp 235–250.

Meagher RB (2000) Phytoremediation of toxic elemental and organic pollutants. *Curr Opin Plant Biol* 3:153–162.

Mejnartowicz L (2001) Influence of nursery environ-ment and pollution on alders. In: Müller-Starck G, Schubert R (eds) Response of Forest Systems to Changing Environmental Conditions. Kluwer Academic Publishers, Dordrecht, Boston, London 70: 63–73.

Mengoni A, Barzanti R, Gonnelli C, Gabbrielli R, Bazzicalupo M (2001) Characterization of nickel-resistant bacteria isolated from serpentine soil. *Environ Microbiol* 3: 691–698.

Merlot Sylvain, HannibalLaure, Sara Martins, Laëtitia Martinelli, Hamid Amir, Michel Lebrunand Sébastien Thomine (2014) The metal transporter PgIREG1 from the hyperaccumulator *Psychotria gabriellae* is a candidate gene for nickel tolerance and accumulation. *J Exp Bot* 65: 1551–1564

Meyer JM (2000) Pyoverdines: Pigments siderophores and potential taxonomic markers of fluorescent Pseudomonas species. *Arch Microbiol* 174: 135–142.

Michel C, Jean M, Coulon S, Dictor MC, Delorme F, Morin D, Garrido F (2007) Biofilms of As (III)-oxidising bacteria: Formation and activity studies for bioremediation process development. *Appl Microbiol Biotechnol* 77: 457–467.

Mikus M, Bobak M, Lux A (1992) Structure of protein bodies and elemental composition of phytin from dry germ of maize (*Zea mays* L.). *Bot Acta* 105:26–33.

Mishra S, Jha AB, Dubey RS (2011) Arsenite treatment induces oxidative stress, upregulates antioxidant system, and causes phytochelatin synthesis in rice seedlings. *Protoplasma* 248: 565–577.

Morris CA, Nicolaus B, Sampson V, Harwood JL, Kille P (1999) Identification and characterization of a recombinant metallothionein protein from a marine alga, *Fucus vesiculosus*. *Biochem J* 338: 553–560

Moustakas M, Lanaras T, SymeonidisL, Karataglis S (1994) Growth and some photosynthetic characteristics of field grown *Avena sativa* under copper and lead stress. *Photosynthetica* 30: 389–396.

Mulligan CN, Yong RN, Gibbs BF (2001) Remediation technologies for metalcontaminated soils and groundwater: An evaluation. *Eng Geol* 60: 193–207.

Nagajyoti PC, Lee KD, Sreekanth TVM (2010) Heavy metals, occurrence and toxicity for plants: Areview. *Environ Chem Lett* 8: 199–216

Nath K, Saini S, Sharma YK (2005) Chromium in tannery industry effluent and its effect on plant metabolism and growth. *J Environ Biol* 26:197–204.

Nishida S, Mizuno T, Obata H (2008) Involvement of histidine-rich domain of ZIP family transporter TjZNT1 in metal ion specificity. *Plant Physiol Biochem* 46: 601–606.

Noctor G, Arisi A, Jouanin L, Kunert K, Rennenberg H, Foyer C (1998) Glutathione: Biosynthesis, metabolism and relationship to stress tolerance explored in transformed plants. *J Exp Bot* 49: 623–647.

Norman AG (1962) The Uniqueness Of Plants. *Am Sci* 50: 436–449.

Nriagu JO (1989) A global assessment of natural sources of atmospheric trace metals. *Nature* 338: 47–49.

Oberschall A, Deak M, Torok K, Sass L, Vass I, Kovacs I, Feher A, Dudits D, Horvath GV (2000) A novel aldose/aldehyde reductase protects transgenic plants against lipid peroxidation under chemical and drought stress. *Plant J* 24: 437–446.

Pauwels M, Saumitou-Laprade P, Holl AC, Petit D, Bonnin I (2005) Multiple origin of metallicolous populations of the pseudo metallophyte *Arabidopsis halleri* (Brassicaceae) in Central Europe: The cpDNA testimony. *Mol Ecol* 14: 4403–4414.

Payne KA, Bowen HC, Hammond JP, Hampton CR, Lynn JR, Mead A, Swarup K, Bennet, MJ, White PJ, Broadley MR (2004) Natural genetic variation in caesium (Cs) accumulation by *Arabidopsis thaliana*. *New Phytol* 162: 535–548.

Pence NS, Larsen PB, Ebbs SD, Letham DL, Lasat MM, Garvin DF, Eide D, Kochian LV (2000) The molecular physiology of heavy metal transport in the Zn/Cd hyperaccumulator *Thlaspi caerulescens*. *PNAS USA,* 25: 4956–4960.

Persans MW, Nieman K, Salt DE (2001) Functional activity and role of cation-efflux family members in Ni hyperaccumulation in *Thlaspi goesingense*. *PNAS USA* 98: 9995–10000.

Pettersson O (1977) Differences in cadmium uptake between plant species and cultivars. *Swed J Agric Res* 7: 21–24.

Peuke AD, Rennenberg H (2005) Phytoremediation: Molecular biology, requirements for application, environmental protection, public attention and feasibility. *EMBO Rep* 6:497–501.

Pilon-Smits E (2005) Phytoremediation. *Ann Rev Plant Biol* 56: 15–39.

Pilon-Smits E, Pilon M (2002) Phytoremediation of metals using transgenic plants. *Crit Rev Plant Sci 21*: 439–456.

Prasad MNV, Freitas HMO (2003) Metal hyperaccumulation in plants - Biodiversity prospecting for phytoremediation technology. *Electr J Biotech* 6: doi: 10.2225/vol6-issue3-fulltext-6.

Prus-Gowacki W, Chudziñska E, Wojnicka-Pótorak A, Kozacki L, Fagiewicz K (2006) Effects of heavy metal pollution on genetic variation and cytological disturbances in the *Pinus sylvestris* L. Population. *J Appl Genet* 47: 99–108.

Rauser WE (1999) Structure and function of metal chelators produced by plants: The case for organic acids, amino acids, phytin and metallothioneins. *Cell Biochem Biophys* 31:19–48.

Rauser WE (1995) Phytochelatins and related peptides: Structure, biosynthesis, and function. *Plant Physiol* 109:1141–1149.

Rea PA (2012) Phytochelatin synthase: Of a protease a peptide polymerase made. *Physiol Planta* 145: 154–164.

Reeves RD, Baker AJM (2000) Metal-accumulating plants. In: Raskin I, Ensley BD (eds) Phytoremediation of Toxic Metals: Using Plants to Clean Up the Environment. Wiley, New York pp 193–229.

Rengel Z (2000) Ecotypes of *Holcus lanatus* tolerant to zinc toxicity also tolerate zinc deficiency. *Ann Bot* 86: 1119–1126.

Rogers S, Ong S, Kjartanson B, Golchin J, Stenback G (2002) Natural attenuation of polycyclic aromatic hydrocarbon-contaminated sites: Review. *Pract Period Hazard Toxic Radioact Waste Manag* 6: 141–155.

Rogers EE, Eide DJ, Guerinot ML (2000) Altered selectivity in an *Arabidopsis* metal transporter. *PNAS USA,* 97: 12356–12360.

Rout GR, Samantaray S, Das P (1999) *In vitro* selection and biochemical characterisation of zinc and manganese adapted callus lines in Brassica spp. *Plant Sci* 146: 89–100.

Rylott EL, Jackson RG, Edwards J, Womack GL, Seth-Smith H M, Rathbone DA, Strand SE, Bruce NC (2006) An explosive degrading cytochrome P450 activity and its targeted application for the phytoremediation of RDX. *Nat Biotechnol* 24: 216–219.

Salt DE, Smith RD, Raskin I (1998) Phytoremediation. *Ann. Rev. Plant Physiol. Plant Mol Biol* 49: 643–668.

Salt DE, Blaylock M, Kumar NPBA, Dushenkov V, Ensley BD, Chet I, Raskin I (1995) Phytoremediation: Anovel strategy for the removal of toxic metals from the environment using plants. *Biol Technol* 13: 468–474.

Salt DE, Kato N, Kräme U, Smith RD, Raskin I (2000) The role of root exudates in nickel hyperaccumulation and tolerance in accumulator and nonaccumulator species of Thlaspi. In: Terry N, Banuelos G (eds) Phytoremediation of Contaminated Soil and Water. CRC Press LLC, Boca Raton.

Sandalio LM, Rodr´iguez-Serrano M, del Rio LA, Romero-Puertas MC (2009) Reactive oxygen species and signalling in cadmium toxicity.In: Rio LA, PuppoA (eds) *Reactive Oxygen Species in Plant Signaling* Springer, Berlin, Germany pp 175–189.

Sandermann H Jr (1994) Higher plant metabolism of xenobiotics; The 'green liver' concept. *Pharmacogenetics* 4: 225–241.

Schäffner A, Messner B, Langebartels C, Sandermann H (2002) Genes and enzymes for *In-Planta* phytoremediation of air, water and soil. *Acta Biotechnol* 22: 141–152.

Schaller J, Brackhage C, Mkandawire M, Dudel EG (2011) Metal/metalloid accumulation/remobilization during aquatic litter decomposition in freshwater: A review. *Sci Tot Environ* 409: 4891–4898.

Schat H, Llugany M, Voojis R, Harley-Whitaker J, Bleeker PM (2002).The role of Phytochelatin in constitutive and adaptive heavy metal tolerances in hyperaccumulator and non-hyperaccumulator metallophytes. *J Exp Bot* 53: 2381–2392.

Shah K, Nongkynrih JM (2007) Metal hyperaccumulation and bioremediation. *Biol Plant* 51: 618–634.

Shah K, Kumar RG, Verma S, Dubey RS (2001) Effect of cadmium on lipid peroxidation, superoxide anion gener- ation and activities of antioxidant enzymes in growing rice seedlings. *Plant Sci* 161: 1135–1144.

Shanker AK, Cervantes C, Loza-Tavera H, Avudainayagam S (2005) Chromium toxicity in plants. *Environ. Int.,* 31: 739–753.

Siciliano SD, Germida JJ, Banks K, Greer CW (2003) Changes in microbial community composition and function during a polyaromatic hydrocarbon phytoremediation field trial. *Appl Environ Microbiol* 69: 483–489.

Singer A (2006) The chemical ecology of pollutants biodegradation. In: Mackova M (eds) Phytoremediation and Rhizoremediation: Theoretical Background. *Springer,* Germany pp 5–21.

Smith SE, McNair MR (1998) Hypostatic modifiers cause variation in degree of copper tolerance in *Mimulus guttatus*. *Heredity* 80: 760–768.

Smith SR (2009) A critical review of the bioavailability and impacts of heavy metals in municipal solid waste composts compared to sewage sludge. *Environ Int* 35: 142–156.

Sonoki T, Kajita S, Ikeda S, Uesugi M, Tatsumi K, Katayama Y, Iimura Y (2005) Transgenic tobacco expressing fungal laccase promotes the detoxification of environmental pollutants. *Appl Microbiol Biotechnol* 67: 138–142.

Mariusz S, Seta-Koselska A, Patrzylas P, Betlej A, Skorzynska-Polit E (2012) Phytodegradation and biodegradation in rhizosphere as efficient methods of reclamation of soil contaminated by organic chemicals (Areview).*Acta Agrophy* 19: 155–169.

Srivastava S, Dubey RD (2011) Manganese-excess induces oxidative stress, lowers the pool of antioxidants and elevates activities of key antioxidative enzymes in rice seedlings. *Plant Gro Reg* 64: 1–16.

Stearns JC, Shah S, Greenberg BM, Dixon DG, Glick BR (2005) Tolerance of transgenic canola expressing 1-aminocyclopropane-1-carboxylic acid deaminase to growth inhibition by Ni. *Plant Physiol Biochem* 43:701–708.

Summers AO (1986) Organization, expression, and evolution of genes for mercury resistance. *Annu Rev Microbio* 40: 607–634.

Takahashi M, Nakanishi H, Kawasaki S, Nishizawa NK, Mori S (2001) Enhanced tolerance of rice to low iron availability in alkaline soils using barley nicotianamine aminotransferase genes. *Nat Biotechnol* 19: 466–469.

Tangahu BV, Abdullah SRS, Basri H, Idris M, Anuar N, Mukhlisin M (2011) A review on heavy metals (As, Pb, and Hg) uptake by plants through phytoremediation. *Int J Chem Eng* ID 939161.

Tanou G, Molassiotis A, Diamantidis G (2009) Induction of reactive oxygen species and necrotic death-like destruction in strawberry leaves by salinity. *Environ Exp Bot* 65: 270–281.

Thomas JC, Davies EC, Malick FK, Endreszl C, Williams CR, Abbas M, Petrella S, Swisher K,Perron M, Edwards R, Ostenkowski P, Urbanczyk N, Wiesend WN, Murray KS (2003) Transgenic Indian mustard plants for phytoremediation of metal contaminated mine tailings. *J Environ Qual* 32: 432–440.

Thomine S, Wang R, Ward JM, Crawford NM, Schroeder JI (2000) Cadmium and iron transport by members of a plant metal transporter family in *Arabidopsis* with homology to Nramp genes. *PNAS USA,* 97: 4991–4996.

Tripathi RD, Tripathi P, Dwivedi S, Dubey S, Chatterjee S, Chakrabarty D, Trivedi PK (2012) Arsenomics: Omics of arsenic metabolism in plants. *Front Physiol* 3: 275.

Tuomainen M, Nunan N, Lehesranta S, Tervahauta A, Hassinen V, Schat H, Auriola S, McNicol J, Karenlampi S (2004) Proteomics and metal-responsive proteins in *Thlaspi*. Abstracts of COST Action 859 1st WG2 Workshop. Exploiting "omics" approaches in phytotechnologies pp 42.

Uchida E, Ouchi T, Suzuki Y, Yoshida T, Habe H, Vamaguchi I (2005) Secretion of bacterial xenobiotic-degrading enzymes from transgenic plants by an apoplastic expressional system: An applicability for phytoremediation. *Environ Sci Tech* 39: 7671–7677.

United States Environmental Protection Agency (USEPA) (2000) Introduction to Phytoremediation. EPA 600/R-99/107 U.S. Environmental Protection Agency, Office of Research and Development, Cincinnati, OH.

United States Environmental Protection Agency (USEPA) (2009) United States Environmental Protection Agency: Municipal Solid Waste in the United States. http://www.epa.gov/osw/nonhaz/municipal/pubs/msw2009rpt.pdf

Van de Mortel J, Rigola D, Talukdar S, Fiers M, Pieper B, Moeller B, Schat H, Aarts M (2004) Comparative genomics of Zn accumulation in *Thlaspi caerulescens* and *Arabidopsis thaliana*, Abstracts of COST Action 859 1st WG2 Workshop Exploiting "omics" approaches in phytotechnologies pp 8.

van Steveninck RFM, Babare A, Fernando DR, Steveninck ME (1993) The binding of zinc in rootcells of crop plants by phytic acid. *Plant Soil* 155–156:525–528.

Van der Zaal BJ, Neuteboom LW, Pinas JE, Chardonnens AN, Schat H, Verkleij JAC, Hooykaas PJJ (1999) Overexpression of a novel *Arabidopsis* gene related to putative zinc-transporter genes from animals can lead to enhanced zinc resistance and accumulation. *Plant Physiol* 119: 1047–1055.

Vatamaniuk OK, Mari S, Lu Y-P, Rea PA (1999) AtPCS1, a phytochelatin synthase from Arabidopsis: Isolation and *in vitro* reconstitution. *PNAS USA,* 96: 7110–7115.

Vert G, Grotz N, Dédaldéchamp F, Gaymard F, Guerinot ML, Briat JF, Curie C (2002) IRT1, an *Arabidopsis* transporter essential for iron uptake from the soil and for plant growth. *Plant Cell* 14: 1223–1233.

Vinit-Dunand F, Epron D, Alaoui-Sosse B, Badot PM (2002) Effects of copper on growth and on photosynthesis of mature and expanding leaves in cucumber plants. *Plant Sci* 163: 53–58.

Wang Jian-Wu, Yan Li, Yu-Xiu Zhang, Tuan-Yao Chai (2013) Molecular cloning and characterization of a *Brassica juncea* yellow stripe-like gene, *BjYSL7*, whose overexpression increases heavy metal tolerance of tobacco. *Plant Cell Reports* 32: 651-662

White MC, Decker AM, Chancy RL (1979) Differential cultivar tolerance in soybean to phytotoxic levels of soil Zn. I. Range of cultivar response. *Agron J* 71: 121–126.

Whiting SN, de Souza MP, Terry N (2001) Rhizosphere bacteria mobilize Zn for hyperaccumulation by *Thlaspi caerulescens*. *Environ Sci Technol* 35: 3144–3150.

Yamamoto Y, Hachiya A, Matsumoto H. (1997) Oxidative damage to membranes by a combination of aluminum and iron in suspension-cultured tobacco cells. *Plant Cell Physiol* 38: 1333–1339.

Zrobek-Sokolnik A, Asard H, Gorska-Koplinska K, Gorecki RJ (2009) Cadmium and zinc-mediated oxidative burst in tobacco BY-2 cell suspension cultures. *Acta Physiol Planta* 31: 43–49.

Zantopoulos N, Antoniou V, Nikolaidis E (1999) Copper, zinc, cadmium, and lead in sheep grazing in North Greece. *Bull Environ Cont Toxicol* 62: 691–699.

Zenk MH (1996) Heavy metal detoxification in higher plants-a review. *Gene,* 179: 21–30.

Zhu Y, Pilon-Smits EAH, Jouanin L, Terry N (1999). Overexpression of glutathione synthetase in *Brassica juncea* enhances cadmium tolerance and accumulation. *Plant Physiol* 119: 73–79.

Zwarich MA, Mills JG (1982) Heavy metal accumulation by some vegetable crops grown on sewage-sludge-amended soils. *Can J Soil Sci* 62: 243–247.

In: Heavy Metal Remediation
Editors: Dharmendra Kumar Gupta and Soumya Chatterjee
ISBN: 978-1-63321-568-9
© 2014 Nova Science Publishers, Inc.

Chapter 9

PHYTOREMEDIATION OF MULTIPLY METAL-CONTAMINATED ENVIRONMENTS: SYNERGISTIC AND COMPETITIVE EFFECTS BETWEEN HEAVY METALS DURING UPTAKE AND TRANSPORT

Esra Üçüncü[1]*, Alper Devrim Özkan[2], Tolga Tarkan Ölmez[2] and Evren Tunca[3]

[1]Ankara University, Department of Biology, Faculty of Science, Ankara, Turkey
[2]Bilkent University, UNAM-Institute of Materials Science and Nanotechnology, Ankara, Turkey
[3]Ordu University, Department of Marine Science and Technology Engineering, Fatsa, Ordu, Turkey

ABSTRACT

Phytoremediation is a promising alternative to conventional metal treatment methods; however, most phytoremediation studies separately consider the removal of each individual metal, which may not fully reflect the situation present in real world contamination sites. Metal-contaminated environments seldom contain a single species of metal, and are instead host to several types of toxic metals and other contaminants. Consequently, the synergistic and antagonistic effects displayed between essential and non-essential metals, as well as these between metallic and non-metallic contaminants, are an important factor in determining the bioremediative efficiencies of plant species. The present chapter outlines the uptake, transport and sequestration mechanisms relevant to heavy metal accumulation, considers the potential competitive and cooperative interactions that occur between metals during these processes, details the current literature regarding bioremediation in multiply metal-contaminated environments and offers insights into the biochemical interactions underlying the trends observed for the beneficial and detrimental effects displayed between the accumulations of certain metals. We also illustrate the potential of metal remediation by aquatic macrophytes, a group

---

* Corresponding Author. Dr. EsraÜçüncü. Department of Biology, Faculty of Science, Ankara University, Ankara-06100, Turkey. Phone:0090-5057830703; Fax:0090-312-2232395; E. Mail:esra.ucuncu@gmail.com.

known for the effective remediation of multiple metals, which possess life histories that render them particularly conductive to studies investigating the impact of multiple metals on metal uptake.

Keywords: Phtyoremediation, Synergistic, Antagonistic, Transport, Heavy metal

1. INTRODUCTION

Industrial, agricultural and domestic processes all contribute strongly to the release of metal compounds into the environment, often in forms more available to biological systems than the metallic compounds naturally present in soils and sediments. Unlike many other types of contaminants, metals do not degrade naturally over time, and their capacity to accumulate progressively through the food chain renders them particularly dangerous to apex predators, including humans. Both essential and non-essential metals display toxic effects, primarily involving developmental defects and various neoplasms, above a threshold concentration. As such, it is imperative to control the extent of metal release into the environment, and to reduce the amount that is already present in natural soil and freshwater sources.

While effective methods, such as chemical oxidation or reduction, ion exchange, filtration, electrochemical treatment, reverse osmosis, membrane technologies and evaporation recovery, have been developed for the removal of metals from industrial wastes, the costs associated with these processes prevent their application over large areas of metal-contaminated soil or water (Zahoor and Rehman 2009). In addition, such methods frequently rely on mechanisms that are impossible to implement in natural environments without significantly damaging the local ecosystem. Consequently, several alternative approaches have been proposed for metal remediation in natural environments, and phytoremediation in particular has attracted much attention as a cost-effective means of metal removal in such locales (Yao et al. 2012). Phytoremediation, the sorption, reduction or sequestration of metals by dead or living plant tissues, allows the removal of contaminants without leaving a lasting impact on the environment, which renders this method ideal for metal remediation in metal-contaminated soils and freshwater sources, either by itself or in tandem with conventional metal removal techniques (Ali et al. 2013).

Metal removal characteristics of plants are well-described in the literature. Terrestrial plants and free-floating macrophytes are exposed to metals primarily by their root surfaces, while root, stem and leaf tissues of emergent and submerged aquatic plants are all in contact with the metal-contaminated environment, which figures heavily into the accumulation trends displayed by soil- and waterborne plants (Figueira et al. 2012; Verbruggen et al. 2013). In addition, while all plant material is expected to display some amount of metal uptake, certain plants are known to preferentially sequester certain metals (such as the zinc hyperaccumulator *Arabidopsis halleri* or the chromium hyperaccumulator *Leersia hexandra*) and may accumulate metal concentrations ~1000 times that of the environment in their tissues (Mishra et al. 2008; Liang et al. 2009; Liu et al. 2011). While the plant species is an important determiner of remediation capacity, metal accumulation also depends on the length of exposure, the metal of interest, its concentration, environmental parameters (*e.g.* temperature, salinity and pH) and the presence synergistic or antagonistic interactions with other metals in the environment. Depending on the valence, concentration and uptake mechanisms of "competing" metals, their presence may assist in, hinder, or be altogether irrelevant to the remediation characteristics of the metal of interest; and since polluted areas are seldom contaminated with only a single type of metal, interactions between multiple metal species are inevitable in most real-world applications of phytoremediation.

Given the importance of metal-metal interactions in the uptake and transport of metals, the present chapter will be devoted to the mechanisms by which metal entry and transportation occur in plants, and the changes that occur in accumulation behavior when multiple metals compete or cooperate within these pathways.

2. Metal Uptake, Transport and Sequestration Mechanisms in Plants

2.1. General Trends in Metal Accumulation in Plants

Plants can be grouped under four categories according to their accumulation behavior: non-specialists (or "ordinary plants"), bioindicators, excluders and hyperaccumulators (van der Ent et al. 2013). The majority of plant species can be categorized as non-specialists with regards to survival in metal-contaminated environments, and are capable of tolerating small amounts of metals, but do not possess the specialized mechanisms necessary for alleviating the increased stress associated with high metal concentrations. Bioindicators are hardy plants that tolerate contaminants to a greater degree than non-specialists, and the metal concentrations in their tissues often reflect the extent of metal contamination in the environment, which renders them important for the monitoring of metal pollution. In contrast, excluders resist metal contamination by preventing metal ions from entering their metabolism, though they also experience toxic effects at higher doses of metals, against which their contingency mechanisms begin to falter. Finally, hyperaccumulators store much higher concentrations of metals within their tissues, potentially utilize these metals as a form of defense mechanism, and experience little to no toxic effects in return, sometimes relying on metals to such an extent that concentrations that would be fatal to non-specialists, excluders and bioindicators may be necessary for the survival of a hyperaccumulator species (Rascio and Navari-Izzo 2011; van der Ent et al. 2013). It should be noted that a plant may display different accumulation trends for different contaminants, e.g. by hyperaccumulating only a select number of pollutants and displaying no such capacity for others (Antiochia et al. 2007). For a plant to be classified as a hyperaccumulator of a given metal, it must be able to tolerate concentrations above a set threshold for that metal; this threshold concentration is 100 μgg^{-1} for Cd, Se and Tl, 300 μgg^{-1} for Cu, Co and Cr, 1000 μgg^{-1} for Ni, As and Pb, 3000 μgg^{-1} for Zn and 10000 μgg^{-1} for Mn (Baker 1981; McGrath et al. 2000; van der Ent et al. 2013).

Following (or sometimes concurrent with) uptake, five broad types of mechanisms can facilitate the remediation of air, water or soil-borne contaminants: phytoextraction, phytovolatilization, rhizofiltration, phytodegradation and phytostabilization (Figure 1) (Cummings 2009; Valida et al. 2010; Dordio and Carvalho 2011). Of these, phytodegradation and phytovolatization are less applicable to metals, given that metals cannot be broken down into nontoxic materials and do not usually form volatile compounds in biological systems. Phytostabilization and rhizofiltration involve the modification and sequestration of toxic metals at the uptake site, while phytoextraction entails both the uptake of metal ions from the surrounding soil or water, and their transport from the roots to the other parts of the plant.

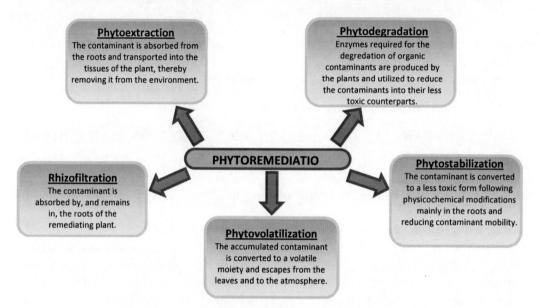

Phytoextraction
The contaminant is absorbed from the roots and transported into the tissues of the plant, thereby removing it from the environment.

Phytodegradation
Enzymes required for the degradation of organic contaminants are produced by the plants and utilized to reduce the contaminants into their less toxic counterparts.

PHYTOREMEDIATIO

Rhizofiltration
The contaminant is absorbed by, and remains in, the roots of the remediating plant.

Phytostabilization
The contaminant is converted to a less toxic form following physicochemical modifications mainly in the roots and reducing contaminant mobility.

Phytovolatilization
The accumulated contaminant is converted to a volatile moiety and escapes from the leaves and to the atmosphere.

Figure 1. Mechanisms by which plants facilitate the removal of pollutants from the environment.

Metal uptake in terrestrial plants and free-floating macrophytes occurs primarily through the roots, as metals and their compounds are usually non-volatile, and solid particles that are deposited on above-ground tissues are not easily recovered by plants. As metal cations are readily available in water, however, all tissues of submerged macrophytes can take part in metal uptake. In both aquatic and terrestrial plants, uptake begins with the transitory association of metal ions to the plant surface by adsorption, followed by proton pump-, membrane transporter- or ion channel-mediated internalization (Hall 2002). In addition, metal ions or complexes may directly penetrate cell membranes without the aid of a transporter protein, though chelating mechanisms exist to prevent the undesired metal entry in this manner (Simkiss 1983; Macfie and Welbourn 2000).

Plant symbionts may intimately interact with the metabolism of their hosts and, by extension, play a role in metal uptake by plants. Rhizobacteria (PGPR) are a group of bacterial symbionts that enhance nutrient uptake and contribute to plant defense systems, and their presence is also known to enhance the mobilization of metal ions by acidification, redox reactions and the production of chelating agents, such as siderophores. Rhizobacteria can also enhance the dissolution of metal ions from bulk particles, which is a prerequisite of metal uptake (Evangelou et al. 2007). Arbuscular mycorrhizal fungi (AMF) may also assist in the entry of metals into plant roots; however, there is some evidence that these fungi may also function as a filter for metals, thereby preventing metal uptake by plant tissues (Hildebrandt et al. 2007; Zhuang et al. 2007). Little is known about the AMF-mediated pathways that regulate metal uptake by plant roots; however, the metallothionein gene of *Gigaspora margarita* has been found to be up regulated upon Cu introduction, while GintZnT1 gene expression in *Glomus intraradices* is reported to be increased under Zn overexposure, and GintABC1 in response to Cd and Cu (Lanfranco et al. 2002; Gonzalez-Guerrero et al. 2005; Clemens 2006a). As such, metallothioneins, phytochelatins and metal transporter genes of symbiotic fungi also appear to be important for the metal uptake of their hosts.

2.2. Metal Transport Mechanisms

Due to the detrimental effects of many metals, plants generally lack the capacity for their specific uptake and transport, and instead possess mechanisms that exclude them from their tissues. However, despite the lack of specialized mechanisms for the uptake of elements with no metabolic functions, many non-essential and even severely toxic metals are readily recovered by plant tissues, as similarities in valence states, hydrodynamic radii or other chemical properties may allow a non-essential metal to utilize the mechanisms evolved for the transport of other metals (some toxic effects of non-essential metals are also caused by this similarity, which permits them to replace cofactors in enzymes and therefore disrupt enzymatic activity). Cd, for example, has been reported to utilize the metabolic pathways that function for the transport of Zn (Clemens 2006b), and the divalent cation-transporting protein IRT1 may transport Cd^{+2} in addition to essential ions such as Fe^{+2}, Mn^{+2} or Co^{+2} (Cohen et al. 1998). Likewise, chromate (CrO_4^{-2}) anions can utilize pathways intended for sulfate transport, while arsenate and selenium are sufficiently similar to phosphate and sulfur to be actively recovered by plants. This lack of specificity may allow essential and non-essential metals to compete over a shared transport pathway, and competitive interactions may also exist between groups of chemically similar essential metals (Jadia and Fulekar 2009). Consequently, the concentrations of both essential and non-essential metals in the environment contribute considerably to the efficiency of phytoremediation efforts.

A great variety of transporter proteins function in the transfer of metal ions within and between cells and tissues (Table 1). These include metal transporting ATPases, the natural resistance associated macrophage protein (NRAMP) family, the cation diffusion facilitator (CDF) family, the ZRT/IRT (Zn regulated transporter/iron regulated transporter) like protein (ZIP) family, the Ca^{2+}-sensitive cross complementer 1 (CCC1) family, the yellow-stripe 1-like (YSL) subfamily, the iron-regulated protein (IREG) family and the copper transporter (COPT) family. Other membrane proteins involved in the transport of transition metals are multidrug resistance-associated proteins (MRP), the ABC transporters of the mitochondria (ATM), the cation exchanger (CAX) family, three subfamilies of ATP-binding cassette (ABC) transporters and the pleiotropic drug resistance (PDR) transporters. In addition, pytochelatins, metallothioneins and certain organic acids, amino acids and phosphate derivatives are known to display metal-binding functions. AtFRD3 (Ferric Reductase Defective 3) and AtZIF1 (Zinc Induced Facilitator 1) are other proteins suspected to be heavily involved in the transport of metals (Guerinot 2000; Williams et al. 2000; Rogers and Guerinot 2002; Green and Rogers 2004; Lee et al. 2005; Kramer et al. 2007; Manara 2012).

Table 1. Proteins and other organic materials involved in metal uptake, transfer or sequestration

Metabolite name	Classification	Metals	Mechanism*	Reference
Type 2 metallothionein	MT	Cd, Cu, Zn	3	Hildebrandt et al. 2007
PCS (phytochelatin synthase)	PC	Cd, As, Hg	3	Hildebrandt et al. 2007
HSP90	Heat shock	Cd, Cu, Zn		Hildebrandt et al. 2007
GST	GSH	Cd, Cu, Zn	3	Hildebrandt et al. 2007
ABC-type transporter protein	Vacuole transport protein	Cd, Mg	2	Lu et al. 1997
Anthocyanins	Secondary metabolite	Mn, Cd, Zn, Co, Ni, Mg	3	Pilon-Smits and Pilon 2002
IRT1	ZIP family	Cd, Zn, Fe	2	Meagher 2000
Zn transporter	ZIP family	Fe, Mn, Zn	2	Hildebrandt et al. 2007
AtHMA4	P-type ATPase	Zn, Cd	2	Yang et al. 2005
CDF family proteins	CE family	Zn, Co, Cd	2	Yang et al. 2005
OsNramp1, 2, 3	Nramp	Cd, Mn, Co, Zn	2	Belouchi et al. 1997
Glomalin	Glycoprotein	Cu, Cd, Pb	4	Gonzalez-Chavez et al. 2004
EDTA (HEDTA, DTPA, CDTA, EGTA etc.)	Aminopolycarboxylic acid	Cd, Ni, Pb, Zn, Cu	1	Evangelou et al. 2007
Phytosiderophores	Siderophore	Fe, Zn, Cu, Mn	1	Yang et al. 2005
TgMTP1, COT1, ZRC1	Vacuolar metal ion transporter (CE family)	Ni, Cd, Co, Zn	4	Persans et al. 2001
ACC deaminase	Deaminase	Cd, Co, Cu, Ni, Pb, Zn	1	Grichko et al. 2000
YCF1 (transgenics)	Recombinant protein	Pb, Cd	4	Kramer 2005
HMA4 (transgenics)	Recombinant protein	Zn, Cd	2	Kramer 2005

Mechanisms are divided into four parts; 1) Uptake from environment or extracellular matrix, 2) Transportation systems, 3) Chelation mechanisms and 4) Segregation or sequesteration in vesicular structures.

2.3. Sequestration of Accumulated Metals

Once within plant tissues, metals are eliminated under three principal mechanisms: They can be neutralized by the cell membrane, sequestered within the cell following internalization, or retained outside the cell (Basile et al. 2012). Within each category, several specific pathways exist for the minimization of detrimental effects following metal uptake (Figure 2). In cell membrane-mediated neutralization, a negatively charged, membrane-bound residue fixes the metal group to the cell membrane and prevents its entry into the cell, which prevents the metal from interacting with intracellular materials. Keeping the metal ions outside the cytoplasm entails both the blockage of metal ion entry, which involves decreases in membrane permeability and transporter expressions, and the expulsion of intracellular metal ions by specialized transporters. Metal ions that are already present within the cell can also be deposited within apoplasts by the action of membrane proteins, or rendered harmless by metal-binding moieties such as metallothioneins, organic acids, amino acids and phytochelatins. Once bound, the metal-ligand complex is subsequently deposited within a vacuole. Tonoplast transporters are also effective in sequestering metal ions within vacuoles (Manara 2012).

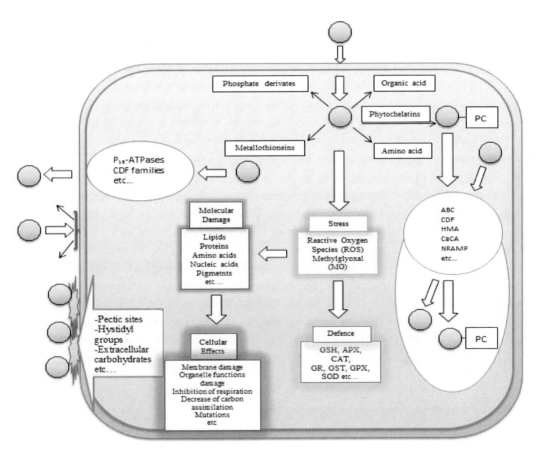

Figure 2. Response mechanisms for the presence of excess metal ions within the cell (Hossain et al. 2012; Manara 2012; Zitka et al. 2013).

While some metals are essential for living organisms, other metals participate in no known metabolic activity and are not necessary to sustain life. Non-essential metals, as well as excess amounts of essential metals, are exported outside the cell or sequestered within a vacuole or metal-ligand complex (Peng and Gong 2014). However, if these compensatory mechanisms are insufficient to counteract the excess metal concentrations, these metals cause intracellular damage under three principal mechanisms, (a) by interacting with thiol, histidyl and carboxyl groups present in peptides, (b) by stimulating the formation of reactive oxygen species (ROS) and (c) by displacing essential metals as cofactors and therefore interfering with protein function (Schutzendubel and Polle 2002). ROS are regularly produced as a result of many intracellular reactions, but the compensatory mechanisms are normally able to alleviate the potential damage that would be caused by these molecules. Metal ions are known to stimulate the formation of free radicals and ROS such as singlet oxygen ($^1O_2$), superoxide radicals ($O_2^{\cdot-}$), hydrogen peroxide (H_2O_2), and hydroxyl radicals ($^{\cdot}OH$) (Sharma and Dietz 2009). The creation of additional ROS presence by metal ions may therefore overwhelm the response mechanisms in place. These radicals then react with cellular components to create various types of cellular damage, such as lipid peroxidation, protein oxidation, enzyme inactivation and DNA damage (Hossain et al. 2012). These effects, in turn, result in physiological or metabolic damage to the cell.

3. EFFECT OF MULTIPLE METALS ON METAL UPTAKE AND TRANSPORT

3.1. Mechanisms Underlying Synergistic and Antagonistic Effects between Metals

Non-essential metal uptake and transport mechanisms generally utilize pathways normally involved in the absorption of essential metals, and mechanisms for their exclusion or sequestration are often shared between different types of metal species (Pence et al. 2000; Williams et al. 2000). Consequently, the presence of an essential or non-essential metal may alter the uptake, transport and sequestration of other metals. These interactions may include direct effects, such as competition over specific binding sites or co-uptake by transport proteins, as well as more indirect mechanisms in which the presence of one metal activates defensive processes that protect the plant from other metals (or, conversely, trigger the enhanced uptake of another metal). In addition, remediative efforts using live plants are obviously futile if a contaminant in the environment is fatal to the intended remediative agent, even if the plant in question may effectively sequester the remaining pollutants (a chromium hyperaccumulator, for example, cannot necessarily be used in locales contaminated with both chromium and arsenic, unless it possess sufficient resistance to arsenic in addition to chromium). As such, the ability of a plant to remediate a contaminated environment depends on the environmental conditions present in the surrounding medium, including not only the metallic nutrients and their uptake mechanisms, but also the precise composition of the metal mixture present in the environment. These metal-metal interactions can be classified under three closely related categories:

3.1.1. Binding-Mediated Effects (Competition and Co-uptake)

While non-essential metals are often considered in their capacity to compete with essential metals, shared use of identical uptake and transport mechanisms may also force multiple non-essential metal species to compete over a limited number of binding sites. Conversely, metals utilizing these mechanisms will tend to co-accumulate if a competitive environment is absent. Major classes of metal-binding proteins, such as phytochelatins and metallothioneins, are not specific to a single metal (but may heavily favor complexes with a specific metal, e.g. for phytochelatins and Cd) and the adsorption-mediated initiation of metal uptake depends on the surface chemistry of the plant and the metal ion, allowing metals with similar valence states to potentially substitute for each other (Zenk 1996). As such, metals displaying similar affinities to common binding sites present on plant surfaces or in tissues and cells may show similar trends in accumulation, and potentially exclude each other in higher concentrations. This dose-dependent effect potentially contributes to the complex, dose- and tissue-specific interplay of antagonistic and synergistic interactions observed in some studies (Liu et al. 2008).

3.1.2. Compensatory Mechanism-Mediated Effects

The presence of excess metal concentrations triggers compensatory processes that prevent the entry of metals into plant tissues, allowing the plant to survive in environments that would otherwise be fatal (Steffens 1990; Maksymiec 2007). These mechanisms, which rely on the above-mentioned binding and chelation effects, are often general and may sequester a large variety of metals, allowing the plant to exclude or co-accumulate multiple metal species that are present in the environment, even if the defensive mechanism in question was activated by a single species of metal. These pathways may also alter the manner in which the uptakes of essential elements are maintained, which disrupts cellular homeostasis and contributes to the tissue damage created by heavy metal presence (Hall 2002). Element depletion may also activate scavenging pathways that are utilized by metals to facilitate tissue or cell entry, and therefore enhance metal remediation. As such, the lack of an essential metal, such as Fe, may trigger the upregulation of membrane transporters that non-specifically uptake other metals, such as Cd (Cohen et al. 1998; Thomine et al. 2000).

3.1.3. Toxicity-Based Effects

Non-essential metals, as well as excess amounts of essential metals interfere with the function of enzymes, and indirectly facilitate the creation of reactive oxygen species responsible for many forms of cellular damage. In addition, environments contaminated with metals often feature other forms of pollution, and species intended for use as live phytoremediation agents must be sufficiently resistant to any contaminant that is present at the site of interest, and should preferably accumulate all such pollutants. However, combinations of metals may be more toxic than when administered individually, and the presence of a severely detrimental element may hamper remediative efforts with a plant species that displays effective uptake of other metals. As such, the additive or synergistic toxicity of metals should be taken into account when real-world applications of phytoremediation are considered. The reverse (and unlikely) case, of decreased metal toxicity due to competitive effects, and should not be considered significant for live plants intended for use in bioremediation, and may be undesirable as the competition may also decrease the amount of metal accumulated by the plant, thereby lowering remediation efficiency.

3.2. Specific Examples of Synergy and Antagonism between Metal Pairs

A large number of synergistic and antagonistic interactions between metals are described in the literature, some of which are presented in Table 2. The interactions of important and widespread pollutants, such as Cd, Zn and Pb, are relatively well-characterized; however, the nature of these interactions may vary significantly between individual studies (Chaoui et al. 1997; Grispen et al. 2006). These discrepancies are in line with both the complexity of multi-metal interactions, and the variable nature of multi-metal uptake mechanisms; as transporters that assist in the transfer of two or more metals may create synergistic or antagonistic interactions depending on the availability of each metal, and the impact of metal toxicity on plant metabolism may affect the uptake of other metals. Plant species, metal concentrations and environmental parameters are therefore expected to significantly alter the outcome of uptake in multi-metal environments. Such concentration-dependent interactions have been noted between Cd and Zn, which are known to share transport proteins, as well as between Pb and Zn, and Cd and Pb (Lombi et al. 2001; Zhao et al. 2002; Grispen et al. 2006; Angelova et al. 2008).

It is notable that antagonistic effects are more frequently noted in phytoremediation research, while synergistic effects are comparatively more pronounced in studies that concern the toxicity of metals. This situation may be interpreted as a result of the differences in the models and metal concentrations utilized in these two types of research. In toxicity studies, near-lethal doses are usually applied, resulting in rapid, synergistic lethality. In remediation studies, hardier plants and tolerable metal concentrations are used, potentially bringing competitive interactions to the fray.

4. NON-METAL CONTRIBUTORS TO METAL REMEDIATION

While the present chapter underlines the effects of metal contaminants on the uptake profiles of each other; non-metal contaminants, chelating agents, symbiotic organisms and stress factors may display supportive or detrimental effects similar to these recorded for mixtures of metals (Table 3). The inclusion of EDTA or other chelating agents, for example, are known to solubilize metals and better facilitate their uptake from the soil, and the deliberate introduction of these materials has been suggested as a means to improve remediation efficiency (Meers et al. 2005; Evangelou et al. 2007). However, these materials may also allow the metals present on the surface to leach through to deeper layers (Wu et al. 2004). Other environments, such as these provided by rhizospheres, instead serve to decrease metal uptake (Meagher and Heaton 2005). Non-metal contaminants, such as organic hydrocarbons, may also affect metal uptake, and usually create synergistically toxic effects (e.g. for PCP and Cu in *Lolium perenne* and *Raphanus sativus*, or for nitrilotriacetate and Cd, Cu and Zn in *L. perenne* and *Lactuca sativa*) (Kulli et al. 1999; Lin et al. 2006).

Table 2. Synergistic and antagonistic interactions between metal accumulations and toxicities in higher plants

Organism(s)	Metal/Metalloid	Nature of effect*	Reference
Glycine max	As/Cd, As/Pb, As/Cd/Pb	S (As/Cd, As/Cd/Pb)/A (As/Pb)	Luan et al. 2008
Brassica spp.	Cu/Zn	A (Zn influenced by Cu but not vice-versa)	Ebbs and Kochian 1997
Pelargonium hortorum	Cu/Zn	A	Orrono et al. 2012
Pisum sativum	Cd/Mn	A	Hernandez et al. 1998
Brassica napus	Cd/Zn	S	Grispen et al. 2006
Brassica napus	Cd/Pb, Cd/Zn, Pb/Zn	S/A (dependent on tissue and treatment)	Angelova et al. 2008
Higher plants	Cd/Fe	S/A (S at low doses, A otherwise)	Siedlecka and Krupa 1999
Amaranthus spp.	Fe/Ni	A	Shevyakova et al. 2011
Allium fistulosum	Hg/Se	A	Afton and Caruso 2009
Glycine max	Hg/Se	A	Yathavakilla and Caruso 2007
Brassica juncea	Hg/Se	A	Mounicou et al. 2006
Beta vulgaris	Cd/Mn	A	Singh and Agrawal 2007
Phaseolus vulgaris	Cd/Zn	A	Chaoui et al. 1997
Submerged aquatic plants	Cd, Cu, Hg, Pb in mixtures	S	Jana and Choudhuri 1984
Triticum aestivum	Cd/As	S	Liu et al. 2007
Oryza sativa	Cd/Cu	S (Cd influenced by Cu but not vice-versa)	Huang et al. 2009
Lemna minor	Cd/Pb, Cd/Zn, Pb/Zn	A	Mohan and Hosetti 1997
Vetiveria zizanioides	Cd/Zn	S	Xu et al. 2009
Lactuca sativa	Fe/Cd	A	Thys et al. 1991

* S denotes a synergistic relationship between metal(loid) ions; A denotes an antagonistic relationship.

5. AQUATIC MACROPHYTES: AN IDEAL GROUP FOR MULTIPLE METAL CONTAMINATION STUDIES?

5.1. Macrophyte Biology and Remediation Potential

Macrophytes, aquatic higher plants, are the dominant plants in the shores of flowing or still freshwater sources, and may be submergent, emergent or free-floating. Emergent macrophytes grow near the shore and break the water surface, though their roots and part of their stem are below the water. Submerged macrophytes, in contrast, are wholly below the water, except possibly for their flowers, while free-floating macrophytes are largely above the water surface; they may be loosely attached to the substrate by their roots or be altogether rootless. Macrophytes are ecologically important due to their release of oxygen into the freshwater ecosystem, as well as their status as a principal food source for herbivorous fish. In addition, a thick covering of these plants serve as a refuge to invertebrates and small fish, and protect these animals from predation.

Table 3. Non-metal materials reported to affect the uptake of metals

Materials	Description	Metal(loid)s	Reference
Anthocyanins	Vacuolar Pigment	Mn, Cd, Zn, Co, Ni, Mg	Pilon-Smits and Pilon 2002
Phytosiderophores	Siderophore	Fe, Zn, Cu, Mn	Yang et al. 2005
EDTA	Synthetic aminopolycarboxylic acid	Zn, Cu, Cd, Ni	Meers et al. 2005
Rhizosphere	Root environment	Hg, As	Meagher and Heaton 2005
Tartaric acid	Low mw org. acids	Cd, Pb, Cu, Zn	Ke et al. 2006
EDDS (ethylene diamine disuccinate)	Natural aminopolycarboxylic acid	Cu, cd, Zn, Pb	Yip et al. 2009
TCE (trichloroethylene)	Linear halogenated carbons	Hg	Zhang et al. 2013
TNT (trinitrotoluene)	Nitroaromatics	Cd, Pb	Lee et al. 2007
Dioxin	PCB (polychlorinatedbiphenyls)	Cd, Cu	Wu et al. 2012
Benzoapyrene	PAH (polycyclic aromatic hydrocarbons)	Cd, Cu, Pb	Sun et al. 2011

Macrophytes are moderately capable metal accumulators, and can deposit environmental toxins in their root, stem or leaf tissues (Axtell 2003; Miretzky et al. 2004). Their ability to readily remediate metals from an aquatic medium makes them model research subjects in the field of toxicology (Vardanyan and Ingole 2006). In addition to their remediative capacity, macrophytes are easy to harvest and culture, serve as bioindicator species for a variety of metal species (Garnczarska and Ratajczak 2000), proliferate rapidly and serve as the initial link between aquatic toxins and higher steps of the food chain (Singh et al. 2006), which makes them preferred organisms in phytoremediation studies. For example *Lemna minor* is one of the most commonly utilized duckweed species in academic studies (figure 3). *L. minor* has been reported for the effective remediation of several metals, with high removal rates within 24 h of exposure to Pb and Cr (Hurd and Sternberg 2008; Üçüncü et al. 2013). In addition to *L. minor*, other macrophytes (e.g. *L. gibba*, *Microspora* spp.) have been successfully tested in remediation studies using aquatic media.

Figure 3. *Lemna minor* fronds in (a) wilderness and (b) laboratory culture.

5.2. Potential Uses of Macrophytes in Phytoremediation

In addition to land-based metal removal efforts, there is a considerable amount of research performed on the phytoremediation of contaminated freshwater ecosystems (Table 4). However, large-scale studies in natural environments are lacking in this area. Laboratory experiments are generally limited to the remediation of small volumes of water, which may not be sufficiently predictive of the *in situ* remediative potential of a plant species, as the success of phytoremediation efforts depends on a large number of environmental variables. As such, pilot studies in large bodies of water are necessary to evaluate whether aquatic plant-based treatment methods are sufficient for the remediation of contaminated freshwater sources. Examples of such large-scale studies include the removal of wastewater metals in alga- or duckweed-containing pools (Sekomo et al. 2012), and the use of *L. minor* for the remediation of a eutrophic lake (Ansari and Khan 2008).

Tablo 4. Macrophyte species used for bioremediation studies, and their accumulation capacities

Family species	Heavy metals	Accumulation/removal rates (%)	References
Araceae *Lemna minor*	Cu Cr Pb	37.17%-51% Over 99% 89.96-96.78%	Üçüncü et al. 2013
Azollaceae *Azolla filiculoides*	Cd Cu	1623.20 g g^{-1} 6013.1 g g^{-1}	Valderrama et al. 2013
Araceae *Lemna minor*	As	430 mg kg^{-1} DW	Favas et al. 2012
Azollaceae *Azolla caroliniana*		397 mg kg^{-1} DW	
Araceae *Lemna gibba* L.	Zn	4.23 to 25.88 mg g^{-1} DM	Khellaf and Zerdaoui 2012
Araceae *Spirodela polyrhiza* L.	As	400–900 mg kg^{-1} DW	Zhang et al. 2011
Pontederiaceae *Eichhornia crassipes*	Hg, As	In roots 0.45 ± 0.02 µg g^{-1} (Hg), 0.34 ± 0.012 µg g^{-1} (As) In leaves 0.29 ± 0.02 µg g^{-1} (Hg), 0.25 ± 0.01 µg g^{-1} (As)	Mishra et al. 2008
Araceae *Lemna minor*		In root 0.38 ± 0.03µg g^{-1} (Hg), 0.29 ± 0.01µg g^{-1} (As) İn leaves 0.25 ± 0.01µg g^{-1} (Hg), 0.21 ± 0.001µg g^{-1} (As	
Spirodela polyrrhiza		In root 0.35 ± 0.01µg g^{-1} (Hg), 0.26 ± 0.01 µg g^{-1} (As) İn leaves 0.23 ± 0.02 µg g^{-1} (Hg), 0.16 ± 0.01 µg g^{-1} (As)	
Pontederiaceae *Eichhornia crassipes*	As	600 mg As ha^{-1} d 140 mg As ha^{-1} d	Alvarado et al. 2008
Araceae *Lemna minor*	Cu	$6,135$ µg Cu g^{-1}	
Araceae *Lemna minor* L.	Pb, Cd	1116 µg g^{-1} (Exposed to 50 µg Pb m L-1)	Saygıdeğer and Doğan 2004
Araceae *Lemna minor*	Pb, Ni	% 76(Pb), % 82(Ni)	Axtell 2003

In addition to accumulative potential, the toxicity of the contaminant on the remediative organism is an important aspect of bioremediation. In most phytoremediation studies, the detrimental effects that the contaminant may have had on the plant are also evaluated, and understanding the cellular or tissue stress responses that the remediative agent may produce in response to the contaminant is important to determine how the remediation process occurs. By extension, the behaviors of the remediative agent can also be taken to be representative of the physiological and morphological responses displayed by contaminant-exposed organisms. These responses are often severe, and their details are frequently described in the literature. For example, in a study using *Chlorococcum hemicolum*, the presence of Ni was found to decrease total sugar, chlorophyll and carotenoid levels due to metal stress-related effects (Harish et al. 2008). In another study, the effects of sewer water Cu on the seeds of *L. minor* and *Raphanus sativus* were determined, and the first 8-16 days of the 64 day-long study were marked by ammonia-derived toxicity, as the higher pH was found to be detrimental for *Lemna* (Fjallborg 2003). In a third study, two-metal combinations of Cr, Pb and Cu were tested for toxic effects on *L. minor*, and high biomass inhibition was observed in every mixture containing Cu. (Üçüncü et al. 2013).

It is also notable that different sections of a plant are subject to different remediative capacities and characteristics; while some plants uptake metals using their roots; others accumulate metals in their leaves. Three aquatic macrophytes (*Eichhornia crassipes*, *L. minor* and *Spirodela polyrrhiza*) were shown to remediate As and Hg more effectively with their roots, compared to their leaves, in the wastewater of a coal mine. Likewise, in *Acacia victoria*, Pb accumulation was shown to be concentrated in the roots (Mahdavi et al. 2014). On the other hand, some species store metals in their shoots, such as *Schoenoplectus lacustris*, which was shown to be a shoot accumulator for Mn and Cd (Duman et al. 2007).

Consortiums are also important in this field of research, and may be more effective than phytoremediation efforts involving a single species. A study, utilizing the plants *Pistia stratiotes*, *Eichhornia crassipess*, *Hydrocotyleum bellatta*, *Lemna minor*, *Tyhpa latifolia*, and *Scirpus acutus*, has demonstrated that mixtures of plants are more capable phytoremediators compared to individual plants, suggesting that a cooperative effect may exist when tissues from different plants are used (Farid et al. 2014).

In addition to their ecological utility, phytoremediation studies are also relevant to the fields of molecular biology and genetics, as the selection of metal-accumulating strains, or the insertion of genes that confer metal resistance, may result in the emergence of strains with enhanced bioremediation capacity.

5.3. Efficiency of Macrophytes for Metal-Metal Interaction Studies

Due to their small size, ease of procurement and rapid growth, macrophytes are popular models for toxicology research, and these features also render them desirable for use in multiple-metal studies. In addition, as water as a highly uniform medium and ensures the even distribution of metal ions, the use of macrophytes eliminates the problem of non-uniform metal concentrations that may be present in field studies with land plants, as well as the possibility of local metal depletion caused by metal uptake (Gerhardt et al. 2009). The existence of emergent, submergent and free-floating species also allows the testing of multiple metal uptake methods on closely related species, which presumably have similar mechanisms for metal transport, but may display different uptake properties due to different tissues being exposed to metals. Further, the ready availability of metals in aquatic environments makes macrophytes ideal for large-scale applications, and especially for commercial uses of phytoremediation, as these easy-to-grow plants can be procured at a low costs and utilized for the removal of metals in large volumes of freshwater. Single metal studies incorporating many of the ecologically important metals have been performed on macrophytes (Table 4), and the analysis of changes in metal accumulation capacities following multiple metal concentrations should allow greater insight into the competitive and cooperative interactions that occur for metal uptake and transport in aquatic environments. While uptake mechanisms in aquatic and terrestrial environments bear close similarities, whether the synergies and antagonisms present in soil-borne metals are closely reflected in an aqueous environment is nonetheless another question that merits attention.

CONCLUSION

Metal uptake capacities in both terrestrial and aquatic plants are determined by a great variety of factors, including not only environmental conditions, but also the physiological state of the phytoremediation agent and other contaminants present in the vicinity. As metal contaminations are rarely found in isolation, future studies involving the real world applications of phytoremediation must consider the network of interactions behind the uptake, transport, chelation and sequestration of metals, metalloids, organic contaminants and other environmental pollutants. These interactions are often complex and may switch between synergy and antagonism depending on the concentrations of the interacting metals, as well as the presence of a third metal. As such, greater insight into the mechanisms underlying metal uptake and transport is required to predict the nature of metal-metal interactions in a given system. In addition to the synergistic or antagonistic effects caused by multiple metal presence, the effect of other chemicals, such as non-metal pollutants, chelating agents or local bacterial flora, will affect remediation behavior.

Macrophytes, due to their ease of maintenance, rapid growth and tendency to readily recover heavy metals from the surrounding water, are promising plants for the study of heavy metal uptake in both singly and multiply contaminated environments. Further, their heavy metal uptake characteristics are well-known in single-metal studies, allowing easier comparisons between single-metal and multi-metal comparison behaviors.

REFERENCES

Afton S, Caruso J (2009) The effect of Se antagonism on the metabolic fate of Hg in *Allium fistulosum*. *J Analytl Atom Spectrom* 24: 759–766.

Ali H, Khan E, Sajad M (2013) Phytoremediation of heavy metals-Concepts and applications. *Chemosphere* 91: 869–881.

Alvarado S, Guedez M, Lue-Meru MP, Nelson G, Alvaro A, Jesus AC, Gyula Z (2008) Arsenic removal from waters by bioremediation with the aquatic plants Water Hyacinth (*Eichhornia crassipes*) and Lesser Duckweed (*Lemna minor*). *Biores Technol* 99: 8436–8440.

Angelova V, Ivanova R, Todorov G, Ivanov K (2008) Heavy metal uptake by rape. *Comm Soil Sci Plant Anal* 39: 344–357.

Ansari AA, Khan FA (2008) Remediation of eutrophic water using *Lemna minor* in a controlled environment. *Afri J Aquat Sci* 33: 275–278.

Antiochia R, Campanella L, Ghezzi P, Movassaghi K (2007) The use of vetiver for remediation of heavy metal soil contamination. *Anal Bioanal Chem* 388: 947–956.

Axtell N (2003) Lead and nickel removal using Microspora and *Lemna minor*. *Biores Technol* 89: 41–48.

Baker AJM (1981) Accumulators and excluders-strategies in the response of plants to heavy metals. *J Plant Nutr* 3: 643–654.

Basile A, Sorbo S, Conte B, Cobianchi RC, Trinchella F, Capasso C, Carginale V (2012) Toxicity, accumulation, and removal of heavy metals by three aquatic macrophytes. *Int J Phytorem* 14: 374–387.

Belouchi A, Kwan T, Gros P (1997) Cloning and characterization of the OsNramp family from *Oryza sativa*, a new family of membrane proteins possibly implicated in the transport of metal ions. *Plant Mol Biol* 33: 1085–1092.

Chaoui A, Ghorbal M, El-Ferjani E (1997) Effects of cadmium-zinc interactions on hydroponically grown bean (*Phaseolus vulgaris* L). *Plant Sci* 126: 21–28.

Clemens S (2006a) Evolution and function of phytochelatin synthases. *J Plant Physiol* 163: 319–332.

Clemens S (2006b) Toxic metal accumulation, responses to exposure and mechanisms of tolerance in plants. *Biochimie* 88: 1707–1719.

Cohen C, Fox T, Garvin D, Kochian LV (1998) The role of iron-deficiency stress responses in stimulating heavy-metal transport in plants. *Plant Physiol* 116: 1063–1072.

Cummings SP (2009*) Bioremediation: Methods and protocols* (Methods in Molecular Biology Vol 599). *Humana Press,* Totowa, NJ.

Dordio A, Palace Carvalho AJ (2011) Phytoremediation: An option for removal of organic xenobiotics from water. In: Golubev IA (ed) *Handbook of Phytoremediation,* Nova Science Publishers, New York pp 51–92.

Duman F, Cicek M, Sezen G (2007) Seasonal changes of metal accumulation and distribution in common club rush (*Schoenoplectus lacustris*) and common reed (*Phragmites australis*). *Ecotoxicology* 16: 457–463.

Ebbs S, Kochian LV (1997) Toxicity of zinc and copper to Brassica species: Implications for phytoremediation. *J Environ Qual* 26: 776–781.

Evangelou M, Ebel M, Schaeffer A (2007) Chelate assisted phytoextraction of heavy metals from soil: Effect, mechanism, toxicity, and fate of chelating agents. *Chemosphere* 68: 989–1003.

Farid M, Irshad M, Fawad M, Awan ZA, Eneji AE, Aurangzeb N (2014) Effect of cyclic phytoremediation with different wetland plants on municipal wastewater. *Int J Phytorem* 16: 572–581.

Favas PJC, Pratas J, Prasad MNV (2012) Accumulation of arsenic by aquatic plants in large-scale field conditions: Opportunities for phytoremediation and bioindication. *Sci Total Environ* 433: 390–397.

Figueira E, Freitas R, Pereira E, Duarte A (2012) Mercury uptake and allocation in *Juncus maritimus*:Implications for phytoremediation and restoration of a mercury contaminated salt marsh. *J Environ Monit* 14: 2181–2188.

Fjallborg B (2003) Toxicity of copper in sewage sludge. *Environ Int* 28: 761–769.

Garnczarska M, Ratajczak L (2000) Metabolic responses of *Lemna minor* to lead ions-1:Growth, chlorophyll level and activity of fermentative enzymes. *Acta Physiol Plant* 22: 423–427.

Gerhardt K, Huang X, Glick B, Greenberg B (2009) Phytoremediation and rhizoremediation of organic soil contaminants: Potential and challenges. *Plant Sci* 176: 20–30.

Gonzalez-Chavez M, Carrillo-Gonzalez R, Wright S, Nichols K (2004) The role of glomalin, a protein produced by arbuscular mycorrhizal fungi, in sequestering potentially toxic elements. *Environ Pollut* 130: 317–323.

Gonzalez-Guerrero M, Azcon-Aguilar C, Mooney M, Valderas A, MacDiarmid C, Eide D, Ferrol N (2005) Characterization of a *Glomus intraradices* gene encoding a putative Zn transporter of the cation diffusion facilitator family. *Fung Genet* Biol 42: 130–140.

Green LS, Rogers EE (2004) FRD3 controls iron localization in *Arabidopsis*. *Plant Physiol* 136: 2523–2531.

Grichko V, Filby B, Glick B (2000) Increased ability of transgenic plants expressing the bacterial enzyme ACC deaminase to accumulate Cd, Co, Cu, Ni, Pb, and *Zn*. *J Biotechnol* 81: 45–53.

Grispen V, Nelissen H, Verkleij J (2006) Phytoextraction with *Brassica napus* L.: A tool for sustainable management of heavy metal contaminated soils. *Environ Pollut* 144: 77–83.

Guerinot ML (2000) The ZIP family of metal transporters. *Biochim Et Biophy ActaBiomemb* 1465: 190–198.

Hall J (2002) Cellular mechanisms for heavy metal detoxification and tolerance. *J Exp Bot* 53: 1–11.

Harish Sundaramoorthy S, Kumar D, Vaijapurkar SG (2008) A new chlorophycean nickel hyperaccumulator. *Biores Technol* 99: 3930–3934.

Hernandez L, Lozano-Rodriguez E, Garate A, Carpena-Ruiz R (1998) Influence of cadmium on the uptake, tissue accumulation and subcellular distribution of manganese in pea seedlings. *Plant Sci* 132: 139–151.

Hildebrandt U, Regvar M, Bothe H (2007) Arbuscular mycorrhiza and heavy metal tolerance. *Phytochemistry* 68: 139–146.

Hossain MA, Piyatida Pda Silva JAT, Fujita M. (2012) Molecular mechanism of heavy metal toxicity and tolerance in plants: Central role of glutathione in detoxification of reactive oxygen species and methylglyoxal and in heavy metal chelation. *J Bot* 1: 37.

Huang Y, Hu Y, Liu Y (2009) Combined toxicity of copper and cadmium to six rice genotypes (*Oryza sativa* L.). *J Environ Sci* 21: 647–653.

Hurd NA, Sternberg SPK (2008) Bioremoval of aqueous lead using *Lemna minor*. Int J Phytorem 10: 278–288.

Jadia C, Fulekar M (2009) Phytoremediation of heavy metals: Recent techniques. *Afr J Biotechnol* 8: 921–928.

Jana S, Choudhuri M (1984) Synergistic effects of heavy-metal pollutants on senescence in submerged aquatic plants. *Water Air Soil* Pollut 21: 351–357.

Ke X, Li P, Zhou Q, Zhang Y, Sun T (2006) Removal of heavy metals from a contaminated soil using tartaric acid. *J Environ Sci* 18: 727–733.

Khellaf N, Zerdaoui M (2012) Development of a kinetic model for the removal of zinc using the aquatic macrophyte *Lemna gibba* L. *Water Sci Technol* 66: 953–957.

Kramer U (2005) Phytoremediation: Novel approaches to cleaning up polluted soils. *Curr Opi Biotechnol* 16: 133–141.

Kramer U, Talke IN, Hanikenne M (2007) Transition metal transport. *FEBS Lett* 581: 2263–2272.

Kulli B, Balmer M, Krebs R, Lothenbach B, Geiger G, Schulin R (1999) The influence of nitrilotriacetate on heavy metal uptake of lettuce and ryegrass. *J Environ Qual* 28: 1699–1705.

Lanfranco L, Bolchi A, Ros E, Ottonello S, Bonfante P (2002) Differential expression of a metallothionein gene during the presymbiotic versus the symbiotic phase of an arbuscular mycorrhizal fungus. *Plant Physiol* 130: 58–67.

Lee I, Baek K, Kim H, Kim S, Kim J, Kwon Y, Chang Y, Bae B (2007) Phytoremediation of soil co-contaminated with heavy metals and TNT using four plant species. *J Environ Sci Heal Part A -Toxic/Hazard Sub Environ Engg* 42: 2039–2045.

Lee M, Lee K, Lee J, Noh EW, Lee Y (2005) AtPDR12 contributes to lead resistance in arabidopsis. *Plant Physiol* 138: 827–836.

Liang H, Lin T, Chiou J, Yeh K (2009) Model evaluation of the phytoextraction potential of heavy metal hyperaccumulators and non-hyperaccumulators. *Environ Pollut* 157: 1945–1952.

Lin Q, Wang Z, Ma S, Chen Y (2006) Evaluation of dissipation mechanisms by *Lolium perenne* L. and *Raphanus sativus* for pentachlorophenol (PCP) in copper co-contaminated soil. *Sci Total Environ* 368: 814–822.

Liu J, Duan C, Zhang X, Zhu Y, Lu X (2011) Potential of *Leersia hexandra* Swartz for phytoextraction of Cr from soil. *J Hazard Mater* 188: 85–91.

Liu J, Zho Q, Sun T, Ma L, Wang S (2008) Growth responses of three ornamental plants to Cd and Cd-Pb stress and their metal accumulation characteristics. *J Hazard Mater* 151: 261–267.

Liu X, Zhang S, Shan X, Christie P (2007) Combined toxicity of cadmium and arsenate to wheat seedlings and plant uptake and antioxidative enzyme responses to cadmium and arsenate co-contamination. *Ecotoxicol Environ Saf* 68: 305–313.

Lombi E, Zhao F, McGrath S, Young S, Sacchi G (2001) Physiological evidence for a high-affinity cadmium transporter highly expressed in a *Thlaspi caerulescens* ecotype. *New Phytol* 149: 53–60.

Lu Y, Li Z, Rea P (1997) AtMRP1 gene of *Arabidopsis* encodes a glutathione S-conjugate pump: Isolation and functional definition of a plant ATP-binding cassette transporter gene. *PNAS USA* 94: 8243–8248.

Luan Z, Cao H, Yan B (2008) Individual and combined phytotoxic effects of cadmium, lead and arsenic on soybean in Phaeozem. *Plant Soil Environ* 54: 403–411.

Macfie S, Welbourn P (2000) The cell wall as a barrier to uptake of metal ions in the unicellular green alga *Chlamydomonas reinhardtii* (Chlorophyceae). *Arch Environ Contam Toxicol* 39: 413–419.

Mahdavi A, Khermandar K, Asbchin SA, Tabaraki R (2014) Lead accumulation potential in *Acacia Victoria*. *Int J Phytorem* 16: 582–592.

Maksymiec W (2007) Signaling responses in plants to heavy metal stress. *Acta Physiolog Planta* 29: 177–187.

Manara A (2012) Plant Responses to Heavy Metal Toxicity. In: Furini A (ed) *Plants and Heavy Metals, Springer Briefs in Biometals* 27–53.

McGrath SP, Dunham SJ, Correll RL (2000) Potential for phytoextraction of zinc and cadmium from soils using hyperaccumulator plants. In: Terry N, Banuelos G (eds)

Phytoremediation of Contaminated Soil and Water. Lewis Publishers, Boca Raton, USA pp 109–128.

Meagher R (2000) Phytoremediation of toxic elemental and organic pollutants. *Curr Opi Plant Biol* 3: 153–162.

Meagher R, Heaton A (2005) Strategies for the engineered phytoremediation of toxic element pollution: Mercury and arsenic. *J Ind Microbiol Biotechnol* 32: 502–513.

Meers E, Ruttens A, Hopgood M, Samson D, Tack F (2005) Comparison of EDTA and EDDS as potential soil amendments for enhanced phytoextraction of heavy metals. *Chemosphere* 58: 1011–1022.

Miretzky P, Saralegui A, Cirelli A (2004) Aquatic macrophytes potential for the simultaneous removal of heavy metals (Buenos Aires, Argentina). *Chemosphere* 57: 997–1005.

Mishra VK, Upadhyay AR, Pandey SK, Tripathi BD (2008) Concentrations of heavy metals and aquatic macrophytes of Govind Ballabh Pant Sagar an anthropogenic lake affected by coal mining effluent. *Environ Monit Assess* 141: 49–58.

Mohan B, Hosetti B (1997) Potential phytotoxicity of lead and cadmium to *Lemna minor* grown in sewage stabilization ponds. *Environ Pollut* 98: 233–238.

Mounicou S, Shah M, Meija J, Caruso J, Vonderheide A, Shann J (2006) Localization and speciation of selenium and mercury in *Brassica juncea* - Implications for Se-Hg antagonism. *J Analyt Atom Spectrom* 21: 404–412.

Orrono D, Schindler V, Lavado R(2012) Heavy Metal availability in *Pelargonium Hortorum* rhizosphere: Interactions, uptake and plant accumulation. *J Plant Nutr* 35: 1374–1386.

Pence N, Larsen P, Ebbs S, Letham D, Lasat M, Garvin D, Eide D, Kochian L (2000) The molecular physiology of heavy metal transport in the Zn/Cd hyperaccumulator *Thlaspi caerulescens. PNAS USA* 97: 4956–4960.

Peng J, Gong J (2014) Vacuolar sequestration capacity and long-distance metal transport in plants. *Front Plant Sci* 5: 19.

Persans M, Nieman K, Salt D (2001) Functional activity and role of cation-efflux family members in Ni hyperaccumulation in *Thlaspi goesingense. PNAS USA* 98: 9995–10000.

Pilon-Smits E, Pilon M (2002) Phytoremediation of metals using transgenic plants. *Crit Rev Plant Sci* 21: 439–456.

Rascio N, Navari-Izzo F (2011) Heavy metal hyperaccumulating plants: How and why do they do it? And what makes them so interesting? *Plant Sci* 180: 169–181.

Rogers EE, Guerinot ML (2002) FRD3, a member of the multidrug and toxin efflux family, controls iron deficiency responses in Arabidopsis. *Plant Cell* 14: 1787–1799.

Saygıdeger S, Dogan M (2004) Lead and cadmium accumulation and toxicity in the presence of EDTA in *Lemna minor* L. And *Ceratophyllum demersum* L. *Bull Environ Contam Toxicol* 73: 182–189.

Schutzendubel A, Polle A (2002) Plant responses to abiotic stresses: Heavy metal-induced oxidative stress and protection by mycorrhization. *J Exp Bot* 53: 1351–1365.

Sekomo CB, Rousseau DPL, Saleh SA, Lens PNL (2012) Heavy metal removal in duckweed and algae ponds as a polishing step for textile wastewater treatment. *Ecolog Engg* 44: 102–110.

Sharma SS, Dietz KJ (2009)The relationship between metal toxicity and cellular redox imbalance. *Trends Plant Sci* 14: 43–50.

Shevyakova N, Cheremisina A, Kuznetsov V (2011) Phytoremediation potential of Amaranthus hybrids: Antagonism between nickel and iron and chelating role of polyamines. *Russ J Plant Physiol* 58: 634–642.

Siedlecka A, Krupa Z (1999) Cd/Fe interaction in higher plants - its consequences for the photosynthetic apparatus. *Photosynthetica* 36: 321–331.

Simkiss K (1983) Lipid solubility of heavy-metals in saline solutions. *J Mar Biol Assoc* UK 63: 1–7.

Singh S, Eapan S, D'Souza SF (2006) Cadmium accumulation and its influence on lipid peroxidation and antioxidative system in an aquatic plant *Bacopa monnieri* L. *Chemosphere* 62: 233–246.

Singh RP, Agrawal M (2007) Effects of sewage sludge amendment on heavy metal accumulation and consequent responses of *Beta vulgaris* plants. *Chemosphere* 67: 2229–2240.

Steffens J (1990) The heavy metal binding peptides of plants. *Ann Rev Plant Physiol Plant Mol Biol* 41: 553–575.

Sun Y, Zhou Q, Xu Y, Wang L, Liang X (2011) Phytoremediation for co-contaminated soils of benzo[a]pyrene (B[a]P) and heavy metals using ornamental plant *Tagetes patula*. *J Hazard Mater* 186: 2075–2082.

Thomine S, Wang R, Ward J, Crawford N, Schroeder J (2000) Cadmium and iron transport by members of a plant metal transporter family in *Arabidopsis* with homology to Nramp genes. *PNAS USA* 97: 4991–4996.

Thys C, Vanthomme P, SchrevensE, DeproftM (1991) Intractions of Cd with Zn, Cu, Mn and Fe for Lettuce (*Lactuca satival* L.) in hydroponic culture. *Plant Cell Environ* 14: 713–717.

Üçüncü E, Tunca E, Fikirdesici S, Özkan AD, Altindag A (2013) Phytoremediation of Cu, Cr and Pb mixtures by *Lemna minor*. *Bull Environ Cont Toxicol* 91: 600–604.

Valderrama A, Tapia J, Penailillo P, Carvajal DE (2013) Water phytoremediation of cadmium and copper using *Azolla filiculoides* Lam. in a hydroponic system. *Water Environ J* 27: 293–300.

Valida AZ, Alirzayeva E, Shirvani T (2010) Plant resistance to anthropogenic toxicants: Approaches to phytoremediation. In: Ashref M, Ozturk M, Ahmad MSA (eds) *Plant Adaptation and Phytoremediation: Springer Verleg* pp 173–192.

van der Ent A, Baker AJM, Reeves RD, Pollard AJ, Schat H (2013) Hyperaccumulators of metal and metalloid trace elements: Facts and fiction. *Plant Soil* 362: 319–334.

Vardanyan LG, Ingole BS (2006) Studies on heavy metal accumulation in aquatic macrophytes from Sevan (Armenia) and Carambolim (India) lake systems. *Environ Internat* 32: 208–218.

Verbruggen N, Juraniec M, Baliardini C, Meyer C (2013) Tolerance to cadmium in plants: The special case of hyperaccumulators. *Biometals* 26: 633–638.

Williams L, Pittman J, Hall J (2000) Emerging mechanisms for heavy metal transport in plants. *Biochim Biophy Acta Biomem* 1465: 104–126.

Wu L, Li Z, Han C, Liu L, Teng Y, Sun X, Pan C, Huang Y, Luo Y, Christie P (2012) Phytoremediation of soil contaminated with cadmium, copper and polychlorinated biphenyls. *Int J Phytorem* 14: 570–584.

Wu L, Luo Y, Xing X, Christie P (2004) EDTA-enhanced phytoremediation of heavy metal contaminated soil with Indian mustard and associated potential leaching risk. *Agricule Ecosys Environ* 102: 307–318.

Xu W, Li W, He J, Singh B, Xiong Z (2009) Effects of insoluble Zn, Cd, and EDTA on the growth, activities of antioxidant enzymes and uptake of Zn and Cd in *Vetiveria zizanioides*. *J Environ Sci* 21: 186–192.

Yang XE, Feng Y, He Z, Stoffella P (2005) Molecular mechanisms of heavy metal hyperaccumulation and phytoremediation. *J Trace Elem Med Biol* 18: 339–353.

Yao Z, Li J, Xie H, Yu C, Jinhui L, Hualong H (2012) Review on remediation technologies of soil contaminated by heavy metals. *Seventh International Conference on Waste Management and Technology (ICWMT 7).* 16: 722–729.

Yathavakilla S, Caruso J (2007) A study of Se-Hg antagonism in *Glycine max* (soybean) roots by size exclusion and reversed phase HPLC-ICPMS. *Analyt Bioanalyt Chem* 389: 715–723.

Yip T, Tsang D, Ng K, Lo I (2009) Empirical modeling of heavy metal extraction by EDDS from single-metal and multi-metal contaminated soils. *Chemosphere* 74: 301–307.

Zahoor A, Rehman A (2009) Isolation of Cr(VI) reducing bacteria from industrial effluents and their potential use in bioremediation of chromium containing wastewater. *J Environ Sci* 21: 814–820.

Zenk M (1996) Heavy metal detoxification in higher plants - A review. *Gene* 179: 21–30.

Zhang Y, Liu J, Zhou Y, Gong T, Wang J, Ge Y (2013) Enhanced phytoremediation of mixed heavy metal (mercury)-organic pollutants (trichloroethylene) with transgenic alfalfa co-expressing glutathione S-transferase and human P450 2E1. *J Hazard Mater* 260: 1100–1107.

Zhang X, Hu Y, Liu YX, Chen BD (2011) Arsenic uptake, accumulation and phytofiltration by duckweed (*Spirodela polyrhiza* L.). *J Environ Sci* 23: 601–606.

Zhao F, Hamon R, Lombi E, McLaughlin M, McGrath S (2002) Characteristics of cadmium uptake in two contrasting ecotypes of the hyperaccumulator *Thlaspi caerulescens*. *J Exp Bot* 53: 535–543.

Zhuang X, Chen J, Shim H, Bai Z (2007) New advances in plant growth-promoting rhizobacteria for bioremediation. *Environ Int* 33: 406–413.

Zitka O, Krystofova O, Hynek D, Sobrova P, Kaiser J, Sochor J, Zehnalek J, Babula P, Ferrol N, Kizek R, Adam V (2013) Metal Transporters in Plants. In: Gupta DK, Corpas FJ, Palma JM (eds) *Heavy Metal Stress in Plants,* Springer Verlag pp 19–41.

In: Heavy Metal Remediation   ISBN: 978-1-63321-568-9
Editors: Dharmendra Kumar Gupta and Soumya Chatterjee © 2014 Nova Science Publishers, Inc.

Chapter 10

EXPLORING POTENTIAL OF USING PHYTOREMEDIATION FOR CO-CONTAMINATED SOILS

Chibuike Chigbo[1] *and Ernest O. Nnadi[2]*

[1]School of Geography, Earth and Environmental Sciences,
University of Birmingham, UK
[2]Sustainable Drainage Applied Research Group, Coventry University, UK

ABSTRACT

Contaminated soils often contain mixtures of different organic and inorganic compounds which require a more complex remediation process. This chapter reviews the use of phytoremediation for removal of organic and inorganic contaminants with consideration as to whether phytoremediation technique can be used for the treatment of co-contaminated soils. Literature suggests that plants can be successfully used for remediation of co-contaminated soils however; the interactions between plants and the microbial communities in the contaminated soil could be a major factor.

Keywords: Phytoremediation, Co-contamination, Organics, Inorganics

1. INTRODUCTION

Co-contaminated soils could be described as soils that are simultaneously contaminated with pollutants of different nature (Almeida et al. 2009). For example, sites that are contaminated with trace metals are frequently contaminated with other chemicals of different nature such as petroleum hydrocarbon, pesticides, surfactants, etc. It is difficult to quantify the extent to which land is contaminated. Over two million sites have been termed as

---

[*] Corresponding author. Dr. Chibuike Chigbo. School of Geography, Earth and Environmental Sciences, University of Birmingham, UK. Phone: 0044-7533419052; E. Mail: chuddychigbo@yahoo.com.

contaminated in Europe (European Environment Agency 2005) and about a sixth of that in the UK (Ashworth et al. 2005). According to Environment Agency about 30,000 to 40,000 sites covering an area of about 55,000 to 80,000 ha have been identified as being affected by contamination in England and Wales. Co-contaminated sites are in abundance and those contaminated with organic and inorganic compounds are most difficult to remediate. Although there are technological advances in land remediation, most contaminated land techniques are unsustainable as they mostly involve certain processes like 'dig and dump', which is the removal of soil to landfill (Batty and Anslow 2008). This method although effective just moves the contaminated soil (problem) elsewhere and due to the implementation of the European Union landfill directive (99/31/EC) that aims at reducing the negative impact of land filling of waste to the environment in the EU, this has become an unviable process (Jones and Hills 2002). Alternative methods, which include the application of other substances that could be potentially harmful to the environment or even thermal treatment, which destroys soil structure, are also unsustainable. Hence, sustainable approaches to land remediation, which include the use of plants and microbes to transform or uptake toxic substances, have been proposed. There are indications that these techniques are not been widely applied due to time restraints, problem of identification of appropriate species for remediation and cost - in the case of use of microbes (Chen et al. 2004). As much as these remediation technologies (both sustainable and unsustainable) have shown promise for individual pollutants (Gao and Zhu 2004), it has not been the case for sites that are contaminated by more than one pollutant. The challenge for soil remediation is that most contaminated sites do not contain one pollutant but instead a number of different substances (Lin et al. 2008).Consequently, a combination of traditional techniques is usually used to remediate these soils, which of late have included methods that use microbes. These techniques utilize energy in many cases and with the emphasis on sustainability, low energy and environmentally friendly technologies are required. Hence, phytoremediation technique has the potential to provide solution to this problem. This chapter provides information on the current knowledge surrounding phytoremediation of pollutants in co-contamination soils and discusses the evidence for the use of plants to remediate co-contaminated sites.

1.1. Phytoremediation

Phytoremediation is a broad term that incorporates different processes that plants use to remove, transform or stabilize pollutants in soil, water or atmosphere. It is a plant based remediation technology that is applied to both inorganic and organic contaminants in soil, water and sediments globally (Nwoko 2010). Natural processes by which plants and their associated microbes degrade and/or sequester inorganic and organic pollutants are incorporated in this technology which makes it a cheaper and environmentally sustainable option to other methods of removal of contaminants from soil (Nwoko 2010). It also generates fewer secondary wastes and less environmental impact than would be obtained using other traditional methods (Mohanty et al. 2010). Results of research for phytoremediation potential show that it is applicable to a broad range of contaminants including metals (Jadia and Fulekar 2009), radionuclides (Kaushik et al. 2008), organic compounds e.g, chlorinated solvents, BTEX- benzene, toluene, ethylbenzene and xylene (Weishaar et al. 2009), polychlorinated biphenyl (Chen et al. 2010), PAHs (Denys et al. 2006) and pesticides (Chang et al. 2005).The success of phytoremediation depends on the plants' ability to assimilate and/or accumulate organic and inorganic contaminants in their cellular structures and to carry out deep oxidative degradation of organic xenobiotics (Kvesitadze et al. 2006).The main disadvantage to phytoremediation is the length of time it takes to achieve the target concentrations, although it may be possible to address this by using species with a short growth cycle and high biomass (Olson et al. 2007). Also, remediation is limited to the rooting depth of the plants but again deeper rooting species can be used where necessary. Before considering the potential application of phytoremediation to co-contaminated soils, it is necessary to examine the application to individual contaminant types.

1.2. Phytoremediation of Organic Contaminants

Organic contaminants contain carbon and can be released into the environment via a range of industrial activities such as timber treatments (Mills et al. 2006; Robinson and Anderson 2007), oil exploration (Rogge et al. 1997), and gas works (Cofield et al. 2008). These vary widely in types which include the polyaromatic hydrocarbons (PAHs), trichloroethylene (TCE), petroleum hydrocarbons, 2,4,6 trinitrotoulene, benzene, toluene, ethylbenzene and xylene (BTEX), polychlorinated phenol, methyl-tert-butyl ether (MTBE), gasoline etc. PAHs are mostly common organic pollutant in contaminated soils because they are widespread due to human activities and by-products of major industrial processes such as pyrolysis reaction (Ledesma et al. 2000; Barbosa et al. 2006). One of the challenges of remediation of organic compounds is that they exist in different structural forms and chemical compositions. In order for phytoremediation to take place, the compounds needs to be mineralized into non-toxic compounds such as CO_2, NO_3^-, Cl^- and NH_4^+ (Meagher 2000), and also be in forms that are available to plants or microbes (Parrish et al. 2005). Typical examples are PAHs, which are less soluble in water due to their non-polar nature (Nazzal, 2007). Their solubility decreases with increase in molecular weight (Werner 2003) as they become increasingly hydrophobic and may become sorbed to the soil (Neuhauser et al. 2006). The more strongly sorbed they are, the less bioavailable and biodegradable they become (Neuhauser et al. 2006). When plants absorb organic contaminants to their roots, the fate of the organic compound varies (Cunningham et al. 1996) and depending on the organic contaminant in question, the partitioning between the roots and the above ground tissues will also vary (Alkorta and Garbisu 2001). These compounds can be extracted, degraded, volatilized or stabilized (Greipson 2011) depending on the organic their chemical nature, external temperature, type of plant and stage of growth of the plant (Kvesitadze et al. 2009). According to Gao and Zhu (2003), the process of organic contaminant uptake in plant roots is complicated and occurs through active and/or passive transport. In the passive process, the pollutants accompany the mobility of transpiration fluid through the plant and transporters such as carrier proteins are involved with active transport (Nardi et al. 2002). However, because organic compounds are man-made except for hydrocarbons which are naturally formed compounds (but with increased accumulation in the environment through anthropogenic sources), there are no transporters for their uptake in plants; rather transport takes place by diffusion and are dependent on the hydrophilic or hydrophobic nature of the contaminants (Widdel and Rabus 2001). The hemicelluloses in the cell wall and the lipid bilayer of plant membrane have been shown to bind hydrophobic organic pollutants effectively (Cherian and Oliveira 2005). Hydrophobicity is determined by the octanol-water partition coefficient (Log K_{OW}) and a range of 0.5 to 3.0 is termed moderately hydrophobic (Alkorta and Garbisu 2001). This range is sufficient for organic contaminants to move through the lipid bilayer of membranes and taken up by plants (Pilons-Smith 2005). However, with a log K_{OW} of less than 0.5, passage through the membranes and subsequent uptake becomes impossible. However, there are disparities in organic contaminant uptake and translocation among plant species in addition to the factors that affects their bioavailability (Alkorta and Garbisu 2001). Studies have shown that the age of the compound plays an important role during phytoremediation of organic contaminants. According to Smith et al. (2006), the process of ageing of PAHs makes extraction by plants more difficult and thus compromises phytoremediation. However, this could be advantageous to living organisms in contact with the soil, as aged PAHs would be less accessible to their competitors. The process of ageing starts with the binding or sorbing of PAHs to the humin, fulvic and humic acid components of the soil (Li and Liu 2005). This process (soil-PAH contact time) is very important to the fate and transportation of PAHs in soil (Hwang and Cutright 2002) as it causes slow desorption of organic contaminants leading to low microbial degradation. If organic compounds age in the soil, there could be a decline in their lability and bioavailability with less effect on the total concentration. For example, Cofield et al. (2008) observed that with the presence of *Festuca arundinacea* and *Panicum virgatum*, the non-labile PAHs were unaffected whilst the total PAHs in the soil decreased. In recent years, non-aged PAH spiked soils have been used for phytoremediation studies (Olsen et al. 2007). However some studies have shown that the age of contaminants in the soil limits their degradation and as such spiking of soils with fresh PAH could likely give results that do not indicate real environmental condition of soil (Allard et al. 2000), hence sparking controversies in phytoremediation research. In as much as these controversies exist, some attempts at phytoremediation of organic contaminants have been successful. Some studies have shown that some plants including the grasses and legumes have successfully remediated organic contaminants. For example, the major mechanism of PAH dissipation in vegetated soil is associated with the microbial activity in the rhizosphere, therefore remediation varies across plant species and type of environment (Lee et al. 2008). The grasses have been successful mainly because of their short growth season with large fibrous root system that results in increased rhizospheric soil and the legumes have the ability to germinate when nutrient availability is poor and are able to fix atmospheric nitrogen (Lee et al. 2008; Smith et al. 2006). Lee et al. (2008) showed that the legumes (*Astragalus membranaceous* and *Aeschynomene indica*) withstood phenanthrene and pyrene contamination better than grasses (*Panicum bisulcatum* Thunb and *Eschinochloa crus-galli*). However the results are of limited value as comparisons were made with no indication of starting concentrations of phenanthrene and pyrene. A variety of plant trials for remediation of organics have been reported and the most common include willows, grasses and herbs (Trapp and Karlson 2001). Success of phytoremediation is also dependent on the organic contaminant in the soil.

According to Gao and Zhu (2004), there were significant differences in phenanthrene and pyrene accumulation in shoot and root of *Glycine max, Phaseolus vulgaris, Capsicum annum, Solanum melongena, Brassica parachinensis, Lolium multiflorum, Amaranthus tricolor, Raphanus sativus, Ipomoea aquatica, Brassica chinenis, Brassica oleracea* and *Spinacea oleracia*. The probable uptake route could be through uptake of volatilized portion of contaminants from the soil as well as root to shoot translocation. There is also evidence of removal of volatile organic compounds through volatilization. For example, the presence of trees in naphthalene contaminated site helped in direct volatilization of naphthalene to the atmosphere (Marr et al. 2006). The key to success of phytoremediation of organic contaminants is not the plant alone, but the interaction between the plants and the consortium of microorganisms in the rhizosphere also known as phytodegradation. These microbes degrade the organic contaminants, which is enhanced with the presence of plants. For example, PAHs degraded faster in planted soils when compared to unplanted soils (White et al. 2006). This was as a result of increased microbial numbers, which results in increased activity (Lu et al. 2010). When compared to the bulk soil, there are more PAH-degrading microorganisms in the rhizosphere (Parrish et al. 2005). For example, in the rhizosphere of Bermuda grass (*Cynodon dactylon*), there was a 400% increase in the number of pyrene degraders when compared to the bulk soil (Krutz et al. 2005). This increase could be associated with the release of phenolics and salicylates by plants (Chen and Aitken 1999) as flavones such as morusin, morusinol, and kuwanon which are phenolic compounds have showed support for PCB degrading bacteria in some plant species (Leigh et al. 2002). In phytoremediation trials involving aliphatic and aromatic hydrocarbons, clear correlations have been reported between the number of microbes in the rhizosphere and the dissipation of the hydrocarbon. For example, Günter et al. (1996) showed that the microbial plate count values increased with increased removal of artificially applied aliphatic hydrocarbon from the rhizosphere when planted with *Lolium perenne*. Similarly Fan et al. (2008) showed that residual pyrene concentration in soil planted with *Medicago sativa* was lower in the rhizosphere with increased microbial numbers in this part of the plant. Conversely, Kaimi et al. (2006), preferred soil dehydrogenase activity to number of aerobic bacteria as the reason for total petroleum hydrocarbon (TPH) dissipation due to lack of correlation between TPH and the number of aerobic bacteria whenthe plot was planted with *Medicago sativa*. Also, there are suggestions that the microbial population differs according to plant species. Kirk et al. (2005) observed that after the seventh week of study, the microbial population was higher in plots planted with *Medicago sativa* than with *Lolium perenne* and that the combination of *Medicago sativa* and *Lolium perenne* showed the greatest microbial number differentiation from the bulk soil. However, the degradation of organic contaminants is highly problematic, with few microorganisms with the ability to use high molecular weight PAHs as their sole source of carbon. Hence it is expected that remediation with microbes independently will be likely inefficient (Huang et al. 2004). Even in cases where bacteria from PAH contaminated sites were used, or when nutrients were supplemented, bacteria remediation was ineffective (Cunningham et al. 1996). Huang et al. (2004) showed that bioremediation alone was ineffective for the removal of benzo[*a*] pyrene and dibenzo[*ah*] pyrene until the establishment of *Festuca arundinacea*. This shows that with the right plant, the rate of degradation of organic contaminants will be improved during bioremediation. Some examples are shown in Table 1.

Table 1. Selected examples of phytoremediation trials for organic contaminants

Pollutant	Soil concentration (mg kg^{-1})	Plant species	Growth condition	Amendment /Fertilizer	Measure of success	Reference
Phenanth-rene, Pyrene	Phe-332.06 (av), Pyrene-321.42 (av)	*Sorghum vulgare L.*	Greenhouse	None	Phenanthrene and Pyrene dissipated	Xin et al. 2009
PAH	1251.7	*Vicia faba, Zea mays, Triticum aesitivum*	Field	None	PAH dissipated	Diab 2008
Benzo[a] pyrene	100	*Medicago sativa L*	Glasshouse	None	B[a] P removal	Shiliang et al. 2004
Alkylated PAHs	9175	*Lolium arundinaceum, Lolium multiflorum, Cynodon dactylon.*	Field	Fertilized	Greater degradation for anthracenes and phenanthracenes	White et al. 2006
Pyrene	100	*Zea mays*	Greenhouse/ Spiked soil	NPK	Pyrene removal	Zhang et al. 2009a
TNT	80	*Vetiveria zizanioides*	Glasshouse/ Spiked	Urea	Removal of TNT helped by urea.	Das et al. 2010
PAH	Unknown	*Festuca arundinacea, Lolium multiflorum*	Glasshouse	Compost	PAH removal	Parrish et al. 2005
TPH	6400	*Lolium perenne*	Glasshouse	None	Loss of TPH	Hou et al. 2010
Chrysene	500	*Lolium perenne, Trifolium repens L*	Glasshouse/ Spiked soil	None	Degradation of chrysene	Johnson et al. 2004
Phenanthrene, Pyrene	Phenanthrene-87.56	*Panicum bisulcatum, Echinogalus crusgalli, Astragalus membranaceus, Aeschynomene indica*	Greenhouse/ Spiked soil	N	Greater pyrene removal	Lee et al. 2008
Pyrene	500	*Zea mays*	Greenhouse/ Spiked soil	N	Pyrene removal	Lin et al. 2008
Hydrocar-bons	11400 (av)	*Pinus sylvestris, Populus deltoids, Trifolium repens*	Field	Fertilized	65% hydrocarbon removal	Palmroth et al. 2006

All concentrations are maximum values except otherwise stated.

Table 2. Selected examples of successful phytoremediation trial for inorganic contaminants

Pollutant	Soil concentration (mg kg^{-1})	Plant species	Growth condition	Amendment /Fertilizer	Measure of success	Reference
Pb	20	*Vetiveria zizanioides*	Greenhouse	EDTA	Removal of metal	Gupta et al. 2008
Cu	1200	*Elsholtzia splendens*	Glasshouse, Field	Urea, KH$_2$PO$_4$	Removal of Cu	Jiang et al. 2004
Cu, Pb, Mn, Zn	Cu- 640 Pb- 2400 Mn- 27000 Zn- 7800	*Brassica juncea*	Greenhouse	None	Removal of metals	Bennett et al. 2003
Zn, Cd	Zn- 25200 Cd- 170	*Thlaspi caerulescens*	Greenhouse	Compost	Removal of metals	Escarre et al. 2000
Cd, Zn, Pb	Cd- 20 Zn- 500 Pb- 1000	*Dianthus chinensis, Vetiveria zizanioides*	Greenhouse	EDTA	Removal of metals greater with EDTA	Lai and Chen 2004
Cr	10	*Trigonella foenumgraecum. L Spinacia oleracea, Brassica campestris*	Glasshouse	None	Removal of Cr	Dheri et al. 2007
Cr	90	*Pterocarpus indicus Jatropha curcas L.*	Glasshouse	Compost	Removal of chromium	Mangkoedihardjo et al. 2008
Zn, Ni	Ni- 109 Zn- 1300	*Salix sp. Populus sp. Alnus sp.*	Field	N	Removal of Zn and stabilization of Ni	French et al. 2006
Cd	1.6 (av)	*Averrhoa carambola*	Field	N	Removal of metal	Li et al. 2009
Cd, Zn	Zn- 600 Cd- 8	*Pennisetum americanum, Pennisetum atratum*	Greenhouse, spiked soil	Basic fertilizer	Removal of metal	Zhang et al. 2010

All concentrations are maximum values except stated otherwise.

1.3. Phytoremediation of Inorganics

Inorganic contaminants are mineral-based and unlike organics, they cannot be mineralized or degraded. Therefore their remediation must be through physical removal, conversion into biologically inert form and stabilization (Cunningham et al. 1996). However, as physical removal cannot be fully accomplished, conversion into biological inert form and stabilization should be a priority. Some plants have the ability of accumulating, transferring or stabilizing inorganic compounds. For the latter, the plant species only need to be tolerant to the inorganic compounds and avoid uptake, while for the former, hyperaccumulator plants have shown to accumulate high concentrations of inorganic compounds thereby removing the contaminants from the soil (Ghosh and Singh 2005). According to Baker (1981) hyperaccumulators are plants (when growing in their natural habitat) with the ability to accumulate high concentration of metals without toxic effects when compared to other species (or genotype) and also the ratio of shoot to root or leaf to root concentration of metals accumulated is greater than one. Presently, there are about 400 plants that hyperaccumulate metals. *Brassicaceae, Asteraceae, Caryophyliaceae, Cyperaceae, Cunouniaceae, Fabaceae, Flacourtiaceae, Lamiaceae, Poaceae, Violaceae and Euphorbiaceae* dominate the 45 families (Prasad and Freitas 2003). Most of the hyperaccumulators accumulate nickel while, manganese, cadmium, zinc and cobalt are accumulated by others. *Thlaspii caerulescens*, which is a hyperaccumulator of zinc and cadmium, has been identified as one of the most studied hyperaccumulators (Wang et al. 2006). The uptake of metals into plant occurs from aqueous phase except in the case of mercury, Therefore, in order to control the uptake of metals, speciation of metals within the soil is very important. In non-accumulating plants, there are indications of enhanced metal uptake even when some essential metals are not available. One of the ways this occurs is that the plants cause rhizospheric changes such as the release of phytosiderophores or increase acidification to increase the mobility of some metals (Marschner, 2002). However, in hyperaccumulators there are limited processes for enhanced uptake. For example, increased acidification of the rhizosphere does not enhance metal uptake (Jing et al. 2007), but release of exudates have shown some promises in few studies (McGrath et al. 2001). Once metals are taken up into plants, they are stored within the tissues, which can be harvested. Some of these metals inside the plant are very insoluble and so do not freely move in the vascular system, and therefore carbonates, sulphates or phosphates are formed (Ghosh and Singh 2005). However, selenium and mercury can be transformed within plants and volatilized if released to the atmosphere (Meagher 2000), which is dependent on root uptake absorption as in the case of organics (Moreno et al. 2008). Some groups of plants are also able to survive and reproduce in highly metal contaminated soil without hyperaccumulating the metals. These are known as pseudometallophytes and they achieve this by developing tolerance through rhizospheric precipitation of metals. For example, Dahmani-Muller et al. (2000) showed that metal (Pb, Zn, Cu and Cd) concentration in *Agrostis tenuis* was higher in roots than in leaves which suggested the immobilization of metals in roots. Studies have indicated that amendment of soil increases the availability of metals for uptake during phytoremediation process. For example, *Pterocarpus indicus* and *Jatropha curcas. L* removed higher amount of chromium with addition of compost (Mangkoedihardjo et al. 2008) while ethylenediaminetetraacectic acid (EDTA) enhanced the uptake of Pb by *Vetiveria zizanioides* (Gupta et al. 2008). Other compounds such as citrate, oxalate, tartrate, malate, acetate and some synthetic chelates have been used as chelators of metals (Prasad and Freitas 2003). However, their effects on the microbial communities in the soil have not been well studied. Microbial communities within the rhizosphere can also play an important role during phytoremediation of inorganics. For example, the presence of rhizospheric bacteria increased the concentration of Zn in *Thlaspi caerulescens* (Whiting et al. 2001) and Ni in *Alyssum murale* (Abou-Shanab 2003). The increase in metal concentration in the respective plants is evidence of the role plant growth promoting rhizobacteria (PGPR) plays. They can affect heavy metal mobility and availability to plant by releasing chelating agents, acidification and redox changes. Also, they can improve plant growth and nutrition though nitrogen fixing and transformation of nutrient elements (Jing et al. 2007). However, under high soil contaminant level, the growth of plant growth promoting bacteria can be inhibited. For example, Nie et al. (2002) showed a 30% germination of seeds of canola irrespective of the presence or absence of plant growth promoting bacteria. Many glasshouse and laboratory studies on phytoremediation of inorganics have been successfully carried out as shown in Table 2. However, full-scale application has been limited compared with organics. Some species that have been used include *Elsholtzia splendens* (Jiang et al. 2004) for Cu, *Salix sp., Populus sp. and Alnus sp.* (French et al. 2006) for phytoextraction of zinc and stabilization of nickel, and *Brassica juncea* for phytoextraction of Pb, Zn, Cu and Cd.

Table 3. Few phytoremediation trials for mixed contaminants

Pollutant	Soil concentration (mg kg⁻¹)	Plant species	Growth condition	Amendment /Fertilizer	Measure of success	Reference
Pyrene, Cd	Pyrene- 100 Cd- 4.5	*Zea mays*	Glasshouse/ Spiked	Fertilized: NPK	Pyrene uptake stimulated by presence of Cd	Zhang et al. 2009b
Benzo[a]pyrene, Cu, Cd, Pb	B[a]P – 5 Cd- 50 Cu- 500 Pb- 3000	*Tagetes patula*	Glasshouse/ Spiked	None	Greater degradation of B[a]P in the presence of Cd	Sun et al. 2011
Pyrene, phenanthrene, Cd	Pyrene- 250 Phe- 250 Cd- 50	*Juncus subsecondus*	Glasshouse/ Spiked	Fertilized	Dissipation of PAH influenced by Cd.	Zhang et al. 2011
PCP, Cu	PCP- 100 Cu- 300	*Lolium perenne L. Raphanussa tivus*	Greenhouse/ Spiked	Fertilized	Higher dissipation of PCP under 50mg/kg with increasing Cu concentration.	Lin et al. 2006
Pyrene, Cu	Pyrene- 500 Cu- 100	*Zea mays L*	Greenhouse/ Spiked	Fertilized	Increasing concentration of pyrene alleviated inhibition of Cu to *Zea mays*. Also presence of Cu increased residual pyrene in soil	Chigbo et al. 2013
B[a]P, Cr	Cr-100 B[a]P- 10	*Zea mays*	Greenhouse/ Spiked	None	Increasing concentration of B[a]P increased the accumulation of Cr in *Zea mays*.	Chigbo and Batty 2013a
B[a]P, Cr	Cr-50 B[a]P- 10	*Medicago sativa*	Greenhouse/ Spiked	EDTA+Citric acid	Higher dissipation of B[a]P and Cr with combined application of amendments	Chigbo and Batty 2013b

All concentrations are maximum values.

1.4. Phytoremediation of Co-contaminants

Phytoremediation of mixed contaminated soils (mixture of organic and inorganic) is poorly understood but very important as most sites are exposed to mixed contaminants (Zhang et al. 2011; Chigbo et al. 2013). The approaches for the remediation of these sites are different. It is very important to understand the interaction between both contaminants, which could affect their availability, and form. When pollutants are mixed or combined, phytoremediation could be influenced as contaminants may interact with themselves as well as with plants and the rhizosphere (Almeida et al. 2009). Previous research has shown that an increase in metal bioavailability can occur when plants interact with organic compounds (Chen et al. 2004; Gao et al. 2006; Chigbo and Batty 2013a). In addition, severe inhibition of biodegradation of organic pollutants by toxic metals such as cadmium (Maslin and Maier 2000), stimulation of microbial activity has been shown. A comprehensive review on the impacts of metals on biodegradation of organic pollutants was provided by Sandrin and Maier (2003). The review however highlighted a wide range of concentrations of metals that could cause inhibitory effects. The non-specificity of concentrations was attributed to limited information on metal speciation as well as variety in experimental protocol. Degradation of organic pollutants during phytoremediation depends extensively on the presence of suitable microbes that are active and favourable environmental conditions. Hence, if availability of metals have negative impact on microbes and limiting their activity, the success of phytoremediation could be severely compromised. Dobbler et al. (2000) observed that heavy metals decreased the number of specific populations of microbes and microbial diversity. Furthermore, the combinations of organic and inorganic contaminants have been shown to have negative effects, such as effect on plant growth and toxicity (Sun et al. 2011; Chigbo et al. 2013b). Palmaroth et al. (2006) showed in a field based study that the removal of hydrocarbon by *Pinus sylvestris* and *Populus deltoides x wettsteinii* was enhanced in the presence of metals such as Zn, Pb and Cu. However, about 80% of the trees died due to toxicity. Cadmium was shown to improve the root and shoot accumulation of pyrene in *Zea mays* L., but the more important factor for pyrene dissipation was plant-promoted biodegradation in the rhizosphere (Zhang et al. 2009a). However, Zhang et al. (2011) showed that the presence of phenanthrene and pyrene at 50 or 250 mg kg^{-1} partially alleviated the toxicity of cadmium to *Juncus subsecundus*. Also 50 to 500 mg kg^{-1} of pyrene, increased shoot yields of *Zea mays* L. in the presence of Cu (Lin et al. 2008), suggesting the potential alleviation of toxicity of Cu to *Zea mays* L. by pyrene. A study conducted by Sun et al. (2011), revealed that although plant growth was affectedthe presence of Cd, Pb and Cu reduced the uptake of benzo[*a*]pyrene in the ornamental plant- *Tagetes patula*. Also, 2, 4 dichlorophenol was shown to reduce the accumulation of zinc in the shoots of *Lolium perenne* L. (Chen et al. 2004) and low concentration of Cu and Cd (0.01 mg L^{-1}) increased the biodegradation of benzoate and 2-chlorophenol by 185 and 168% respectively (Kuo and Genthner 1996). The occurrence of B[a]P had an enhancing effect on the accumulation and translocation of Cr in shoot of *Zea mays* (Chigbo and Batty 2013a). The issue of co-contamination could be addressed by using diverse plant communities. Plant diversity has shown to have an effect upon microbial community in their associated rhizosphere (Kowalchuk et al. 2002). For example, a combination of *Lolium perenne* L and *Medicago sativa* increased the number of bacteria in the rhizosphere as well as the number of bacteria capable of degrading petroleum contamination (Kirk et al. 2005). Also, when *Lolium perenne*,

Trifolium repens and *Apium graveolens* were used in mixed culture in a PAH contaminated soil, the average amount of PAH remaining in soil was significantly lower than in monocultures although plant uptake contributed under 2% (Meng et al. 2011). Since diversity of plant and bacteria community are mostly affected in polluted environment (Travis et al. 2008), it is necessary during phytoremediation, to choose plants with known capabilities of degrading or accumulating contaminants, that can also complement each other rather than those that compete with each other. For example, when *Echinochloa crus-galli, Helianthus annuus* and *Abutilon avicennae* and *Aeschynomene indica* were used as mixed and mono-cultures in a 2,4,6- trinitrotoluene, Cd and Pb phytoremediation trial, trinitrotoluene was removed irrespective of mixed or monocultures. Moreover, more Cd was removed by mono-culture than mixed culture and there appeared to be competition as slower growth rate was reported in the mixed culture (Lee et al. 2007). When different plant species interact, the normal response of a plant to a contaminant may change. For example, in a mixed culture of *Carex flava, Centaurea angustifolia* and *Salix caprea*, the negative effect of Zn in *Carex flava* was improved in the presence of *Salix caprea* (Koelbener et al. 2008). Very little phytoremediation trials on mixed pollutant has been carried out and examples are shown in Table 3.

Conclusion

In this Chapter, exploring the potential of phytoremediation of co-contaminated soils with different plant species, soils with contrasting properties, range of metals and PAH concentrations, and the presence of organic and inorganic chelates represented a challenge to rigorous review of this area of research. The degree to which these tests could explain the ability of remediating co-contaminated soils with plants appeared to be metal-PAH specific with the metal-PAH interactions influencing the way different plants simultaneously removes metals and dissipates PAHs from soils. It is evident that phytoremediation could be applied to co-contaminated soils; therefore research on the commercialization of this technology is suggested.

References

Abou-Shanab R, Angle J, Delorme T, Chaney R, Van-Berkum P, Moawad H, Ghanem K, Ghozlan H (2003) Rhizobacterial effects on nickel extraction from soil and uptake by *Alyssum murale*. *New Phytol* 158: 219–224.

Alkorta I, Garbisu C (2001) Phytoremediation of organic contaminants in soils. *Bioresour Technol* 79: 273–276.

Allard A, Remberger M, Neilson A (2000) The negative impact of aging on the loss of PAH components in a Creosite-contaminated soil. *Int Biodeter Biodegrad* 46: 43–49.

Almeida C, Dias A, Mucha A, Bordalo A, Vasconcelos M (2009) Study of the influence of different organic pollutants on Cu accumulation by *Halimione portulacoides*. *Estuar Coast Shelf Sci* 85: 627– 632.

Ashworth A, Barnes B, Oates W, Slade N (2005) Indication for land contamination. Environment Agency Science Report SC030039/SR. Bristol Environment Agency. pp 40.

Baker A (1981) Accumulators and excluders- strategies in the response of plants to heavy metals. *J Plant Nutr* 3: 643–654.

Barbosa J, Re-Poppi N, Santiago-Silva M (2006) Polycyclic aromatic hydrocarbons from wood pyrolysis in charcoal production furnaces. *Environ Res* 101: 304–311.

Batty LC, Anslow M (2008) Effect of polycyclic aromatic hydrocarbon on the phytoremediation of zinc by two plant species (*Brassica Juncea* and *Festuca Arundinacea*). *Int J Phytorem* 10: 236–251.

Bennett L, Burkhead J, Hale K, Terry N, Pilon M, Pilon-Smits E (2003) Analysis of transgenic Indian mustard plants for phytoremediation of metal contaminated mine tailings. *J Environ Qual* 32: 432-440.

Chen S, Aitken M (1999) Salicylate stimulates the degradation of high molecular weight polycyclic aromatic hydrocarbons by *Pseudomaonas saccharophilia* P15. *Environ Sci Technol* 33: 435–439.

Chang S, Lee S, Je C (2005) Phytoremediation of Atrazine in poplar trees: Toxicity, uptake and transformation. *J Environ Sci Heal* 4: 801–811.

Chen Y, Lin Q, He F, Tian M (2004) Behaviour of Cu and Zn under combined pollution of 2, 4- dichlorophenol in the planted soil. *Plant Soil* 261: 127–134.

Chen Y, Tang X, Cheema S, Liu W, Shen C (2010) β- Cyclodextrin enhanced phytoremediation of aged PCBs – contaminated soil from e- waste recycling area. *J Environ Monit* 12: 1482–1489.

Cherian S, Oliviera M (2005) Transgenic plants in phytoremediation: Recent advances and new possibilities. *Environ Sci Technol* 39: 9377–9390.

Chigbo C, Batty L (2013a) Phytoremediation of Cr and B (a) P co-contaminated soil. *Environ Sci Pollut Res* 21: 3051–3059.

Chigbo C, Batty L (2013b) Effect of EDTA and citric acid on phytoremediation of Cr and B (a) P co-contaminated soil. *Environ Sci Pollut Res (In press)*. DOI 10.1007/s11356-013-1883-7.

Chigbo C, Batty L, Bartlett R (2013) Interactions of copper and pyrene on phytoremediation potential of *Brassica juncea* in copper–pyrene co-contaminated soil. *Chemosphere* 90: 164–169.

Cofield N, Banks M, Schwab A (2008) Liability of polycyclic aromatic hydrocarbons in the rhizosphere. *Chemosphere* 70: 1644–1652.

Cunningham S, Anderson T, Schwab A, Hsu F (1996) Phytoremediation of soil contaminated with organic pollutants. *Adv agron* 56: 55–114.

Dahmani-Muller H, Van Oort F, Gelie B, Balabane M (2000) Strategies of heavy metal uptake by three plant species growing near a metal smelter. *Environ Pollut* 109: 231–238.

Das P, Datta R, Maknis K, Sarker D (2010) Vetiver grass is capable of removing TNT from soil in the presence of Urea. *Environ Pollut* 158: 1980–1983.

Denys S, Rollin C, Guillot F, Baroudi H (2006) In-situ phytoremediation of PAHs contaminated soils following a bioremediation treatment. *Water Air Soil Pollut*: Focus 6: 299–315.

Dheri G, Brar M, Malhi S (2007) Comparative phytoremediation of chromium contaminated soils by fenugreek, spinach and raja. *Comm Soil Sci Plant Anal* 38: 1655–1672.

Diab E (2008) Phytoremediation of polycyclic aromatic hydrocarbon (PAHs) in a polluted desert soil with special reference to biodegradation of the soil carcinogenic PAHs. *Aust J Basic App Sci* 2: 757–762.

Dobbler R, Saner M, Bachofen R (2000) Population changes of soil microbial communities induced by hydrocarbon and metal contamination. *Biorem J* 4: 41–56.

Escarre J, Lefebure C, Gruber N, Leblanc M, Lepart J, Riviere Y, Delay B (2000) Zinc and cadmium hyperaccumulation by *Thalspi caerulescens* from metalliferous and non-metaliferrous sites in the Mediterranean area: Implication for phytoremediation. *New Phytol* 145: 429–437.

European Environment Agency (2005) Progress in Management of contaminated sites [Online]. Available from <http://www.eea.europa.eu/data-and-maps/indicators/progr ess-in-management-of-contaminated-sites/progress-in-management-of-contaminated> (10/06/2011).

Fan S, Li P, Gong Z, He N (2008) Promotion of pyrene degradation in rhizosphere of alfalfa (*Medicago sativa L.*) *Chemosphere* 71: 1593–1598.

French C, Dickingson J, Putwain P (2006) Woody biomass phytoremediation of contaminated brownfield site. *Environ Pollut* 141: 387–395.

Gao Y, Xiong W, Ling W, Xu J (2006) Sorption of Phenanthrene by soils contaminated with heavy metals. *Chemosphere* 65: 1355–1361.

Gao Y, Zhu L (2003) Phytoremediation and its models for organic contaminated soils. *J Environ Sci* 15: 302-310.

Gao Y, Zhu L (2004) Plant uptake, accumulation and translocation of phenanthrene and pyrene in soils. *Chemosphere* 55: 1169–1178.

Ghosh M, Singh S (2005) A review on phytoremediation of heavy metals and utilization of its byproducts. *Asi J Ener Environ* 6: 214–231.

Greipsson S (2011) Phytoremediation. Nature Education Knowledge 2(1) 7 [Online]. Available from <http://www.nature.com/scitable/knowledge/library/phytoremediatio n-17359669> (04-06-2011).

Günter T, Dornberger U, Fritsche W (1996) Effects of ryegrass on biodegradation of hydrocarbons in soil. *Chemosphere* 33: 203–215.

Gupta DK, Srivastava A, Singh VP (2008) EDTA enhances lead uptake and facilitated phytoremediation by vitiver grass. *J Environ Biol* 29: 903– 906.

Hou F, Milke M, Leung D, Macpherson D (2010) Variations in phytoremediation performance with diesel contaminated soil. *Environ Technol* 22: 215–222.

Huang X, El-Alawi Y, Penrose D, Glick B, Greenberg B (2004) A multi- process phytoremediation system for removal of polycyclic aromatic hydrocarbons from contaminated soils. *Environ Pollut* 130: 465–476.

Hwang S, Cutright T (2002) Biodegradability of aged pyrene and phenanthrenein a natural soil. *Chemosphere* 47: 891–899.

Jadia C, Fulekar M (2009) Phytoremediation of heavy metals: recent techniques. *Afr J Biotechnol* 8: 921–928.

Jiang L, Yang X, He Z (2004) Growth response and phytoextraction of copper at different levels in soils by *Elshotzia splendens*. *Chemosphere* 55: 1179–1187.

Jing Y, He Z, Yang X (2007) Role of rhizobacteria in phytoremediation of heavy metal contaminated sites. *J Zhejiang Uni Sci B* 8: 192–207.

Johnson D, Maguire K, Anderson D, McGrath S (2004) Enhanced dissipation of chrysene in planted soil. The impact of rhizobial inoculum. *Soil Biol Biochem* 36: 33–38.

Jones HM, Hills CD (2002) The regeneration of contaminated land by stabilization/solidification: The findings of a study mission to the USA. *Land contam reclam* 10: 231–237.

Kaimi E, Mukaidani T, Miyoshi S, Tamaki M (2006) Ryegrass enhancement of biodegradation in diesel- contaminated soil. *Environ Exp Bot* 55: 110–119.

Kaushik C, Raj K, D'Souza S (2008) Phytoremediation of 137-Cesium and 90-Strontium from solutions of low- level nuclear waste by *Vetiveria zizanoids*. *Ecotoxicol Environ Saf* 69: 206–311.

Kirk J, Kllronomos J, Lee H, Trevors J (2005) The effects of perennial ryegrass and alfalfa on microbial abundance and diversity in petroleum contaminated soil. *Environ Pollut* 133: 455–465.

Koelbener A, Ramseier D, Suter M (2008) Competition alters plant species response to nickel and zinc. *Plant Soil* 303: 241–251.

Kowalchuk G, Buma D, De Boer W, Klinkhamer P, Van Veen J (2002) Effects of above - ground plant species composition and diversity on the diversity of soil- borne microorganisms. *Antonie van Leeuwenhoek* 81: 509–520.

Krutz L, Beyrouty C, Gentry T, Wolf D, Reynolds C (2005) Selective enrichment of a pyrene degrader population and enhanced pyrene degradation in Bermuda grass rhizosphere. *Biol Fert Soils* 41: 359–364.

Kuo C, Genther B (1996) Effect of added heavy metal ions on biotransformation and biodegradation of 2- chlorophenol and 3-chlorobenzoate in anaerobic bacterial consortia. *App Environ Microbiol* 62: 2317–2323.

Kvesitadze G, Khatisashvili G, Sadunishrili T, Ramsden J (2006) Biochemical mechanisms of detoxification in higher plants: *Basis of phytoremediation.* Springer- Verlag: Berlin, Germany.

Kvesitadze E, Sadunishvili I, Kvesitadze G (2009) Mechanisms of organic contaminants uptake and degradation in plants. *World Acad Sci Engg Technol* 55: 458–468.

Ladesma E, Kalish M, Wornat M, Mackie J (2000) Formation and fate of PAH during the pyrolysis and fuel rich combustion of coal primary tar. *Fuel* 79: 1801–1814.

Lai H, Chen Z (2004) Effects of EDTA on solubility of cadmium, zinc, and lead and their uptake by rainbow pink and vetiver grass. *Chemosphere* 55: 421–430.

Lee I, Baek K, Lim H, Kim S, Kim J, Kwon Y, Chang Y, Bae B (2007) Phytoremediation of soil co-contaminated with metals and TNT using four plant species. *J Environ Sci Heal A. Tox/Hazard sub Environ Engg* 42: 2039–2045.

Lee S, Lee W, Lee C, Kim J (2008) Degradation of phenanthrene and pyrene in rhizosphere of grasses and legumes. *J Hazard Mat* 153: 892–898.

Leigh M, Fletcher J, Fu X, Schimtz F (2002) Root turnover: An important source of microbial substances in rhizosphere remediation of recalcitrant contaminants. *Environ Sci Technol* 36: 1579–1593.

Li J, Liao B, Dai Z, Zhu R, Shu W (2009) Phytoextraction of cadmium contaminated soil by carambola (*Averrhoa carambola*). *Chemosphere* 76: 1233–1239.

Li A, Liu X (2005) Combined effects of aging and co-solvents on sequestration of phenanthrene in soils. *J Environ Engg Asce* 131: 1068–1072.

Lin Q, Shen K, Zhao H, Li W (2008) Growth response of *Zea mays* L. in pyrene-copper co-contaminated soil and fate of pollutants. *J Hazard Mat* 150: 515–521.

Lin Q, Wang, Z, Ma S, Chen Y (2006) Evaluation of dissipation mechanisms by *Lolium perenne* L, and *Raphanus sativus* for pentachlorophenol (PCP) in copper co-contaminated soil. *Sci Total Environt* 368: 814–822.

Liu J, Zhou Q, Sun T, Ma L, Wang S (2008) Growth response of three ornamental plants to Cd and Cd-Pb stress and the metal accumulation characteristics. *J Hazard Mat* 151: 261–267.

Lu M, Zhang Z, Sun S, Wei X, Wang Q, Su Y (2010) The use of Goose grass (*Elcusine indica*) to remediate soil contaminated with petroleum. *Water Air Soil Pollut* 209: 181–189.

Mangkoedihardjo S, Ratnawati, Alfianti N (2008) Phytoremediation of hexavalent chromium polluted soil using *Pterocarpus indicus* and *Jatropha curcas. L. World App Sci J* 4: 338–342.

Marr LC, Booth E, Anderson R, Widdowson W, Novak J (2006) Direct volatilization of naphthalene to the atmosphere at a phytoremediation site. *Environ Sci Technol* 40: 5560–5566.

Marschner H (2002) Mineral nutrition of higher plants (2nd ed) Academic press, London: UK.

Maslin P, Maier R (2000) Rhamnolipid- enhanced mineralization of phenanthrene in organic – metal co- contaminated soils. *Biorem J* 4: 295– 308.

McGrath S, Zhao F, Lambi E (2001) Plant and rhizospheric processes involved in phytoremediation of metal- contaminated soils. *Plant Soil* 232: 207–214.

Meagher R (2000) Phytoremediation of toxic elemental and organic pollutants. *Curr Opi Plant Biol* 3: 153–162.

Meng L, Qiao M, Arp H (2011) Phytoremediation efficiency of a PAH contaminated industrial soil using ryegrass, white clover and celery as mono and mixed cultures. *J Soil Sed* 11: 482–490.

Mills T, Arnold B, Sivakumaran S, Northcott G, Vogeter L, Robinson B, Norling C, Leonil D (2006) Phytoremediation and long term site management of soil contaminated with pentachlorophenol (PCP) and heavy metals. *J Environ Manag* 79: 232–241.

Mohanty M, Dhai N, Patra P, Das B, Reddy P (2010) Phytoremediation: A novel approach for utilization of iron-ore wastes. *Rev Environ Cont Toxicol* 206: 29–47.

Moreno FN, Andrew C, Stewart R, Robinson B (2008) Phytofiltration of mercury-contaminated water: Volatilization and plant accumulation aspects. *Environ Exp Bot* 62: 78–85.

Nardi S, Pizzeghello D, Muscolo A, Vaniello A (2002) Physiological effects of humic substances on higher plants. *Soil Biol Biochem* 34: 1527–1536.

Nazzal J (2007) The presence of polycyclic aromatic hydrocarbons (PAH) in oil obtained at pyrolysis of Jordan oil shale. J Poly Sci 24 (3) [Online]. Available from <http://www.freepatentsonline.com/article/Oil-Shale/199194874.html> (25/02/2011).

Neuhauser E, Kreitinger J, Nakles D, Hawthorne S, Doherty F, Ghosh V, Khalil M, Ghosh R, Jonker M, Van der Heijden S (2006) Bioavailability and toxicity of PAHs at MGP sites. *Land Cont Reclam* 14: 261–266.

Nie L, Shah S, Burd G, Dixon D, Glick B (2002) Phytoremediation of arsenate contaminated soil by transgenic canola and the plant growth promoting bacterium *Enterobacter cloacae CAL2. Plant Physiol Biochem* 40: 355–361.

Nwoko C (2010) Trends in phytoremediation of toxic elemental and organic pollutants. *Afr J Biotechnol* 9: 6010–6016.

Olsen P, Castro A, Joern M, Duteau NM, Pillon-Smits E, Reardon K (2007) Comparison of plant families in a greenhouse phytoremediation study on an aged polycyclic aromatic hydrocarbon contaminated soil. *J Environ Qual* 36: 1461–1469.

Palmroth M, Koskinen P, Pichtel J, Vaajasaari K, Joutti A, Tuhkanene T, Puhakka J (2006) Field- scale assessment of phyto-treatment of soil contaminated with weathered hydrocarbons and heavy metals. *J Soils Sed* 6: 128–136.

Parrish Z, Banks M, Schwab A (2005) Effectiveness of phytoremediation as a secondary treatment for polycyclic aromatic hydrocarbons (PAHs) in composted soil. *International J Phytorem* 6: 119–137.

Pilon-Smits E (2005) Phytoremediation. *Ann Rev Plant Biol* 56: 15–39.

Prasad, M, Freitas H (2003) Metal hyperaccumulation in plants- Biodiversity prospecting for phytoremediation technology. *Elect J Biotechnol* 6: 285–321.

Robinson B, Anderson C (2007) Phytoremediation in New Zealand and Australia. *Phytorem Methods Biotechnol* 23: 455–468.

Rogge W, Hildemann L, Mazurek M, Cass G (1997) Sources of fine organic aerosols. 8 boilers burning no 2 distillate fuel oil. *Environ Sci Technol* 31: 2731–2737.

Sandarin T, Maier R (2003) Impacts of metals on the biodegradation of organic pollutants. *Environ Heal Persp* 111: 1093–1101.

Shiliang L, Yongming L, Kequiang D, Hua L, Longhua W, Weign X, Jing S, Hihong C (2004) Enhanced phytoremediation of benzo (a) pyrene contaminated soil with arbiscular mycorrhizal fungi. Acta Pedol Sin [Online]. Available from <http://en.cnki.com.cn/Article_en/CJFDTOTAL-TRXB200403001.htm>Technology 31: 2731– 2737.

Smith M, Flowers T, Duncan H, Alder J (2006) Effects of polycyclic aromatic hydrocarbons on germination and subsequent growth of grasses and legumes in freshly contaminated soil and soil with aged PAHs residues. *Environ Pollut* 141: 519–525.

Sun Y, Zhou Q, Xu Y, Wang L, Liang X (2011) Phytoremediation for co- contaminated coils of benzo(a) pyrene and heavy metals using ornamental plant *Tagetes patula*. *J Hazard Mat* 186: 2075–2082.

Trapp S, Karlson U (2001) Aspects of phytoremediation of organic compounds. *J Soils Sed* 1: 37– 43.

Travis E, Bruce N, Rosser S (2008) Microbial and plant ecology of a long term TNT-contaminated site. *Environ Pollut* 153: 119–126.

Wang A, Angle J, Chaney R, Delorme T, Mcintosh M (2006) Changes in soil biological activities under reduced soil pH during *Thalspi caerulescens* phytoextraction. *Soil Biol Biochem* 38: 1451–1461.

Weishaar J, Tsao D, Burken J (2009) Phytoremediation of BTEX hydrocarbons: potential impacts of diurnal groundwater fluctuation on microbial degradation. *Int J Phytorem* 11: 509– 523.

Werner P (2003) The contribution of natural attenuation processes for the remediation of contaminated sites. In: Kono I, Nishigaki M, Komatsu M (eds) *Groundwater Engineering- Recent Advances*. Swets and Zeitlinger: Lisse.

White P, Wolf D, Thoma G, Reynolds C (2006) Phytoremediation of alkylated polycyclic aromatic hydrocarbons in a crude oil- contaminated soil. *Water Air Soil Pollut* 169: 207–220.

Whiting S, De Souza M, Terry N (2001) Rhizosphere bacteria mobilize Zn for hyperaccumulation by *Thlaspi caerulescens. Environ Sci Technol* 35: 3144–3150.

Widdel F, Rabus R (2001) Anaerobic biodegradation of saturated and aromatic hydrocarbons. *Curr Opi Biotechnol* 12: 259–276.

Xin Y, Shi Qiang W, Shang Wang P (2009) Remediation of phenanthrene and pyrene in soil by Audan grass (*Sorghum vulgare L.*) *J Agro Environ Sci* [Online]. Available from http://en.cnki.com.cn/Article_en/CJFDTotal-NHBH200907018.htm.

Zhang H, Dang Z, Yi X, Yang C, Zheng L, Lu G (2009a) Evaluation of dissipation mechanisms for pyrene by maize (*Zea mays*) in cadmium co-contaminated soil. *Global NEST J* 11: 487–496.

Zhang H, Dang Z, Zheng L, Yi X (2009b) Remediation of soil co- contaminated with pyrene and cadmium by growing maize. *Int J Environ Sci Technol* 6: 249–258.

Zhang X, Xia H, Li Z, Zhang P, Gao B (2010) Potential of four forage grasses in remediation of Cd and Zn contaminated soils. *Biores Technol* 101: 2063–2066.

Zhang Z, Rengel Z, Meney K, Pantelic L, Tomanovic R (2011) Polynuclear aromatic hydrocarbons (PAHs) mediate cadmium toxicity to an emergent wetland species. *J Hazard Mat* 189: 119–126.

In: Heavy Metal Remediation   ISBN: 978-1-63321-568-9
Editors: Dharmendra Kumar Gupta and Soumya. Chatterjee © 2014 Nova Science Publishers, Inc.

Chapter 11

HEAVY METAL REMEDIATION BY DEAD PLANTS AND ALGAE

Reza Panahi [1,] and Mina Ebrahimi [2]*

[1] Chemistry and Chemical Engineering Research Center of Iran, Tehran, Iran
[2] R&D Department, Zistec Ltd., Fatemi Ave., Tehran, Iran

ABSTRACT

Elimination of heavy metals from wastewaters using biomasses is divided in two major categories of accumulation and/or biosorption. The operation, in which the dead plants and algae are used for sorbing, sequestering and immobilizing heavy metals from aqueous solutions, is known as biosorption. Many species of dead plants and algae have been employed as biosorbents to eliminate desired pollutants from aqueous phases in a variety of ways. These biomasses are cheap, inexhaustible and safe, and can be easily disposed by burning. Different types of chemical and physical treatments have been developed to modify these kinds of biosorbents before being applied for heavy metal removal since untreated biomasses may offer low adsorption capacities and weak mechanical properties.

The biosorption may occur by different mechanisms such as adsorption by physical force, complexation, coordination, chelation, ion exchange, precipitation or entrapment, which depends on the chemical nature of pollutant, type of biomass, biosorbent preparation and its specific surface properties, and the environmental conditions. The understanding of metal-biomass interaction mechanism offers the possibilities such as optimizing the process on the molecular level, improving the screening process, and manipulating the biosorption properties of biomass when it is growing. Algae bear large quantities of biopolymers that can bind heavy metals resulting in high metal uptake capacities mainly through ion-exchange mechanism, while biosorption by dead plants can be attributed to the combination of various mechanisms.

The application of biosorbents on commercial scale have some operational limitations related to physical characteristics of biomass such as small particle size, low density, poor mechanical strength and low rigidity. There are just few reports concerning

---

* Corresponding author: Dr. Reza Panahi, Chemistry and Chemical Engineering Research Center of Iran, P.O. Box 14335-186, Tehran, Iran Tel/Fax: 0098-21-88630086, E. Mail: r58panahi@gmail.com.

the application of plant-based and algal biosorbents in commercial scale. It seems that biosorption can be a proper alternative for heavy metal remediation in addition to accumulation.

Keywords: Biosorption, Dead plants and algae, Mechanisms, Commercial biosorbents, Chemical treatments

1. INTRODUCTION

One of the major environmental and health problems of our modern society is attributed to heavy metals toxicity and the danger of their bioaccumulationin the food chain. Several industries related to mining, surface finishing, energy and fuel producing, fertilizer, pesticide, metallurgy, iron and steel, electroplating, electrolysis, electro-osmosis, leather, photography, electric appliance manufacturing, and metal surface treating, as well as aerospace and atomic energy installations are known as the major sources of pollution. Unfortunately, these kinds of wastes are directly or indirectly released into the environment causing serious environmental pollution and even threatening human life (Peng et al. 2006; Nilanjana et al. 2008).

Table 1. Features of current methods for removal of metal ions from wastewaters (Farooq et al. 2010)

Method	Advantages	Disadvantages
Chemical Precipitation	Simple	Large amounts of sludge
	Inexpensive	produced
	Most of metals can be removed	Disposal problems
Chemical coagulation	Sludge settling	High cost
	Dewatering	Large consumption of chemicals
Ion-exchange	High regeneration of materials	High cost
	Metal selective	Less number of metal ions removed
Electrochemical methods	Metal selective	High capital cost
	No consumption of chemicals	High running cost
	Pure metals can be achieved	Initial solution pH and current density
Adsorption Using activated carbon	Most of metals can be removed	Cost of activated carbon
	High efficiency (>99%)	No regeneration
Using natural zeolite	Most of metals can be removed	Low efficiency
	Relatively less costly materials	
Membrane process and ultrafilteration	Less solid waste produced	High initial and running cost
	Less chemical consumption	Low flow rates
	High efficiency (>95% for single metal)	Removal (%) decreases with the presence of other metals

Conventional processes to treat metal-contaminated waste streams consist of chemical precipitation, chemical oxidation and reduction, electrochemical treatment, ion exchange/chelating, filtration and reverse osmosis (Bahadir et al. 2007; Lodeiroet al. 2006; Yang et al. 2007).

Some features of these methods are listed in Table 1. The most efficient classical way for heavy metal elimination is attributed to adsorption by activated carbon which is able to remove more than 99% of certain metal ions. However, the production of activated carbon is expensive and it cannot be regenerated and recycled. It is not effective and economical to use these methods for treatment of wastes with ion concentration lower than 100 mg l^{-1}. Therefore, the development of new methods such as biosorption to remove heavy metals from wastewaters is valuable (Keng et al. 2013; Ceribasi and Yetis 2004; Farooq et al. 2010).

Elimination of heavy metals from aqueous phases using biomasses is divided in two major categories of accumulation and/or biosorption. The operation, in which the dead plants and algae are used for sorbing, sequestering and immobilizing heavy metals from aqueous solutions, is known as biosorption (Naja et al. 2005). This chapter briefly reviews several aspects of heavy metal biosorption using dead plants and algae, including process properties, biomass sources, possible mechanisms, and commercially available biosorbents.

2. BIOSORPTION FEATURES

A lot of research on biosorption process was conducted to remove heavy metals from industrial effluents (e.g. the mining or electroplating industry), processing solutions or the seawater. The metal concentration on biosorbent can be 1000 folds higher than the concentration on the liquid phase, leading to the lower waste volume. Interestingly, biosorption is applicable as a polishing technique for purifying wastewaters with a metal concentration of 1-100 ppm to the drinking water standards. The process produces high quality effluent in spite of low operational cost, and it is applicable under a broad range of working conditions (Ishikawa et al. 2002; Atkinson et al. 1998; Schiewer and Volesky 2000). The other advantages regarding the use of dead biomass for metal removal are referred to its immunity to toxicity, non-biotic external conditions, and precise control of the process (Naja and Volesky 2011). Dead biomasses are easily stored or used for longer time periods without nutrient supply.

The metal ion-saturated biosorbents can be simply desorbed and reused (Baysal et al. 2009, Selatnia et al. 2004). However, the disadvantages regarding the use of non-living biomass in powdered form include mass loss after regeneration, difficulty in separation of biomass from the reaction system, and poor mechanical strength (Arica et al. 2004).

The first step, in the metal removal from solution, is the binding of metals to the solid particle. The laden (dead) biomasses are separated from the system by settling, flotation, filtration, centrifugation, etc. Alternatively, the biomass solids can be immobilized within the column while the liquid lose its metal content by flowing freely through the column (Fig. 1).

Finally, the combustion of the biomass solids is a simple way to collect the metal load in the small amount of ash (Naja and Volesky 2011).

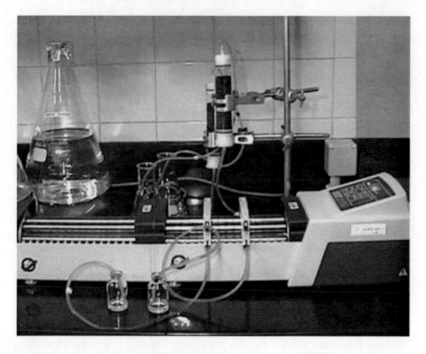

Figure 1. Biosorption of heavy metal ions from aqueous solution using fixed-bed column.

3. BIOSORBENTS

The source of the biosorbent is important where the feasibility of the industrial biosorption process is considered. It is well proved that each biological material has different level of affinity to various pollutants. This is a reason why many kinds of biomass are potentially available for biosorption purposes. Each sorbent has unique physical and chemical characteristics such as porosity, surface area and physical strength. These characteristics and experimental conditions lead to different sorption capacities.

Numerous species of dead plants and algae have been employed as biosorbent for the desired pollutant removal in a variety of ways. These biomasses are cheap, inexhaustible and safe, and can be easily disposed by burning. Agricultural waste materials such as grape stalks (Zouboulis et al. 2002), sawdust (Witek-Krowiak 2013), plant barks (Reddy et al. 2011), sugarcane bagasse (Khoramzadeh et al. 2013), leaves (Reddy et al. 2012), coconut shell (Acheampong et al. 2013), wheat straw (Farooq et al. 2011), wheat bran (Farajzadeh and Monji 2004) and rice husk (Manique et al. 2012) have been already used as biosorbent. Biosorbents are simply inactivated and then pretreated by washing with acid or base before the final drying although chemical pretreatments can also be performed. Subsequently, simple cutting or grinding of dry biomass supplies stable biosorbent particles with desired size (Ebrahimi et al. 2009; Fourest et al. 1994). Examples of heavy metals removal by untreated agriculture wastes are shown in Table 2.

Wheat straw and bran are by-products of the wheat milling industry. World wheat production was more than 600 million tonsin 2007. The wheat straw as a lignocellulosic agricultural waste approximately contains 37–39% cellulose, 30–35% hemicellulose, 14% lignin and sugars as well as other compounds offering different functional groups such as carboxyl, hydroxyl, sulphydryl, amide and amine (Farooq et al. 2010). The wheat bran is the shell of the wheat seed which is produced as a waste in the processing of wheat into flour (Nameni et al. 2008). Both wheat straw and wheat bran have been extensively applied for biosorption of heavy metal ions, in order to decrease the volume of these waste.

Table 2. Untreated dead plant and algae for heavy metal removal

Biosorbent	Metal	Biosorption capacity (mg g^{-1})[*]	References
Plant			
Wheat straw	U(VI)	1.2	Wang et al. (2012)
Wheat straw	Ni(II)	41.8[**]	Dhir and Kumar (2010)
Wheat straw	Cu(II)	11.4[**]	Dang et al. (2009)
Wheat bran	Pb(II)	87[**]	Bulut and Baysal (2006)
Wheat bran	Ni(II)	12	Farajzadeh and Monji (2004)
Wheat bran	Hg(II)	70	Farajzadeh and Monji (2004)
Rice husk	Zn(II)	30.8	Mishra et al. (1997)
Rice husk	Pb(II)	9.45[**]	Tarley et al. (2004)
Rice husk	Au(I)	28.2	Nakbanpote et al. (2002)
Sugarcane bagasse	Cr(VI)	18.2	Wartelle and Marshall (2005)
Soybean hulls	Cr(VI)	13.5	Wartelle and Marshall (2005)
Corn stover	Cr(VI)	18.2	Wartelle and Marshall (2005)
Garcinia cambogia	As (III)	128.1[**]	Kamala et al. (2005)
Olive pomace	Cd	5.5[**]	Pagnanelli et al. (2005)
Algae			
Cystoserta indica (brown alga)	Ni(II)	45	Pahlavanzadeh et al. (2010)
Sargassum glaucescens (brown alga)	Co (II)	27.7	Ebrahimi et al. (2009)
Cladophora glomerata (green alga)	Pb(II)	75	Jalali et al. (2002)
Ulva lactuca (green alga)	Zn(II)	9.5	Areco et al. (2012)
Polysiphonia violacea (red alga)	Pb(II)	100	Jalali et al. (2002)
Gracilaria edulis (red alga)	Cd(II)	27[**]	Hashim and Chu (2004)

[*]The reported data are referred to different experimental conditions
[**]Theoretical value based on isotherm models

The hard outer shell of the rice grain is called rice husk known as the major by-product of rice hulling process, accounting for almost 20% of the rice production. This agricultural residue is readily available in huge amount. It contains high amount of lignin, and its outer surface is covered with silica. In nature, rice husk is tough, woody and insoluble in water, and it has good chemical stability and high mechanical strength. As a lignocellulosic agricultural by-product, rice husk contains cellulose (32.23%), hemicelluloses (21.34%), lignin (21.44%) and mineral ash (15.05%) with high percentage of silica (96.34%) in the mineral ash (Ndazi et al. 2007; Dada et al. 2013; Khan et al. 2014).A large number of researchers have been used this cheap biomass for heavy metals removal from aqueous phases in laboratory scale.

Sugarcane is used as raw material in both the alcohol and the sugar industries. The most important by-product of these industries is bagasse which contains about 50% cellulose, 27% polyoses, and 23% lignin. These biological polymers supply many hydroxyl and/or phenolic functional groups that can be chemically modified, leading to attractive biosorption capacities. For example, the succinic anhydride-modified sugarcane bagasse materials for biosorption of Cu^{2+}, Cd^{2+}, and Pb^{2+} ions from aqueous single metal solutions was reported (Karnitz et al. 2007).

The application of untreated plant wastes as adsorbents in industrial scale can be limited because of low adsorption capacities and weak mechanical properties. Therefore, the modification of plant wastes before being applied for heavy metals removal is rewarding. Treatments have been done using different kinds of modifying agents such as base solutions (sodium hydroxide, calcium hydroxide, sodium carbonate) mineral and organic acid solutions (hydrochloric acid, nitric acid, sulfuric acid, tartaric acid, citric acid, thioglycollic acid), organic compounds (ethylenediamine, formaldehyde, epichlorohydrin, methanol), oxidizing agent (hydrogen peroxide), etc. Examples of modified plant wastes for the removal of heavy metal ions are reported in Table 3 (Ngah and Hanafiah 2008).

Table 3. Modified plant wastes for the removal of heavy metal ions - adapted from Ngah and Hanafiah (2008)

Modifying agent	Biosorbent	Heavy metal	Biosorption capacity (mg g^{-1})
Formaldehyde	Sawdust (*S. robusta*)	Cr(VI)	3.6
Formaldehyde	Sawdust (*Pinus sylvestris*)	Pb(II)	9.78
Formaldehyde	Sawdust (*P. sylvestris*)	Cd(II)	9.29
Formaldehyde	Banana pith	Pb(II)	91.7
Hydrochloric acid	Sawdust (Oak tree)	Cu(II)	3.6
Hydrochloric acid	Sawdust (Oak tree)	Ni(II)	3.37
Hydrochloric acid	Sawdust (Oak tree)	Cr(VI)	1.74
Hydrochloric acid	Spent grain	Cd(II)	17.3
Hydrochloric acid	Spent grain	Pb(II)	35.5
Hydrochloric acid	Carrot residues	Cr(III)	45.09
Hydrochloric acid	Carrot residues	Cu(II)	32.74
Hydrochloric acid	Carrot residues	Zn(II)	29.61
Hydrochloric acid	Sugar beet pulp	Cu(II)	0.15
Hydrochloric acid	Sugar beet pulp	Zn(II)	0.18
Nitric acid	Banana pith	Cu(II)	13.4
Nitric acid	Corncob	Cd(II)	19.3
Sodium bicarbonate	Rice husk	Cd(II)	16.18
Sodium bicarbonate	Sugarcane bagasse	Cu(II)	114
Sodium bicarbonate	Sugarcane bagasse	Pb(II)	196
Sodium bicarbonate	Sugarcane bagasse	Cd(II)	189
Sodium hydroxide	Rice husk	Cd(II)	20.24
Sodium hydroxide	Sawdust (*Cedrus deodara* wood)	Cd(II)	73.62
Sodium hydroxide	Sawdust (*Dalbergia sissoo*)	Ni(II)	10.47
Sodium hydroxide	Sawdust (Poplar tree)	Cu(II)	6.92
Sodium hydroxide	Sawdust (Poplar tree)	Zn(II)	15.8
Sodium hydroxide	Juniper fibre	Cd(II)	29.54
Sodium hydroxide	Cork powder	Cu(II)	18.8
Sodium hydroxide	Alfalfa biomass	Pb(II)	89.2
Sodium hydroxide	*Imperata cylindrica* leaf powder	Pb(II)	13.5
Sulfuric acid	Sawdust (Poplar tree)	Cu(II)	13.95
Sulfuric acid	Peanut husk	Pb(II)	29.14
Sulfuric acid	Peanut husk	Cr(III)	29.14
Sulfuric acid	Peanut husk	Cu(II)	10.15
Sulfuric acid	Wheat bran	Cu(II)	51.5
Sulfuric acid	Wheat bran	Cd(II)	101

Another important source of biosorbent is related to algae biomasses. The term algae refer to a large and diverse group of eukaryotic organisms containing chlorophyll and carrying out oxygenic photosynthesis. These kinds of biomasses are extensively found in aquatic habitats, freshwater, marine and moist soil. The algal groups are composed of *Chlorophyta* (green algae), *Euglenophyta* (euglenoids, protozoa), *Chrysophyta* (golden-brown algae, diatoms), *Phaeophyta* (brown algae), *Pyrrophyta* (dino-flagellates) and *Rhodophyta* (red algae). Numerous kinds of algae were used and investigated as biosorbents for heavy metal removal (Wang and Chen 2009). Some examples regarding the use of intact algae for biosorption of heavy metals are given in Table 2.

Among the three major groups of algae (red, green, brown algae), brown algae have received the most attention because of higher uptake capacity. Researchers have employed modified brown algae to improve the sorption capacity (Brinza et al. 2007; Romera et al. 2006). Treatments which improve ionic interactions generally imply one of two chemical alterations. The first is protonation of the biomass with a strong acid such as HCl whereby the proton displaces the light metal ions from the binding sites (i.e., carboxylic, sulfonic, and others). The second is biomass reaction with an aqueous solution of a given ion at high concentration so that the majority of binding sites are occupied by, for example, calcium, potassium or magnesium. As a modification, the crosslinking with aldehydes such as formalin was reported, which reinforces the biosorbent particles by bridging-binding of their own molecules (Ebrahimi et al. 2009). Although chemically modified biosorbents may increase the uptake capacity, the cost of chemicals and methods of modification must be considered in order to produce low-cost adsorbents.

A great number of marine micro and macro algal species, for instance, the micro algae of Chlamydomonas reinhardtii, Chlorella vulgaris, Lyngbyataylorii, Phaeodactylum tricornutum, Scenedesmus quadricauda, Spirulina platensis, Stichococcus bacillaris, Stigeoclonium tenue, and the macro algae such as *Ascophyllum nodosum, Cladophora crispata, Colpomenia sinuosa, Fucus vesiculosus, Gracilaria fischeri, Jania rubrens, Laminaria digitata, Padina pavonia, Sargassum asperifolium, Turbinaria conoides, Ulva fascia* have been extensively used as biosorbents for heavy metal ions removal (Brinza et al. 2007). It is reported that brown algae are efficient biosorbents for removal of heavy metals such as Cd^{2+}, Cu^{2+}, Ni^{2+}, Pb^{2+} and Zn^{2+}, in comparison with red and green algae. The brown algae can present an approximate maximum sorption capacity of 1 mmol g^{-1} for copper and lead (Romera et al. 2006).

4. BIOSORPTION MECHANISMS

The biosorption may occur by different mechanisms such as adsorption by physical force, complexation, coordination, chelation , ion exchange, precipitation or entrapment (Veglio and Beolchini 1997; Davis et al. 2003; Crist et al. 1999), which depends on the chemical nature of pollutant, type of biomass, biosorbent preparation and its specific surface properties, and the environmental conditions (pH, temperature, ionic strength, existence of competing organic or inorganic ligands in solution) (Lin and Juang 2009; Yang and Volesky 1999; Esposito et al. 2002; Gavrilescu 2004). The understanding of metal-biomass interaction mechanism offers the possibilities such as optimizing the process on the molecular level, improving the screening process, and manipulating the biosorption properties of biomass when it is growing (Gavrilescu 2004). The cell wall composition has substantial effects on the biosorption process. The biosorbent cell wall is typically composed of polysaccharides, proteins and lipids, which makes available a number of functional groups such as hydroxyl, carboxyl, amino, phosphoryl and sulfhydryl for biosorption of heavy metals from aqueous phases (Arief et al. 2008). Ion exchange refers to the interchange of ions based on gaining or losing electrons. For instance, the alginates of marine algae can replace its natural ions of K^+, Na^+, Ca^{2+}, and Mg^{2+} with Co^{2+}, Cu^{2+}, Cd^{2+} and Zn^{2+}. Physical adsorption occurs with the aid of van der Waals' forces. For example, electrostatic interactions between the metal ions and cell walls had been responsible for uranium, cadmium, zinc, copper and cobalt biosorption by dead biomasses of algae (Kuyucak and Volesky 1988) and copper biosorption by *Chiarella vulgaris* (Aksu et al. 1992). The precipitation by dead plants and algae does not dependent on the cellular metabolism. It is as a result of chemical interaction between the metal and the cell surface. Metal complexes consist of a central metal atom or ion surrounded by several atoms, ions or molecules which can have an independent existence. To remove metals from solution, complex is formed on the cell surface by the interaction between the metal and the active groups. It is reported that adsorption and formation of coordination bonds between metals and amino and carboxyl groups of cell wall polysaccharides are dominant mechanisms for biosorption of copper by *C. vulgaris* (Aksu et al. 1992). Metals can form a complex by carboxyl groups found in microbial polysaccharides and other polymers (Huang et al. 2012).

5. BIOSORPTION MECHANISMS BY DEAD PLANTS

Agricultural waste materials generally contain lignin, cellulose, hemicelluloses, lipids, proteins, simple sugars, starches, water, hydrocarbons, ash and many more compounds offering a variety of functional groups. There is high affinity between the biomasses and the heavy metal ions resulting in metal uptake. It occurs through complex processes with combination of several mechanisms such as complexation, ion exchange, chelation, and adsorption by physical forces and entrapment (Basso et al. 2002; Qaiser et al. 2007).

Chromium removal from coastal waters was performed using bagasse as an effective biosorbent. It is found that ion-exchange and adsorption are the most important mechanisms (Krishnani et al. 2004). It is also reported that lignocellulosic biomass of wheat straw and bran offers high complexing capacities (Gauthier et al. 2002). The lignocellulosic materials contain lignin and cellulose. The functional groups in lignin such as alcohols, ketones, and carboxylic can be involved in complexation reactions with cations (Gerente et al. 2000; Reddad et al. 2002a).

Carboxylic groups of the galactouronic acid residues in the sugar beet pulp were responsible for the removal of Pb^{2+}, Cu^{2+}, Zn^{2+}, Cd^{2+} and Ni^{2+} ions from aqueous solutions, with the ion-exchange as the most important mechanism (Reddad et al. 2002b). This cheap biomass has been also used for the removal of Cr(III) and Cr(VI) from aqueous phases. The Cr(VI) removal was attributed to reduction mechanism while the biosorption of Cr(III) ions were related to the ion-exchange mechanism (Reddad et al. 2003). Furthermore, the maximum uptake capacity of sugar beet pulp for Cu^{2+}, Pb^{2+}, and Ni^{2+} ions removal was found at pH 6 with the predominant ion exchange mechanism (Gerente et al. 2000).

Biosorption of heavy metals using the other plants has been reported. Biosorption characteristics of Cd^{2+}, Cu^{2+}, and Pb^{2+} by the fruiting body of jelly fungus *Auricularia polytricha* showed that synergistic ion exchange and surface complexation were the dominant mechanisms in the biosorption process (Huang et al. 2012).

Biosorption of cadmium and nickel using roots and leaves biomass of *Ludwigia stolonifera* were evaluated. The results supported that ion exchange is the major mechanism of the process since the heavy metal ions were bound to the biomass against the discharge of light metal ions such as calcium, magnesium, potassium and sodium (Elifantz and Telor 2002). Biosorption of single- and multi-metal system using Lemna minor biomass was compared. The mechanism was found to be ion-exchange mainly with K^+, Ca^{2+} and Mg^{2+} (Chojnacka 2006).

6. BIOSORPTION MECHANISMS BY ALGAE

The red and brown algae found in seawater along with green algae occurring in fresh water are the major groups of algae (Tamilselvan et al. 2012). The marine algal biosorbents are readily available. They bear large quantities of biopolymers that can bind heavy metals offering high metal uptake capacities (Wang and Chen 2009). They have a consistent quality, and do not require specific immobilization (Kratochvil et al. 1995). Plenty of studies confirm that ion-exchange is dominant mechanism for cations biosorption by seaweeds although complexation is also observable (Davis et al. 2003; Volesky and Holan 1995). For anion uptake, adsorption-coupled reduction is the most important mechanism (Suksabye et al. 2007; Park et al. 2005; Elangovan et al. 2008; Park et al. 2007).

The cell walls of brown algae generally contain cellulose (the structural support), sulphated polysaccharides, and alginic acid (a polymer of mannuronic and guluronic acids) along with the corresponding salts of sodium, potassium, magnesium and calcium (Romera et al. 2007). The alginate contains carboxyl groups as the most abundant acidic groups involved in metal binding. The presence of carboxyl groups in the alginate polymer directly influences the biosorption capacity. Another functional group of the brown seaweed involved in biosorption is sulfonic acid (Davis et al. 2003). The ion exchange properties of alginate confirm the prevalence of this mechanism on biosorption by these kinds of algae (da Costa et al. 2001). The biosorption study on marine brown alga *Gelidium* showed that ion exchange is one of the mechanisms involved in the process (Vilar et al. 2008). Another report by *Fucusserratus* showed the same mechanism (Ahmady-Asbchin et al. 2008).

The biosorption of Cr(VI) by *Fucus vesiculosus* and *Fucus spiralis* (brown), *Ulva lactuca* and *Ulva* spp. (green), and *Palmaria palmata* and *Polysiphonia lanosa* (red) was an adsorption-coupled reduction (Murphy et al. 2009). Although red algae contain cellulose, their main biosorption capacities are related to the presence of sulphated polysaccharides made of galactanes (agar and carraghenates). Green algae mainly consist of cellulose, and proteins bonded to polysaccharides (glycoproteins). These compounds present several functional groups (amino, carboxyl, sulphate, hydroxyl, etc.) which play important role in the biosorption process (Romera et al. 2007). The mechanism of biosorption was identified as ion exchange for biosorption of heavy metals such as Cr(III), Cu(II), Mn(II), Zn(II), and Co(II) to the biomass of green algae, *Chlorella vulgaris* and *Enteromorpha prolifera* (Chojnacka 2007,

2008; Michalak and Chojnacka 2010; Michalak et al. 2011). Mechanism of heavy metal biosorption using microalgae *Chlorella vulgaris* and *Desmodesmus pleiomorphus* was ion exchange and the cells were capable of adsorbing about 90% of the total metal (Mehta et al. 2002; Monteiro et al. 2010). The cell wall functional groups of microalgae such as carboxyl, hydroxyl, phosphate, amino, and sulphydryl present a net negative charge leading to high binding affinity for heavy metal cations (Gupta and Rastogi 2008; Deng et al. 2007; Volesky 2007). Depending on the species and the environmental conditions, various mechanisms can occur simultaneously for biosorption of cations by microalgae since the composition of their cell surface is complex (Franklin et al. 2002).

7. COMMERCIAL BIOSORBENTS

Besides conventional methods, biosorption of heavy metals has been introduced as one of the most promising technologies involved in the removal of toxic metals from industrial waste streams as it offers the advantages of low operating costs, possibility of metal recovery, regeneration of biosorbent, minimization of the volume of chemical and/or biological sludge and high efficiency in detoxifying very dilute effluents (Bahadir et al. 2007; Barros et al. 2007; Vijayaraghavan et al. 2006). Heavy metal removal using biosorbent can be accomplished in a wide range of pH and temperature (Kiran et al. 2007; Witek-Krowiak et al. 2011). The equilibrium state of biosorption process is achieved very fast, for instance as early as after 20 min (Witek-Krowiak et al. 2011). However, the application of biosorption process on commercial scale have some operational limitations related to physical characteristics of biosorbents such as small particle size, low density, poor mechanical strength and low rigidity (McHale and McHale 1994; Iqbal et al. 2007). Additionally, it should be easily possible to recover bound metals from biosorbents and reuse them more and more. The biosorbent recovery or desorption of the metal are strongly influenced by the biosorption mechanisms. Metal-biomass interactions are often reversible and the biosorbents can be regenerated using non-destructive methods. The popular desorption agents are diluted inorganic acids and bases, chelating agents and salt solutions (Dostálek 2011; Tsezos1984). Hydrochloric acid, acetic acid, sodium Chloride (Ghasemi et al. 2011), Calcium chloride (Ebrahimi et al. 2009), Carbonates and bicarbonates (ammonium and sodium) (Strandberget al. 1981; Siegel et al. 1990; de Rome and Gadd 1991) etc. were used for desorption of heavy metals from biosorbents.

However, there are just few reports concerning the application of biosorbent in commercial scale. AlgaSORB, BIO-FIX and B.V. Sorbex are the most important biosorbents originated from dead plants and algae, which were used in large scale for industrial applications. Bio-recovery Systems Inc. has developed ALGASORB^{TM} using a fresh water alga *Chlorella vulgaris* to treat wastewaters. BIO-FIX is a combination of algae and other biomasses. The algae, *S. natans*, *A. nodosum*, *H. opuntia*, *P. pamata*, *C. Crispus*, and *C. vulgaris* are used to produce BV–SORBEX™ (Wang and Chen 2009).

CONCLUSION

Numerous kinds of dead plants and algae are available for biosorption of heavy metals from aqueous solutions. The agriculture wastes such as wheat straw and bran, rice husk and bagasse have substantial potential to be used as biosorbent since these biomasses are cheap and abundant. However, their mechanical properties and adsorption capacities should be improved, for instance, by chemical treatments. Additionally, several industrial requirements should be considered to bring this technology into commercial scale. Beside bioaccumulation, biosorption process is a promising alternative technology for remediation of heavy metals from aqueous solution.

REFERENCES

Acheampong MA, Pakshirajan K, Annachhatre AP, Lens PNL (2013) Removal of Cu(II) by biosorption onto coconut shell in fixed-bed column systems. *J Indust Engg Chem* 19: 841–848.

Ahmady-Asbchin S, Andres Y, Gerente C, Cloirec P (2008) Biosorption of Cu(II) from aqueous solution by *Fucuss erratus*: Surface characterization and sorption mechanisms. *Bioresou Technol* 99: 6150–6155.

Aksu Z, Sag Y, Kutsal T (1992) The biosorption of copper by *C. vulgaris* and *Z. ramigera*. *Environ Technol* 13:579–586.

Areco MM, Hanela S, Duran J, dos Santos Afonso M (2012) Biosorption of Cu(II), Zn(II), Cd(II) and Pb(II) by dead biomasses of green alga *Ulva lactuca* and the development of a sustainable matrix for adsorption implementation. *J Hazard Mater* 213-214: 123–132.

Arica MY, Bayramoglu G, Yilmaz M, Bektas S, Genc O (2004) Biosorption of Hg^{2+}, Cd^{2+}, and Zn^{2+} by Ca-alginate and immobilized wood-rotting fungus *funali atrogii*. *J Hazard Mater* 109: 191–199.

Arief VO, Trilestari K, Sunarso J, Indraswati N, Ismadji S (2008) Recent progress on biosorption of heavy metals from liquids using low cost biosorbents: Characterization, biosorption parameters and mechanism studies. *Clean Soil Air Water* 36: 937–962.

Atkinson BW, Bux F, Kasan CH (1998) Considerations for application of biosorption technology to remediate metal-contaminated industrial effluents. *Water SA* 24: 129–135.

Bahadir T, Bakan G, Altas L, Buyukgungor H (2007) The investigation of lead removal by biosorption: An application at storage battery industry waste waters. *Enz Microb Technol* 41: 98–102.

Barros AJ, Prasad S, Leite VD, Souza AG (2007) Biosorption of heavy metals in upflow sludge columns. *Bioresou Technol* 98: 1418–1425.

Basso MC, Cerrella EG, Cukierman AL (2002) Lignocellulosic materials as potential biosorbents of trace toxic metals from wastewater. *Ind Engg Chem Res* 41: 3580–3585.

Baysal Z, Çinar E, Bulut Y, Alkan H, Dogru M (2009) Equilibrium and thermodynamic studies on biosorption of Pb(II) onto *Candida albicans* biomass. *J Hazard Mater* 161: 62–67.

Brinza L, Dring MJ, Gavrilescu M (2007) Marine micro- and macro-algal species as biosorbents for heavy metals. *Environ Engg Manag J* 6: 237–251.

Bulut Y, Baysal Z (2006) Removal of Pb(II) from wastewater using wheat bran. *J Environ Manag* 78: 107–113.

Ceribasi IH, Yetis U (2004) Biosorption of Ni(II) and Pb(II) by *Phanerochaete chrysosporium* from a binary metal system – kinetics. *Water SA* 27: 15–20.

Chojnacka K (2006) The application of multi elemental analysis in the elaboration of technology of mineral feed additives based on *Lemna minor* biomass. *Talanta* 70: 966–972.

Chojnacka K (2007) Using biosorption to enrich the biomass of *Chlorella vulgaris* with microelements to be used as mineral feed supplement. *World J Microbiol Biotechnol* 23: 1139–1147.

Chojnacka K (2008) Using biosorption to enrich the biomass of seaweeds from the Baltic Sea with microelements to produce mineral feed supplement for livestock. *Biochem Engg J* 39: 246–257.

Crist RH, Martin JR, Crist DR (1999) Interaction of metal ions with acid sites of biosorbents peat moss and *Vaucheria* and model substances alginic and humic acids. *Environ Sci Technol* 33: 2252–2256.

da Costa AC, Mora Tavares AP, Pessôa de França F (2001) The release of light metals from a brown seaweed (*Sargassum* sp.) during zinc biosorption in a continuous system. *Elect J Biotechnol* 4: 125–129.

Dada AO, Ojediran JO, Olalekan AP (2013) Sorption of Pb^{2+} from aqueous solution unto modified rice husk: Isotherms studies. *Adv Phy Chem ID* 842425.

Dang VBH, Doan HD, Dang-Vu T, Lohi A (2009) Equilibrium and kinetics of biosorption of cadmium(II) and copper(II) ions by wheat straw. *Bioresou Technol* 100: 211–219.

Davis TA, Volesky B, Mucci A (2003) A review of the biochemistry of heavy metal biosorption by brown algae. *Wat Res* 37: 4311–4330.

de Rome L, Gadd G (1991) Use of pelleted and immobilized yeast and fungal biomass for heavy metal and radionuclide recovery. *J Ind Microbiol* 7: 97–104.

Deng L, Zhu X, Wang X, Su Y, Su H (2007) Biosorption of copper(II) from aqueous solutions by green alga *Cladophora fascicularis*. *Biodegradation* 18: 393–402.

Dhir B, Kumar R (2010) Adsorption of heavy metals by *Salvinia* biomass and agricultural residues. *Int J Environ Res* 4: 427–432.

Dostálek P (2011) Immobilized biosorbents for bioreactors and commercial biosorbents. In: Kotrba P, Mackova M, Macek T (eds) *Microbial Biosorption of Metals*. Dordrecht, Springer Netherlands pp 19-58.

Ebrahimi M, Panahi R, Dabbagh R (2009) Evaluation of native and chemically modified *Sargassum glaucescens* for continuous biosorption of Co(II). *App Biochem Biotechnol* 158: 736–746.

Elangovan R, Philip L, Chandraraj K (2008) Biosorption of hexavalent and trivalent chromium by palm flower (*Borassus aethiopum*). *Chem Engg J* 141: 99–111.

Elifantz H, Telor E (2002) Heavy metal biosorption by plant biomass of the macrophyte *Ludwigiasto lonifera*. *Water Air Soil Pollut* 141: 207–218.

Esposito A, Pagnanelli F, Vegliò F (2002) pH-related equilibria models for biosorption in single metal systems. *Chem Engg Sci* 57: 307–313.

Farajzadeh M, Monji A (2004) Adsorption characteristics of wheat bran towards heavy metal cations. *Sep Purif Technol* 38: 197–207.

Farooq U, Khan MA, Athar M, Kozinski JA (2011) Effect of modification of environmentally friendly biosorbent wheat (*Triticum aestivum*) on the biosorptive removal of cadmium(II) ions from aqueous solution. *Chem Engg J* 171: 400–410.

Farooq U, Kozinski JA, Khan MA, Athar M (2010) Biosorption of heavy metal ions using wheat based biosorbents – a review of the recent literature. *Bioresou Technol* 101: 5043–5053.

Fourest E, Canal C, Roux JC (1994) Improvement of heavy metal biosorption by mycelial dead biomasses (*Rhizopus arrhizus*, *Mucor miehei* and *Penicillium chrysogenum*): pH control and cationic activation. *FEMS Microbiol Rev* 14: 325–332.

Franklin NM, Stauber JL, Apte SC, Lim RP (2002) Effect of initial cell density on the bioavailability and toxicity of copper in microalgal bioassays. *Environ Toxicol Chem* 21: 742–751.

Gauthier A, Derenne S, Dupont L, Guillon E, Largeau C, Dumonceau J, Aplincourt M (2002) Characterization and comparison of two ligno-cellulosic substrates by ^{13}C CP/MAS NMR, XPS, conventional pyrolysis and thermo chemolysis. *Analyt Bioanalyt Chem* 373: 830–838.

Gavrilescu M (2004) Removal of heavy metals from the environment by biosorption. *Engg Life Sci* 4: 219–232.

Gerente C, Couespel du Mesnil P, Andrès Y, Thibault JF, Le Cloirec P (2000) Removal of metal ions from aqueous solution on low cost natural polysaccharides. *React Funct Poly* 46: 135–144.

Ghasemi M, Keshtkar AR, Dabbagh R, Safdari SJ (2011) Biosorption of uranium in a continuous flow packed bed column using *Cystoseira indica* biomass. *Iran J Environ Heal Sci Engg* 8: 65–74.

Gupta VK, Rastogi A (2008) Equilibrium and kinetic modelling of cadmium(II) biosorption by nonliving algal biomass *Oedogonium* sp. from aqueous phase. *J Hazard Mater* 153: 759–766.

Hashim M (2004) Biosorption of cadmium by brown, green, and red seaweeds. *Chem Engg J* 97: 249–255.

Huang H, Cao L, Wan Y, Zhang R, Wang W (2012) Biosorption behavior and mechanism of heavy metals by the fruiting body of jelly fungus (*Auricularia polytricha*) from aqueous solutions. *App Microbiol Biotechnol* 96: 829–840.

Iqbal M, Saeed A, Zafar SI (2007) Hybrid biosorbent: An innovative matrix to enhance the biosorption of Cd(II) from aqueous solution. *J Hazard Mater* 148: 47–55.

Ishikawa SI, Suyama K, Arihara K, Itoh M (2002) Uptake and recovery of gold ions from electroplating wastes using egg shell membrane. *Bioresou Technol* 81: 201–206.

Jalali R, Ghafourian H, Asef Y, Davarpanah S, Sepehr S (2002) Removal and recovery of lead using nonliving biomass of marine algae. *J Hazard Mater* 92: 253–262.

Kamala CT, Chu KH, Chary NS, Pandey PK, Ramesh SL, Sastry ARK, Sekhar C (2005) Removal of arsenic(III) from aqueous solutions using fresh and immobilized plant biomass. *Wat Res* 39: 2815–2826.

Karnitz OJ, Gurgel LVA, de Melo JCP, Botaro VR, Melo TMS, de Freitas Gil RP, Gil LF (2007) Adsorption of heavy metal ion from aqueous single metal solution by chemically modified sugarcane bagasse. *Bioresou Technol* 98: 1291–1297.

Keng PS, Lee SL, Ha ST, Hung YT, Ong ST (2013) Cheapmaterials to clean heavy metal polluted waters. In: Lichtfouse E, Schwarzbauer J, Robert D (eds) *Green Materials for Energy, Products and Depollution.Dordrecht.* Springer, Netherlands pp 335–414.

Khan T, Isa MH, Chaudhuri M, Mustafa MRU (2014) Acidically prepared rich husk carbon for adsorption of Zn(II) from aqueous solution. *J App Sci*14: 537–541.

Khoramzadeh E, Nasernejad B, Halladj R (2013) Mercury biosorption from aqueous solutions by sugarcane bagasse. *J Tai Instit Chem Engg* 44: 266–269.

Kiran B, Kaushik A, Kaushik C (2007) Biosorption of Cr(VI) by native isolate of *Lyngby aputealis* (HH-15) in the presence of salts. *J Hazard Mater* 141: 662–667.

Kratochvil D, Fourest E, Volesky B (1995) Biosorption of copper by *Sargassum fluitans* biomass in fixed-bed column. *Biotechnol Lett* 17: 777–782.

Krishnani KK, Parimala V, Meng X (2004) Detoxification of chromium(VI) in coastal water using lignocellulosic agricultural waste. *Water SA* 30: 541–545.

Kuyucak N, Volesky B (1988) Biosorbents for recovery of metals from industrial solutions. *Biotechnol Lett* 10: 137–142.

Lin SH, Juang RS (2009) Adsorption of phenol and its derivatives from water using synthetic resins and low-cost natural adsorbents: A review. *J Environ Manag* 90: 1336–1349.

Lodeiro P, Barriada JL, Herrero R, Sastre de Vicente ME (2006) The marine macroalga *Cystoseir abaccata* as biosorbent for cadmium(II) and lead(II) removal: Kinetic and equilibrium studies. *Environ Pollut* 142: 264–273.

Manique MC, Faccini CS, Onorevoli B, Benvenutti EV, Caramão EB (2012) Rice husk ash as an adsorbent for purifying biodiesel from waste frying oil. *Fuel* 92: 56–61.

McHale AP, McHale S (1994) Microbial biosorption of metals: Potential in the treatment of metal pollution. *Biotechnol Adv* 12: 647–652.

Mehta SK, Singh A, Gaur JP (2002) Kinetics of adsorption and uptake of Cu^{2+} by *Chlorella vulgaris*: Influence of pH, temperature, culture age, and cations. *J Environ Sci Heal Part A* 37: 399–414.

Michalak I, Chojnacka K (2010) The new application of biosorption properties of *Enteromorpha prolifera. App Biochem Biotechnol* 160:1540–1556.

Michalak I, Chojnacka K, Marycz K (2011) Using ICP-OES and SEM-EDX in biosorption studies. *Microchim Acta* 172: 65–74.

Mishra SP, Tiwari D, Dubey RS (1997) The uptake behaviour of rice (jaya) husk in the removal of Zn(II) ions—A radiotracer study. *App Rad Isotop* 48: 877–882.

Monteiro CM, Castro PML, Malcata FX (2010) Cadmium removal by two strains of *Desmodesmus pleiomorphus* cells. *Water Air Soil Pollut* 208: 17–27.

Murphy V, Hughes H, McLoughlin P (2009) Enhancement strategies for Cu(II), Cr(III) and Cr(VI) remediation by a variety of seaweed species. *J Hazard Mater*166: 318–326.

Naja G, Volesky B (2011) The mechanism of metal cation and anion biosorption. In: Kotrba P, Mackova M, Macek T (eds) *Microb Biosorp Met Dordrecht.* Springer Netherlands pp 19–58.

Naja G, Mustin C, Berthelin J, Volesky B (2005) Lead biosorption study with *Rhizopus arrhizus* using a metal-based titration technique. *J Coll Interf Sci* 292: 537–543.

Nakbanpote W, Thiravetyan P, Kalambaheti C (2002) Comparison of gold adsorption by *Chlorella vulgaris*, rice husk and activated carbon. *Miner Engg* 15: 549–552.

Nameni M, Alavi Moghadam MR, Arami M (2008) Adsorption of hexavalent chromium from aqueous solutions by wheat bran. *Int J Environ Sci Technol* 5: 161–168.

Ndazi BS, Nyahumwa C, Tesha J (2007) Chemical and thermal stability of rice husks against alkali treatment. *Bioresources* 3: 1267–1277.

Ngah WSW, Hanafiah MAKM (2008) Removal of heavy metal ions from wastewater by chemically modified plant wastes as adsorbents: A review. *Bioresou Technol* 99: 3935–3948.

Nilanjana D, Vimala R, Karthika P (2008) Biosorption of heavy metals–An overview. *Ind J Biotechnol* 7: 159–169.

Pagnanelli F, Mainelli S, De Angelis S, Toro L (2005) Biosorption of protons and heavy metals onto olive pomace: Modelling of competition effects. *Wat Res* 39: 1639–1651.

Pahlavanzadeh H, Keshtkar AR, Safdari J, Abadi Z (2010) Biosorption of nickel(II) from aqueous solution by brown algae: Equilibrium, dynamic and thermodynamic studies. *J Hazard Mater* 175: 304–310.

Park D, Lim SR, Yun YS, Park JM (2007) Reliable evidences that the removal mechanism of hexavalent chromium by natural biomaterials is adsorption-coupled reduction. *Chemosphere* 70: 298–305.

Park D, Yun YS, Park JM (2005) Studies on hexavalent chromium biosorption by chemically-treated biomass of *Ecklonia* sp. *Chemosphere* 60: 1356–1364.

Peng K, Li X, Luo C, Shen Z (2006) Vegetation composition and heavy metal uptake by wild plants at three contaminated sites in xiangxi area, china. *J Environ Sci Heal Part A* 41: 65–76.

Qaiser S, Saleemi AR, Ahmad MM (2007) Heavy metal uptake by agro based waste materials. *Elect J Biotechnol* 10: 409–416.

Reddad Z, Gerente C, Andres Y, Cloirec PL (2003) Mechanisms of Cr(III) and Cr(VI) removal from aqueous solutions by sugar beet pulp. *Environ Technol* 24: 257–264.

Reddad Z, Gerente C, Andres Y, Le Cloirec P (2002a) Adsorption of several metal ions onto a low-cost biosorbent: Kinetic and equilibrium studies. *Environ Sci Technol* 36: 2067–2073.

Reddad Z, Gerente Y, Andres Y, Le Cloirec P (2002b) Comparison of the fixation of several metal ions onto a low cost biopolymer. *Wat Sci Technol: Wat Supp* 2: 217–224.

Reddy DHK, Ramana DKV, Seshaiah K, Reddy AVR (2011) Biosorption of Ni(II) from aqueous phase by *Moringaolei fera* bark, a low cost biosorbent. *Desalination* 268: 150–157.

Reddy DHK, Seshaiah K, Reddy AVR, Lee SM (2012) Optimization of Cd(II), Cu(II) and Ni(II) biosorption by chemically modified *Moringaolei fera* leaves powder. *Carbohyd Polym* 88: 1077–1086.

Romera E, Gonzalez F, Ballester A, Blazquez ML, Munoz JA (2007) Comparative study of biosorption of heavy metals using different types of algae. *Bioresou Techno* l98: 3344–3353.

Romera E, González F, Ballester A, Blázquez ML, Muñoz JA (2006) Biosorption with algae: A statistical review. *Crit Rev Biotechnol* 26: 223–235.

Schiewer S, Volesky B (2000) Biosorption by marine algae. In: Valdes JJ (ed) *Bioremediation*. Dordrecht. Springer Netherlands pp 139–169.

Selatnia A, Madani A, Bakhti MZ, Kertous L, Mansouri Y, Yous R (2004) Biosorption of Ni^{2+} from aqueous solution by a NaOH-treated bacterial dead *Streptomyces rimosus* biomass. *Mineral Engg* 17: 903–911.

Siegel SM, Galun M, Siegel BZ (1990) *Filamentous* fungi as metal biosorbents: A review. *Water Air Soil Pollut* 53: 335–344.

Strandberg GW, Shumate SE, Parrott JR (1981) Microbial cells as biosorbents for heavy metals: accumulation of uranium by *Saccharomyces cerevisiae* and *Pseudomonas aeruginosa*. *App Environ Microbiol* 41: 237–245.

Suksabye P, Thiravetyan P, Nakbanpote W, Chayabutra S (2007). Chromium removal from electroplating wastewater by coir pith. *J Hazard Mater* 141: 637–644.

Tamilselvan N, Saurav K, Kannabiran K (2012) Biosorption of Cr(VI), Cr(III), Pb(II) and Cd(II) from aqueous solutions by *Sargassum wightii* and *Caulerpara cemosa* algal biomass. *J Ocean Uni China* 11: 52–58.

Tarley CRT, Costa Ferreira SL, Zezzi Arruda MA (2004) Use of modified rice husks as a natural solid adsorbent of trace metals: Characterization and development of an on-line pre concentration system for cadmium and lead determination by FAAS. *Microchem J* 77: 163–175.

Tsezos M (1984) Recovery of uranium from biological adsorbents-desorption equilibrium. *Biotechnol Bioengg* 26: 973–981.

Veglio F, Beolchini F (1997) Removal of metals by biosorption: A review. *Hydrometallurgy* 44: 301–316.

Vijayaraghavan K, Palanivelu K, Velan M (2006) Biosorption of copper(II) and cobalt(II) from aqueous solutions by crab shell particles. *Bioresou Technol* 97: 1411–1419.

Vilar VJP, Botelho CMS, Loureiro JM, Boaventura RAR (2008) Biosorption of copper by marine algae *Gelidium* and algal composite material in a packed bed column. *Bioresou Technol* 99: 5830–5838.

Volesky B (2007) Biosorption and me. *Wat Res* 41: 4017–4029.

Volesky B, Holan ZR (1995) Biosorption of heavy metals. Biotechnol Prog 11: 235–250.

Wang J, Chen C (2009) Biosorbents for heavy metals removal and their future. *Biotechnol Adv* 27: 195–226.

Wang X, Xia L, Tan K, Zheng W (2012) Studies on adsorption of uranium (VI) from aqueous solution by wheat straw. *Environ Prog Sust Ener* 31: 566–576.

Wartelle LH, Marshall WE (2005) Chromate ion adsorption by agricultural by-products modified with dimethyloldihydroxyethylene urea and choline chloride. *Wat Res* 39: 2869–2876.

Witek-Krowiak A (2013) Application of beech sawdust for removal of heavy metals from water: Biosorption and desorption studies. *Europ J Wood Wood Prod* 71: 227–236.

Witek-Krowiak A, Szafran RG, Modelski S (2011) Biosorption of heavy metals from aqueous solutions onto peanut shell as a low-cost biosorbent. Desalination 265: 126–134.

Yang C, Guan L, Zhao Y, Yan Y (2007) Sorption of Cu^{2+} and Zn^{2+} by natural biomaterial: Duck feather. *App Biochem Biotechnol* 142: 168–178.

Yang J, Volesky B (1999) Modeling uranium-proton ion exchange in biosorption. *Environ Sci Technol* 33: 4079–4085.

Zouboulis AI, Lazaridis NK, Matis KA (2002) Removal of toxic metal ions from aqueous systems by biosorptive flotation. *J Chem Technol Biotechnol* 77: 958–964.

INDEX

E

F

G

J

K

L

M

N

O

T